PRINCIPLES OF
MODERN ALGEBRA

SECOND EDITION

J. ELDON WHITESITT
Montana State University

PRINCIPLES OF
MODERN ALGEBRA

SECOND EDITION

ADDISON-WESLEY PUBLISHING COMPANY
Reading, Massachusetts ● Menlo Park, California ● London ● Don Mills, Ontario

This book is in the
ADDISON-WESLEY SERIES IN MATHEMATICS

Consulting Editors

Richard S. Pieters
Gail S. Young

MA 1/73 08706

PREFACE

This book is designed primarily as a text for a course in abstract algebra for the training of secondary teachers of mathematics. It can also be used as an introductory course for mathematics majors, especially where such an introduction is desired at the freshman or sophomore level. Details frequently glossed over in more advanced texts have been included in order to make this text as nearly self-teaching as possible. Where a certain level of maturity is often presupposed, this book is intended to develop such maturity, along with the understanding of subject matter necessary to teach modern high-school algebra courses. The material included satisfies the recent recommendations for teacher training set forth by study groups sponsored by the Mathematical Association of America and others.

The purpose of this book is to introduce the subject of abstract algebra in a way which emphasizes the nature of the subject and the techniques of rigorous proof characteristic of modern mathematics. The topics treated were chosen from those felt to be most fundamental and at the same time most closely related to topics appearing in up-to-date high school texts. The point of view adopted is to proceed, wherever this is feasible, from concepts familiar to the beginning student to those which are more abstract and less generally known.

This *second edition* represents a careful revision of the earlier text. Although the general content and purpose have remained unchanged, classroom experience has suggested a number of changes to be made in the text. The first half of the book has been completely rewritten. Chapter 2 has been deleted as a separate chapter. The examples from this chapter have been incorporated into the text at the places where they provide the maximum motivation for theoretical material. Special topics which the author found expedient to skip in a regular course have been omitted and some sections have been condensed or combined. These changes make it possible to proceed more rapidly to a discussion of more important topics.

Several sections in the original text, including the sections on integers and on elementary properties of rings, were so informal in nature as to make later reference difficult. These sections have been rewritten with a more appropriate presentation. More explanation has been given in sections which students found unusually difficult.

Additional exercises have been included to give greater challenge to the better students, without removing the more mechanical problems for the average student. Finally, answers to many exercises and hints for those which require proofs have been added.

Chapter 1 introduces the basic concepts of set, relation, function, and the standard logical terminology which are needed in subsequent chapters. Emphasis is placed on set-theoretic definitions with comparison given to other more traditional definitions. Since modern high-school texts contain much of this material, a careful treatment is important for later use and as a significant part of the teacher's training.

Chapter 2 treats the principle of mathematical induction, ring theory, and an introduction to number theory in a discussion of divisibility in the ring of integers.

Chapter 3 introduces the fields of rational numbers, real numbers, and complex numbers. The rational numbers are discussed most thoroughly with a careful construction based on equivalence sets of ordered pairs of integers. Real and complex numbers are treated more briefly in accordance with CUPM recommendations, but adequately for an introductory course.

Chapter 4 presents the elementary theory of groups with special emphasis on the group of symmetries of the square and groups of permutations. Chapter 5 is a short chapter describing the applications of group theory to Euclidean geometry.

Chapter 6 extends the earlier material on rings and fields, and Chapter 7 discusses the integral domain of polynomials over a field. Emphasis is placed on computational procedures. The theory of equations contained in Chapter 7 is developed in general with exercises and examples relating to specific coefficient domains which include finite fields as well as the fields of rational and real numbers.

This text contains ample material for a semester or a two-quarter course meeting three times a week. Most sections were planned for a single day's work; however, it will occasionally be advisable to spend more time on sections of greater difficulty or more general interest. Chapters 4, 5, 6, and 7 are largely independent and require only Chapters 1 through 3 as background. Chapter 6, in particular, may readily be omitted in a shorter course. If it is desired to place less emphasis on number systems, Chapter 3 may be omitted by assuming that the properties of number systems are known.

The author wishes to apologize for the many topics of interest not adequately covered in this text. The needs of future secondary teachers have been given first priority in selecting the material to be included. In addition, the attempt has been made to provide a sound foundation for advanced work in algebraic theory. It is hoped that the introduction given here will stimulate the reader to pursue these topics further in more course work or through individual study.

Suggestions for this revision have come from many individuals and although it was impossible to incorporate them all, they were greatly appreciated. I would especially like to thank Donald Freeburg, whose thoughtful and detailed comments have been most useful. I also appreciate the encouragement and help provided by the staff of Addison-Wesley in carrying out the project.

Bozeman, Montana   J. E. W.
December 1972

CONTENTS

CHAPTER I

FUNDAMENTAL CONCEPTS

1-1 INTRODUCTION

One of the basic difficulties encountered in the study of any subject is the problem of language. In every field of endeavor, there are terms peculiar to the area which must be mastered before any serious progress can be made. In cases where the terminology is presumed known and therefore not described specifically, a serious obstacle is raised in the path of the student who may be convinced that the subject is beyond his ability or who may try to apply interpretations of words not suited to the subject matter and thus become hopelessly confused. This chapter is an attempt to help overcome this difficulty by discussing certain concepts, terms, and interpretations that are basic to mathematics.

Many of the concepts introduced here are as important in analysis or geometry as in algebra. The notions of set, relation, and function, as well as the meanings of the standard connectives of logic, are important in most areas of mathematics. The concept of an equivalence relation, which appears in many branches of mathematics, is of singular interest in algebra. Its importance in the study of algebra cannot be overemphasized. It will form an essential part of nearly every topic discussed throughout this book.

1-2 LOGICAL TERMS

The terms defined in this section are familiar to the reader. However, the correct mathematical usage is not always compatible with commonly understood usage in other areas of discourse. It is well, then, to spend the time necessary to make sure that these terms which will be used throughout the text are clearly understood at the outset.

By a *statement*, or *proposition*, we will understand the content of any declarative sentence, that is, any sentence which states a fact. It will be assumed that whenever we make a statement, we are asserting the truth of the statement. By the *negation* of a statement we mean the sentence which asserts that the statement is false. The negation of the statement "two is less than three" might be written "it is false that two is less than three," but is more commonly written "two is not less than three." Whatever the wording, the negation of a statement has the property of being false whenever the original statement is true and true whenever the original statement is false. We will designate arbitrary statements by italic lower-case letters such as p or q, and the negation of the statement p by the symbolism "not-p." Thus if p is the statement "it is raining," then not-p is the statement "it is not raining."

There are several ways to combine statements to form new statements. If p and q represent arbitrary statements, we may form the statement "p and q," called the *conjunction* of p with q. This new statement has the property of being true whenever both p and q are true, and false if either or both of p and q are false. Since this usage is customary in ordinary conversation, we will not discuss it further here.

Another way to combine statements p and q is to form the statement "either p or q," called the *disjunction* (more precisely, the inclusive disjunction) of p with q. In mathematical usage this statement will always bear the connotation "either p or q or both." Whenever it is desired to express the alternative meaning "either p or q but not both," the phrase "but not both" will always be included. This last interpretation is referred to as *exclusive disjunction*, and while it is very commonly understood in ordinary conversation, it is rarely intended in a mathematical context. "Either p or q," as used here, will have the property of being true in case either one or both of p and q are true and of being false only in case both p and q are false. For example, both of the following are true statements:

Either three is an odd integer or three is even.
Either three is an odd integer or three is greater than two.

The negation of the statement "p and q" is the statement, "either not-p or not-q." Similarly, the negation of "either p or q" is the statement "not-p and not-q."

Most mathematical theorems are written in the form "if p, then q" for some statements p and q. Consider, for instance, the theorem "if a triangle is isosceles, then the base angles are equal." This type of statement is called a *material implication* and will be written in symbols as $p \rightarrow q$, where p is called the *antecedent* of the implication and q is the *consequent* of the implication. Because such implications are most commonly used where the antecedent is a true statement, a great deal of misunderstanding arises concerning the truth of the statement for the various cases. We will define the statement $p \rightarrow q$ to be true if p is true and q is true, or if p is false no matter whether q is true or false. Then $p \rightarrow q$ will be false only if p is true and q is false. For the following four implications, the first and the last two are true, and only the second is false.

If x is an odd integer, then x^2 is odd.   (True)
If x is an odd integer, then x^2 is even.   (False)
If 2 is odd, then 4 is even.   (True)
If 2 is odd, then 4 is odd.   (True)

The negation of the implication, "if p, then q," is the statement "p and not-q."

Associated with any implication are two others which are very important.

If $p \to q$ is any implication, then the implication $q \to p$ is called the *converse* of the given implication. The converse is a new implication formed from the old which may be true or false independently of the truth or falsity of the original implication. There are many theorems in mathematics whose converses are true, but there are also many others whose converses are false. The theorem "if a triangle is equilateral, then it is isosceles" has as its converse the statement "if a triangle is isosceles, then it is equilateral." Of these, the first is true and the second is false. In stating or proving a theorem, one should be very careful to distinguish between an implication and its converse.

A second implication associated with a given implication $p \to q$ is the implication, "not-$q \to$ not-p," called the *contrapositive* of the given implication. The contrapositive of an implication has the property of being true if and only if the given implication is true. The reader should check this by referring to the definitions of negation and implication. Because of this property, the contrapositive is useful in mathematics. It often happens that a given theorem is difficult to prove, but that if the contrapositive is taken, the proof becomes easy. The proof that the contrapositive is true is an acceptable proof that the theorem holds. As an example, suppose we consider the following theorem concerning the integer x: "If x^2 is odd, then x is odd." Instead of trying to examine all odd square integers, we will prove instead that the contrapositive is true. Namely, "if x is not odd, then x^2 is not odd." To say that x is not odd is to say that $x = 2k$ for some integer k. But then $x^2 = 4k^2$, which is clearly not an odd integer, and the proof is complete.

It should be added that our definition of converse and contrapositive refers to implications with a single antecedent. Implications with more than one antecedent, such as "if p and q, then r," possess more than one converse or contrapositive. We will usually avoid such cases by stating theorems so that the converse or contrapositive can be formed by the rules given here, and leave the more involved cases for advanced courses in logic.

There are various ways in which an implication may be stated in mathematical theorems. Some usages involve the phrases *necessary condition* or *sufficient condition*. For example, instead of saying "if a triangle is equilateral, then it is isosceles," we might equally well say "the fact that a triangle is equilateral is a sufficient condition that it be isosceles," or "in order that a triangle be equilateral, it is necessary that it be isosceles." Several minor variations of this wording arise in forming readable sentences. Still another form is to replace "if p, then q" by the statement "p only if q," which is equivalent. We might say, for example, that "a triangle is equilateral only if it is isosceles." This may be used interchangeably with the statements above. The meanings of these connectives are expressed by the following abbreviated statements, which are equivalent:

> If p, then q.
> q if p.
> p only if q.
> p is a sufficient condition for q.
> q is a necessary condition for p.

In certain theorems we wish to state that an implication $p \rightarrow q$ and its converse $q \rightarrow p$ are both true. Symbolically, we represent this by writing $p \leftrightarrow q$. In words, we state this as "p if and only if q" or as "p is necessary and sufficient for q." The theorem "a triangle is isosceles if and only if the base angles of the triangle are equal" is an example of such a statement. Another example is the theorem "a necessary and sufficient condition that two lines be parallel is that either they have the same slope or neither one has a slope."

We conclude this section with a final remark concerning methods of proof. A *direct proof* of an implication is a proof which begins with the assumption that the antecedent is true and proceeds by logically clear steps to the conclusion that the consequent must also be true. An *indirect proof* is a proof which begins with the assumption that the consequent is false and proceeds by logically clear steps, using any given antecedents, to the conclusion that one of the given antecedents or some known true statement must then be false. We say that this establishes a *contradiction*. Since our logical system presupposes that no such contradictions can exist, our assumption that the consequent is false cannot be correct. Hence the consequent must be true, and the proof is complete. The simplest example of an indirect proof is that in which the contrapositive of the given implication is proved to be true.

EXERCISES

1. Write the negation of each of the following statements without using the phrase "it is false that."

   a) Three is odd and six is even.
   b) Either this triangle is a right triangle or it is isosceles.
   c) If a triangle is isosceles, then the median drawn to one of its sides is perpendicular to that side.
   d) The equation $ax = b$ can be solved for x if and only if a is not zero.

2. Give the converse and the contrapositive of each of the following implications:

   a) If a is less than b, then $2a$ is less than $2b$.
   b) If two lines are perpendicular to the same line, they are parallel.
   c) If $x^2 = 4$, then $x = \pm 2$.
   d) If a function $f(x)$ has a derivative at $x = a$, then it is continuous at $x = a$.

3. Rewrite each of the implications in Exercise 2, using the "only if" terminology.

4. Rewrite each of the implications in Exercise 2, using the word "sufficient."

5. Rewrite each of the implications in Exercise 2, using the word "necessary."

6. Write a true implication whose converse is also true.

7. Write a true implication whose converse is false.

8. Verify directly that the implication "if p, then q" is true or false in exactly the same cases as its contrapositive by considering the three cases, p and q both true, both false, or one true and one false.

1-3   SETS

Certain words in mathematics are so fundamental that they cannot be defined. *Point* and *line* are undefined in plane geometry, although the student quickly develops an intuitive understanding of their meaning from examples and illustrations. Similarly, we will take the words *set* and *element* as undefined. The word set is synonymous with *collection, class,* and *aggregate* and has the property of being associated with certain other objects called elements, which are said to be *members* of the set. Examples of sets are the set of all chairs in a given room, the set of days in a given year, and the set of the names of all past Presidents of the United States. In these examples, each chair is an element in the set of chairs, each day is an element in the set of days, and each name is an element in the set of names. Sets more common in mathematics courses are the set of all right triangles in a plane, the set of all lines through a given point in space, or the set of all numbers. While sets of interest usually contain elements with some rather obvious common property, as in the above examples, this is not a necessary restriction. The mere fact that the elements belong to the same set is itself a common property. Thus a set might consist of this book, the planet Mars, and the six letters of the word "number."

It will be assumed that whenever a set is given, it will be possible to determine from the description whether or not any given object is a member of the set. We say that the set is *well defined* in this case and no other sets will be considered. For instance, "the set of all boys" is not well defined. However, "the set of all living male humans between the ages of 2 and 19 years, inclusive, on July 1, 1971, whose legal residence on this date is within the boundaries of the United States of America" is a well-defined set. Here we must assume that legal residence and the other words are clearly defined. It is usually easier to describe precisely those sets which occur in mathematics than those sets which occur in everyday life. However, in every application of set theory, it is important that the elements which belong to each set be clearly understood. This is equally significant in preparing a legal document and in mathematics.

We will usually denote sets by capital letters and elements of sets by lower-case letters. Suppose that for some set A, x is a member of the set. We will indicate this by writing $x \in A$ and will read this as "x is a member of A," or "x belongs to A," or "x is in A." If y is an element which is not a member of A, we write $y \notin A$. If $\mathbf{Z}$ is used to denote the set of all integers, positive, negative, and zero, we may write $3 \in \mathbf{Z}, -2 \in \mathbf{Z}, \frac{1}{2} \notin \mathbf{Z}$.

There are several ways in which a set may be specified. The most obvious is the method used above where the set was given by describing the elements belonging to the set in a sentence. Another method is to list, within braces, each element of the set. For example, if the set of those positive integers less than 10 is denoted by T, it can be given by writing

$$T = \{1, 2, 3, 4, 5, 6, 7, 8, 9\}.$$

The final notation for sets, sometimes referred to as the *set-builder notation*, consists of a pair of braces within which occur a generic symbol or *variable* followed by a vertical bar and a statement involving the variable.   The set represented by the notation is the set of all objects such that a replacement of the variable in the statement by the name of the object converts the sentence into a true statement. The set is often called the *solution set* of the statement.   The statement may be given in words, or with symbols in the form of an equation or inequality.

For example, if Z denotes the set of all integers, the set T mentioned above may be specified in the following way:

$T = \{x|x \in Z, x$ is positive, and x is less than $10\}$.   We read this notation as "the set of all x such that x is in Z, x is positive, and x is less than 10."   As a further example, the set $S = \{-3, -2, -1, 0, 1, 2, 3\}$ may be expressed as:

$$S = \{x|x \in Z \text{ and } |x| \leq 3\}.$$

In some cases where there is no danger of ambiguity, the notation may be abbreviated by omitting the name of the larger set.   For instance, in a discussion dealing only with integers, the following notations could be used for the sets S and T above:

$$S = \{x| |x| \leq 3\}, \qquad T = \{x|0 < x < 10\}.$$

In some instances a single symbol such as x is not suitable for representing a general element of the set.   For instance, consider the set E of all quadratic equations in the unknown x whose coefficients are integers.   This set is an important one in elementary algebra.   Each member of the set has the form $ax^2 + bx + c = 0$, where a, b, and c are integers.   Hence a suitable notation for the set E would be:

$$E = \{ax^2 + bx + c = 0 | a, b, \text{ and } c \text{ are integers}\}.$$

Example 1–1.   Describe in words the set $\{x\,|\,x^2 < 5 \text{ and } x \in Z\}$.   This set is the set containing all integers whose square is less than 5.   The elements in the set are 0, ± 1, and ± 2.

Example 1–2.   Use one of the notations for sets to specify the set of all values of $\cos x$ for x a real number.   We might denote this set by

$$\{\cos x \,|\, x \text{ is a real number}\},$$

or by

$$\{y \,|\, y = \cos x \text{ for a real number } x\},$$

or by

$$\{z \,|\, -1 \leq z \leq 1 \text{ and } z \text{ is a real number}\}.$$

Each of these notations represents the same set, namely, the possible values of $\cos x$.   There is, of course, no single correct answer.   The set is a specific set but there are many ways in which one may express it.

Example 1–3.   Use one of the notations given to specify the set of all points in the cartesian plane lying outside the circle with center at the origin having radius 5. In analytic geometry, a point in the cartesian plane is represented by a pair (x, y)

of real numbers. Thus we may specify this set of points by the notation $\{(x, y) \mid x^2 + y^2 > 25\}$. The inequality $x^2 + y^2 > 25$ is derived by considering points whose distance from the origin exceeds 5. When the distance formula from analytic geometry is used, this condition requires that the point (x, y) satisfy the condition

$$\sqrt{(x - 0)^2 + (y - 0)^2} > 5,$$

or that $x^2 + y^2 > 25$.

The language of sets is largely self-evident, and is so basic to mathematics that most readers will be familiar with the terminology from earlier courses. We shall formalize the definitions of the more common terms for reference in writing proofs and to ensure a common background of understanding throughout the remainder of this text.

Definition 1. Two sets are *equal* if and only if they contain exactly the same elements.

For example, $\{a, b, c\} = \{b, a, c\}$, but $\{a, b, c\} \neq \{1, 2, 3\}$ and $\{a, b, c\} \neq \{a, b, c, d\}$. It is also clear from the definition that a set is determined by its elements and not by the notation used in expressing the set. Thus

$$\{1, 2, 3\} = \{x \mid x \in \mathbf{Z} \quad \text{and} \quad 0 < x < 4\}.$$

Definition 2. A set X is a *subset* of a set Y if each element which is a member of X is also a member of Y. When X is a subset of Y, we write $X \subseteq Y$. If, in addition, there is at least one element in Y which is not a member of X, we say X is a *proper subset* of Y, and denote this by $X \subset Y$.

For example, both of the statements $\{a, b\} \subseteq \{a, b, c\}$ and $\{a, b\} \subset \{a, b, c\}$ are correct. The latter notation calls attention to the fact that $\{a, b\}$ is a proper subset of $\{a, b, c\}$, but either is a correct statement. We may also state, correctly, that $\{a, b\} \subseteq \{a, b\}$, whereas the statement $\{a, b\} \subset \{a, b\}$ is false.

In many proofs (such as Example 1–8) which require that we show two sets to be equal, it is convenient to note the following relationship:

$$X = Y \quad \text{if and only if} \quad X \subseteq Y \text{ and } Y \subseteq X.$$

The condition that the sets X and Y are equal is clearly equivalent, from our definitions, to the statement that each element in X is a member of Y and each element of Y is an element of X. These two statements are equivalent to stating that each of X and Y is a subset of the other.

Many formulas and theorems which are stated in the language of sets require statements of exception which can be avoided by considering as a special set a set which contains no elements. We call this set the *empty set* and denote it by $\varnothing$. An alternative notation which is often used is the symbol $\{\ \}$, suggesting a listing of no elements. This latter notation should not be confused with the symbol $\{\varnothing\}$ which is not the empty set, but a set having one element, $\varnothing$. We shall have occasion to consider sets whose elements are themselves sets and the symbol $\{\varnothing\}$ might appear in this context, but is never a correct notation for the empty set.

Definition 3. The *empty set*, denoted by $\varnothing$, is a set which contains no elements.

Example 1-4. The set $X = \{a, b, c\}$ contains eight subsets, seven of which are proper subsets. They are $\varnothing$, $\{a\}$, $\{b\}$, $\{c\}$, $\{a, b\}$, $\{a, c\}$, $\{b, c\}$, and $\{a, b, c\}$. The fact that $\varnothing$ is a subset of X can be proved by noting that since $\varnothing$ contains no elements, we can correctly state that each element of $\varnothing$ is an element of X. We sometimes refer to this by saying that the requirement is *vacuously fulfilled*.

In the previous example, note that three of the subsets listed contain a single element. We will always distinguish between a set having one element and the element itself. Referring to this example, it is correct to write $a \in X$ or $\{a\} \subseteq X$. In the first case we are thinking of a as an element in X and in the second case we are thinking of that subset of X which contains the single element a.

In connection with a set and its subsets, there is a special case of considerable interest in algebra. It sometimes happens that for a certain set S there is a collection of subsets $X_1, X_2, \ldots, X_n$ which have the property that every element of the set S is a member of one and only one of the subsets $X_1, X_2, \ldots, X_n$. That is, no two of the X's have an element in common and every element of S is a member of some one of the X's. When this is the case, we say that $X_1, X_2, \ldots, X_n$ form a *partition* of S. For example, the sets, $X_1 = \{1\}$, $X_2 = \{2, 4, 5\}$, and $X_3 = \{3, 6, 7, 8, 9\}$, form a partition of the set T mentioned above. Note that the partition consists of the *three* sets $X_1, X_2,$ and X_3. Each of the sets $X_1, X_2,$ and X_3 is referred to as a *member* of the partition.

Definition 4. If $X_1, X_2, \ldots, X_n$ are subsets of a set S such that each element of S is an element in one and only one of the subsets $X_1, X_2, \ldots, X_n$, then $\{X_1, X_2, \ldots, X_n\}$ is called a *partition* of S, and each of the sets $X_1, X_2, \ldots, X_n$ is a *member* of the partition.

Example 1-5. Give one partition of the set **R** of all real numbers. There are, of course, many correct answers. One such answer is $\{X_1, X_2, X_3\}$, where $X_1 = \{x \mid x \text{ is a real number and } x < 0\}$, $X_2 = \{x \mid x \text{ is a real number and } 0 \leq x \leq 10\}$, and $X_3 = \{x \mid x \text{ is a real number and } x > 10\}$.

There are two ways in which new sets can be formed from given sets that will be important in our discussions. These new sets are described in the following definition.

Definition 5. If X and Y are arbitrary sets, then the *union* of X and Y, denoted $X \cup Y$, is defined to be

$$X \cup Y = \{s \mid \text{either } s \in X \text{ or } s \in Y\},$$

and the *intersection* of X and Y, denoted by $X \cap Y$, is defined to be

$$X \cap Y = \{t \mid t \in X \text{ and } t \in Y\}.$$

The union of two sets is the set formed by combining the given sets. It is composed of those elements which are elements of either one (or both) of the given sets. The intersection of two sets, on the other hand, consists of those elements which are elements of both sets. In the case that the two sets have no elements in common, then the intersection of the sets is the empty set.

Example 1–6. If $X = (a, b, c)$, $Y = (b, c, d)$ and $Z = (d, e, f)$, then $X \cup Y = \{a, b, c, d\}$, $X \cup Z = \{a, b, c, d, e, f\}$, $X \cap Y = \{b, c\}$, and $X \cap Z = \emptyset$.

Example 1–7. We will prove that if X and Y are arbitrary sets, then $X \cap Y \subseteq X$. Let x be any element in $X \cap X$. By definition of intersection, $x \in X$. By definition of subset, we may conclude that $X \cap Y \subseteq X$, since every element of $X \cap Y$ is in X.

Example 1–8. We will prove that if $X \subseteq Y$ then $X \cup Y = Y$.

Proof. Suppose that $X \subseteq Y$. Let s be an arbitrary element of $X \cup Y$. By definition of union, either $s \in X$ or $s \in Y$. But since $X \subseteq Y$, $s \in Y$ in either case by definition of subset. Hence every element of $X \cup Y$ is in Y and $X \cup Y \subseteq Y$.
　　　　Conversely, suppose $t \in Y$. Then, by definition of union, $t \in X \cup Y$. Hence every element of Y is in $X \cup Y$ and $Y \subseteq X \cup Y$. From these two results we conclude that $X \cup Y = Y$.

EXERCISES

1. List all subsets of the set $\{a, b, c, d\}$.

2. Describe in words each of the following sets, where $\mathbf{Z}$ is the set of all integers, positive, negative, and zero.

   a) $\{x \mid x \in \mathbf{Z}$, and x is a prime$\}$. [*Note:* A prime is an integer n, neither 0 nor ± 1, which contains no factors other than $\pm n$ and ± 1.]
   b) $\{x \mid x \in \mathbf{Z}$ and $x \geq 10\}$
   c) $\{x \mid x \in \mathbf{Z}$ and $x - 7 = 3\}$
   d) $\{x \mid x \in \mathbf{Z}$ and x is a multiple of 3$\}$

3. Use one of the notations for sets given in this section to specify each of the following sets.

   a) The set consisting of the three smallest integers which are larger than 10.
   b) The set of all linear equations in two unknowns having real numbers as coefficients.
   c) The set of all values of sin x for x a real number.
   d) The set of all points in the cartesian plane lying on the line which passes through the points (1,0) and (0,1).
   e) The set of all points in the cartesian plane lying above and to the right of the line mentioned in d) above.
   f) The set of all integers which are solutions of the equation $x^2 + x + 1 = 0$.
   g) The set of all points in the cartesian plane lying within or on a circle of radius 2 with center at the origin.

4. Find three different partitions for the set $\mathbf{Z}$ of all integers.

5. Let $X = \{1, 3, 5\}$, $Y = \{2, 4, 6\}$ and $Z = \{3, 4, 5, 6\}$. Find each of the following.

a) $X \cup Y$ b) $X \cup Z$ c) $Y \cup Z$
d) $X \cap Y$ e) $X \cap Z$ f) $Y \cap Z$

6. Let X and Y be arbitrary sets. Prove each of the following.

a) $\varnothing \subseteq X$ b) $X \subseteq X$ c) $X \subseteq X \cup Y$
d) $X \cup X = X$ e) $X \cap X = X$ f) $X \cup \varnothing = X$
g) $X \cap \varnothing = \varnothing$

7. Prove that if $X \subseteq Y$ then $X \cap Y = X$.

8. Determine whether each of the following is true or false. Consider the statement false if the notation is used incorrectly.

a) $\{1, 3, 5\} = \{x \mid x$ is an odd integer between 0 and 6$\}$
b) $\{1, 2\} \subset \{1, 2\}$
c) $\{1, 2\} \subseteq \{1, 2\}$
d) $x \in \{a, x, 7\}$
e) $\{x\} \in \{a, x, 7\}$
f) $\{a, b\} \subseteq \{\{a, b\}, \{c, d\}\}$
g) $\{a, b\} \in \{\{a, b\}, \{c, d\}\}$
h) For all sets X and Y, $X \cup Y = Y \cup X$ and $X \cap Y = Y \cap X$
i) For all sets X, Y, and Z, $X \cap (Y \cup Z) = (X \cap Y) \cup (X \cap Z)$
j) For all sets X and Y, $X \cup (X \cap Y) = X$

1-4 PRODUCT SETS

In analytic geometry the properties of plane figures are studied with the help of a rectangular coordinate system which represents each point in the plane as an ordered pair of real numbers. The word *ordered* refers to the fact that the point (a, b) is distinct from the point (b, a), in case $a \neq b$. This in only one of the possible uses for ordered pairs, which we will interpret as the general elements of product sets, to be defined below.

We define an *ordered pair* to be a set containing exactly two elements, with the additional property that the elements can be distinguished as a first element and a second element. Whereas the set $\{a, b\}$ is identical to the set $\{b, a\}$, the ordered pair (a, b) is distinct from the ordered pair (b, a). We will use parentheses for ordered pairs to emphasize this fact. The first and second elements of an ordered pair may be elements taken from the same set, or from different sets, depending on the circumstances. For instance, in the ordered pairs representing points in a plane, both elements are members of the set of real numbers. However, suppose that seats are to be assigned by number to the members of a class; we might consider a solution of the seating problem to be the finding of a suitable set of ordered pairs in which each first element is a name and each second element a seat number. (Smith, 14) might be one of the ordered pairs selected.

Definition. The *cartesian product*, or simply the *product*, of two sets X and Y

will be denoted by $X \times Y$, and is defined as the set of all ordered pairs (x, y) such that $x \in X$ and $y \in Y$. We can write this in set notation as follows:

$$X \times Y = \{(x, y) \mid x \in X \text{ and } y \in Y\}.$$

Example 1-9. Suppose that $X = \{1, 2, 3\}$ and $Y = \{\$, \# \}$, then

$$X \times Y = \{(1, \$), (1, \#), (2, \$), (2, \#,) (3, \$), (3, \#)\}.$$

Note that $X \times Y \neq Y \times X$. As a further example,

$$Y \times Y = \{(\$, \$), (\$, \#), (\#, \$), (\#, \#)\}.$$

With this definition we see that the cartesian plane of analytic geometry may be interpreted as a geometric representation of the product set $\mathbf{R} \times \mathbf{R}$, where $\mathbf{R}$ is the set of real numbers. If $\mathbf{Z}$ is the set of integers, $\mathbf{Z} \times \mathbf{Z}$ is represented in the plane by the set of all points having integers as coordinates.

Example 1-10. Consider the statistical experiment of rolling together two dice the first red and the second blue. The possible "outcomes" of this experiment may be thought of as the elements of the product set $S \times S$, where $S = \{1, 2, 3, 4, 5, 6\}$. The product set contains as elements the 36 ordered pairs having the integers from 1 through 6 as first and second elements. The first element of each ordered pair represents the face showing on the red die and the second element of each ordered pair represents the face showing on the blue die. Among the elements of this product set are $(1, 1)$, $(1, 2)$, $(2, 1)$, etc.

The concept of the product of two sets can be extended to the product of any number of sets. We have no use for infinite products, so we will define the product of only a finite number n of sets. An *n-tuple* is a set having exactly n elements, with the further property that these elements can be distinguished as first, second, ..., nth elements of the set. The notation $(a_1, a_2, \ldots, a_n)$ is used to denote an n-tuple. This is a natural extension of the notion of ordered pairs. Now, if sets $A_1, A_2, \ldots, A_n$ are given, the *cartesian product* of these sets, in this order, is represented by $A_1 \times A_2 \times \cdots \times A_n$ and is defined as follows:

$$A_1 \times A_2 \times \cdots \times A_n$$
$$= \{(a_1, a_2, \ldots, a_n) \mid a_i \in A_i \quad \text{for each} \quad i = 1, 2, \ldots, n\}.$$

That is, a cartesian product of n sets in a given order is the set of all n-tuples of elements which can be formed such that the ith element of each n-tuple is an element in the ith set. In the case $n = 2$ this definition reduces to that already given for the product of two sets and hence this definition is an extension of the former.

EXERCISES

1. If M is the set $\{1, 3, 4\}$, write out the nine elements of the product set $M \times M$.

2. If N is the set $\{2, 4, 6\}$ and M is the set of Exercise 1, write out the elements of $M \times N$ and of $N \times M$.

3. What set of points in the plane corresponds to the set $\mathbf{Z}^0 \times \mathbf{Z}^0$, where $\mathbf{Z}^0$ is the set of nonnegative integers, that is, $\mathbf{Z}^0 = \{0, 1, 2, 3, \ldots\}$?

4. Construct an example that might occur in business of a product set in which not both elements of the ordered pairs are numbers.

5. Consider the following experiment. Four coins, a penny, a nickel, a dime, and a quarter, are placed in a hat. From the hat a blindfolded person draws a coin. The coin is then flipped and the result is recorded as to which coin is drawn and whether the coin lands heads or tails. Define a product set whose elements may be considered as the eight possible outcomes of this experiment. List all eight elements of the product set.

6. Let $A = \{1, 3, 5\}, B = \{3, 4, 5\}$, and $C = \{0, 1\}$. Determine each of the following sets and list all elements of each set.
   a) $(A \cup B) \times C$
   b) $C \times (A \cap B)$
   c) $(A \cap C) \times (A \cap B)$
   d) $(A \times C) \cap (A \times B)$

7. Let $S = \{1, 2\}$. List the elements of $S \times S \times S$.

1-5   RELATIONS AND THEIR GRAPHS

Relations occur frequently in mathematics and in everyday life. The symbol $\leq$ represents a relation that is satisfied by certain pairs of real numbers. For instance, $1 \leq 2$, but it is not true that $3 \leq 2$. The phrase "is a brother of" is an example of a relation used in everyday conversation.

   In order to be precise, we will formulate a definition of a relation which at first appears to have little connection with the intuitive idea one gains from considering examples like those above, but which we will show includes these examples in a very natural way.

   Definition. A *binary relation R from a subset of X into a set Y* is any subset of the product $X \times Y$.

   The word "binary" will usually be omitted when we speak of relations. As an example, if $X = \{1, 2, 3\}$ and $Y = \{\$, \#\}$, three possible relations from a subset of X into Y are

$$R_1 = \{(1, \$), (1, \#), (2, \$)\}, \qquad R_2 = \{(3, \#)\},$$

and

$$R_3 = \{(2, \$), (2, \#), (3, \$), (3, \#)\}.$$

In any relation R, from a subset of A into B, the subset of elements of A which appear in R as first elements of pairs is called the *domain* of the relation. The set of elements of B which appear in R as second elements of pairs is called the *range* of the relation. The domain of R_3, above, is $\{2, 3\}$, and the range of R_3 is $\{\$, \#\}$, the entire set Y. By a *relation from X into Y* we will mean a relation whose domain is the entire set X.

In many cases where a relation is of interest, the two sets involved are the same set. If a relation R from a subset of S into S is used, it will be referred to as a *relation in S*. Both examples at the beginning of this section are of this type. The relation $\leq$ is a relation in **R**, the set of real numbers. To see that $\leq$ really represents a subset of $\mathbf{R} \times \mathbf{R}$, we consider all pairs of real numbers (a, b) such that $a \leq b$ is a true statement. This subset of $\mathbf{R} \times \mathbf{R}$ is the subset corresponding to the relation $\leq$ We might write that

$$\leq \, = \{(a, b) \,|\, a \leq b \text{ for real numbers } a \text{ and } b\}.$$

Again, if the relation "is a brother of" is designated by the set B, we may say that B is a relation in the set M of all men. That is, B is a subset of $M \times M$, defined as the sets of all pairs (x, y), where x and y are men such that the sentence "x is a brother of y" is true:

$$B = \{(x, y) \,|\, x \text{ and } y \text{ are men and } x \text{ is a brother of } y\}.$$

A custom which is confusing to the beginning student but in very common use involves two quite different uses for the symbol R representing a relation. Suppose that R is a relation from a subset of X into a set Y and that (x, y) is a pair belonging to R. The most natural notation which describes (x, y) as a member of the subset R is to write $(x, y) \in R$. However, it is customary to write $x \, R \, y$ instead.

$$x \, R \, y \quad \text{means} \quad (x, y) \in R.$$

Since this notation is in common use, we will adopt it here, even though it is confusing. With this explanation it should now be clear that $\leq$, as commonly used, is actually a relation satisfying our formal definition. The statements $a \leq b$ and $(a, b) \in \, \leq$ are equivalent, even though they appear quite different.

Since a relation is a set, it should be clear from the discussion of set notations that a relation can be expressed in many ways. It may be given by listing the members of the set, it may be described in words, or it may be given in the usual set notation, using open sentences, equations, or inequalities. Consider the relation $P = \{(x, y) \,|\, x + y = 1\}$ defined in the set of all real numbers. This relation contains as elements the pairs of real numbers representing the points on a line in the cartesian plane. Both the domain and the range of the relation are the set of all real numbers. It is natural to graph this relation in the plane in the way that equations are graphed in elementary algebra and analytic geometry. The graph of the relation is shown in Fig. 1–1.

Graphs of relations from a subset of A into a set B are commonly used where A and B are sets of numbers. These graphs are drawn in the usual rectangular coordinate system.

Example 1–11. Consider the set $S = \{1, 2, 3, 4, 5\}$ and the relation Q in S defined by $Q = \{(x, y) \,|\, x < y\}$. The graph of this relation is shown in Fig. 1–2. The domain of the relation is the set $\{1, 2, 3, 4\}$ and the range is the set $\{2, 3, 4, 5\}$.

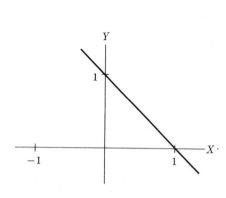

Fig. 1–1.   Graph (incomplete) of the relation $P = \{(x, y) \mid x + y = 1\}$.

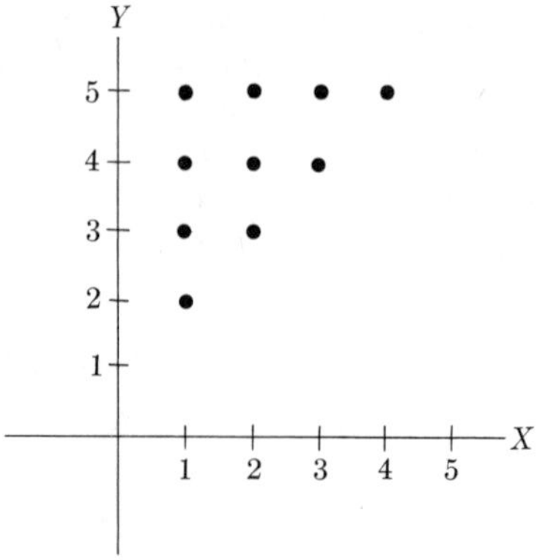

Fig. 1–2.   Graph of the relation $\{(x, y) \mid x < y\}$ in the set $s = \{1, -2, 3, 4, 5\}$.

Example 1–12.   Consider the relation $T = \{(x, y) \mid x^2 + y^2 \leq 4\}$ defined in the set **Z** of all integers.   The graph is given in Fig. 1–3.   Both the domain and the range of this relation are the set $\{-2, -1, 0, 1, 2\}$.

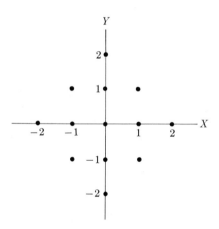

Fig. 1–3.   Graph of the relation $\{(x, y) \mid x^2 + y^2 \leq 4\}$ in the set **Z** of all integers.

Example 1–13.   We will graph a part of the relation $\{(x, y) \mid x + 2y \geq 6\}$ considered as a relation in the set of all real numbers.   Considering first the subset $\{(x, y) \mid x + 2y = 6\}$, we note that the graph is the straight line passing through the points $(0, 3)$ and $(6, 0)$.   Next, any point $P(x_1, y_1)$ in the plane above and to the right of this line can be compared to a point Q on the line with the same ordinate y_1, but having abscissa x_2.   Since $x_1 > x_2$, $x_1 + 2y_1 > x_2 + 2y_1 = 6$, where $x_2 + 2y_1 = 6$ because (x_2, y_1) lies on the line $x + 2y \geq 6$.   Thus the coordinates of the point P satisfy the inequality $x + 2y \geq 6$, indicating that the

point P is included in the graph.   Similarly, any point below and to the left of
the line fails to satisfy the given inequality and hence is not part of the graph.
The graph of the given relation is therefore the half-plane consisting of points
above and to the right of the line $x + 2y = 6$, as well as all points on this line.
Part of the graph is shown in Fig. 1–4.

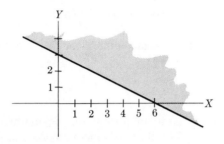

Fig. 1–4.   Graph of part of the relation $\{(x, y) \mid x + 2y \geq 6\}$ in the set of real numbers.

The terminology and notation used here are rapidly becoming standard in
high school texts.   (See Johnson [13], Brumfiel [4], and others)*.   The set specified
by an equation or inequality is often referred to as the *solution set* of the equation or inequality.   Thus we say that the solution set of the equation $3x + 2y = 5$
is the set $\{(x, y) \mid 3x + 2y = 5\}$.   We no longer require a student to "graph the
equation $3x + 2y = 5$," but instead direct him to "graph the solution set of the
equation $3x + 2y = 5$."   This terminology is more precise and provides a better
basis for generalization to advanced course work in college.

This terminology is part of the material often referred to as "new mathematics."   It should be understood that this mathematics is not new at all.   Only
the language is new, and it is much more comprehensible than that used in elementary texts a few years ago.

EXERCISES

1. Graph a reasonable part of the relation $\{(x, y) \mid y = 2x\}$ considered (a) in the set of real
   numbers and (b) in the set of integers.   In each case find the domain and the range of
   the relation.

2. Graph a reasonable portion of the relation $\{(x, y) \mid y = |x|\}$ considered (a) in the set of
   real numbers and (b) in the set of integers.   In each case give the domain and the range
   of the relation.

3. Let X be the set $\{1, 2, 3, 4, 5\}$ and Y be the set $\{1, 2, 3\}$.   Graph the product set $X \times Y$
   and the relation $\{(x, y) \mid x > y\}$ from a subset of X into Y.   Give the domain and the
   range of this relation.

---

* Numbers refer to references following Chapter 7.

4. Graph the relation $\{(x, y) \mid x^2 + y^2 = 25\}$ (a) in the set of real numbers and (b) in the set of integers.

5. Graph a reasonable portion of the relation $\{(x, y) \mid y = x^2\}$ considered as a relation from the set of real numbers into the set of nonnegative real numbers.

6. Graph a reasonable portion of the relation $\{(x, y) \mid y \geq 2x + 1\}$ considered as a relation in the set of real numbers.

7. Describe in words and with set notation the relation "is similar to" in the set of triangles in the plane.

8. Describe in words and with set notation the relation "has the same area as" in the set of all polygons in the plane.

1-6   FUNCTIONS

The concept of a function is an important one in mathematics, equally useful in analysis and in algebra.   The study of functions of a real variable is the central topic of most college freshman mathematics courses.   We are primarily interested in functions defined in various sets other than the real numbers, but it is possible to formulate the definition in such a way that it is adequate for use in any area of mathematics where the concept of function appears.

Definition 1.   A *function from a subset of* X *into a set* Y is a binary relation from a subset of X into Y, with the additional properties that (a) the relation is not the empty set and (b) if (x, a) and (x, b) are both members of the relation, then $a = b$.

In other words, a function is a nonempty relation in which each element in the domain of the relation appears as the first element of only a single ordered pair in the subset defining the relation.   The *domain of a function* and the *range of a function* are defined as for the more general term, relation.   That is, the domain is the set of all first elements and the range is the set of all second elements in the set of pairs which specifies the function.   If the domain of a function from a subset of X into Y is the entire set X, we call the function a function *from* X into Y.   The statement that F is a function from X into Y is sometimes abbreviated to the notation $F: X \rightarrow Y$.   This shortened notation is especially useful in cases where we wish to discuss an arbitrary function F, rather than a particular one specified by an equation or inequality.

If F is a function from a subset of X into Y, then F is a set of ordered pairs (x, y).   Since each x appears only once as a first element of a pair in F, an alternative notation for a function is possible.   We write $F(x) = y$ to represent the fact that the pair (x, y) is an element of F:

$$F(x) = y \quad \text{means that} \quad (x, y) \in F.$$

This notation is usually referred to as *functional notation*.   It would not be satisfactory for the representation of an arbitrary relation because for each x there could be several pairs in the relation containing x as a first element, making the notation $F(x)$ ambiguous. It frequently happens that a single element y appears many times as the second element of pairs in a particular function. For example, the real function sin x consists of those pairs $(x, \sin x)$ for real numbers x. For each real number x there is exactly one value of sin x, but each number from -1 to 1 appears infinitely many times as the sine of a number x. We see that $(0, 0)$, $(\pi, 0)$, and, in general, $(n\pi, 0)$ for any integer n are all pairs in the set describing the function sin x.

In Section 1–5, the relation graphed in Fig. 1–1 is a function. The relations in Fig. 1–2 and Fig. 1–3 are not functions, since some values of x appear in more than one of the pairs of the relation.

The word "mapping" is synonymous with the word "function." It is customary to use *function* in freshman mathematics, in calculus, and in many other places in analysis. *Mapping*, on the other hand, is used much more commonly in algebra and certain other areas of mathematics. We will use these words interchangeably, but in order to conform to standard practice, we will in most instances use mapping.

For the reader who is acquainted with functions but may feel that the definition given here is somewhat abstract, let us consider the definition of a function often given in mathematics texts and compare it with our definition. A common definition reads, "A variable y is said to be a function of a variable x if and only if each value of x determines a unique value of y." First, we point out that a variable is merely a symbol representing an arbitrary element of some set. Thus this definition refers to two sets, the set of permissible values of x and the set of corresponding values of y. Next, suppose that for each value of x and the y that it "determines," we write the pair (x, y). Then the statement that each x determines a unique y is merely the statement that if two pairs contain the same first element, then the second elements of these pairs must be equal. This definition is then equivalent to ours but is considered less rigorous, partly because the word "determines" is not clearly defined and suggests some form of computational procedure or formula which is not an essential requirement of a function.

Mappings (or functions) may be specified in any of the ways mentioned for relations. They may be given by one or more equations, by a listing of pairs, by sentences, or by a variety of ways.

For a given function F, when (x, y) is an element in F, or equivalently when $y = F(x)$, we speak of y as the *value of F at x*. When the word "mapping" is used for F, it is more common to refer to y as the *image of x under the mapping F*. We would still write $y = F(x)$ in this case. Again, where we refer to F as a mapping, the range of F is often called the *image set of F*.

Whenever we consider a mapping from a set X into a set Y, there are some other wordings in common use. We frequently say that we have a mapping *of* X into Y rather than *from* X into Y. Again, if F is the mapping (function) considered, we say that F *maps* X into Y. As when using the word "function," we often denote this mapping by $F: X \to Y$.

In general, mappings are *many-to-one*, by which we mean that many elements in the domain of this mapping have the same image element in the range. Recall, for example, the function sin x mentioned above. We say that a mapping (or function) is *one-to-one* provided that distinct elements in the domain always have distinct images in the range. The mapping $F = \{(x, y) \mid y = 3x - 2\}$ from the real numbers into the real numbers is one-to-one since each value of y in the range of F is the image of only a single x in the domain of F. A more precise definition follows.

Definition 2. A mapping F from a subset of a set X into a set Y is *one-to-one* if and only if whenever (a, y) and (b, y) are pairs in F, it follows that $a = b$.

Example 1–13. Prove that the mapping $F = \{(x, y) \mid y = 3x - 2\}$ from the real numbers into the real numbers is one-to-one.

Proof. Suppose that (a, y) and (b, y) are in F for some real numbers $a, b,$ and y. Then $y = 3a - 2$ and $y = 3b - 2$. Therefore $3a - 2 = 3b - 2$ from which it follows that $a = b$, so F is one-to-one.

Example 1–14. Prove that the mapping $G = \{(x, y) \mid y = x^2\}$ from the real numbers into the real numbers is not one-to-one.

Proof. From the definition of G, we see that the pairs $(2,4)$ and $(-2,4)$ both belong to G. Since $2 \neq -2$, G is not a one-to-one mapping.

Whenever a mapping is specified by listing all pairs explicitly, one can check whether or not the mapping is one-to-one by inspection. For example, the mapping H from the set $\{1, 2, 3\}$ into the set $\{2, 4, 6, 8\}$ given by $H = \{(1,6), (2,2), (3,8)\}$ is clearly one-to-one since no two pairs contain the same second element.

It is sometimes convenient to express the fact that a mapping F from a set X into a set Y has the property that every element of Y is in the image set of the mapping F. We describe this case by saying that F maps X *onto* Y. Thus if F maps X onto Y, for every $y \in Y$ there is an $x \in X$ such that $F(x) = y$. The word "into" which appears in the definition is always correct but when special attention is drawn to this property, the word "onto" is used instead.

Example 1–15. Prove that the mapping $F = \{(x, y) \mid y = 3x - 2\}$ from the set of real numbers into itself is a mapping *onto* the set of real numbers.

Proof. Let r be any real number. Then $(r + 2)/3$ is also a real number. But from the definition of F,

$$f\left(\frac{r + 2}{3}\right) = 3\left(\frac{r + 2}{3}\right) - 2 = r.$$

Hence r is the image of $(r + 2)/3$. Since r was arbitrary, the image set of F is the entire set of real numbers and F is a mapping from the real numbers onto the real numbers.

Example 1–16. Prove that the mapping $K = \{(x, y) \mid x \in \mathbf{Z} \text{ and } y = 2x\}$ is not a mapping from **Z** onto **Z**.

Proof. For every integer x, $K(x) = 2x$ is an even integer. Hence no odd integer is in the image set of K and hence K is not a mapping onto **Z**.

In advanced texts in algebra some other terms are often used to describe the special kinds of mappings we have referred to. A one-to-one mapping from a set X into a set Y is also called an *injection*. A mapping from X onto Y is referred to as a *surjection*. A mapping which is both one-to-one and onto, hence both an injection and a surjection, is often termed a *bijection*. These terms are mentioned to help in the reading of supplementary material, but will not be used further in this text.

A special mapping from a set S onto itself is worthy of comment. It is called the *identity mapping* and consists of the set of all pairs (x, x) for $x \in S$. This mapping is clearly one-to-one and onto. The word "identity" used in describing the mapping comes from a standard use of the term which appears in a later section.

EXERCISES

Exercises 1, 2, and 3 below all refer to the set $S = \{1, 2, 3, 4\}$. In each case a mapping from a subset of S into S is given.

1. $P = \{(1, 4), (2, 1), (3, 2)\}$

   a) What is the domain of P?
   b) What is the image set of P?
   c) Does P map S onto S?
   d) Is P one-to-one?

2. $Q = \{(1, 3), (2, 4)\}$

   a) Is Q a one-to-one mapping from a subset of S into S?
   b) Is Q a one-to-one mapping from a subset of S onto S?
   c) Is Q a mapping from S into S?

3. $R = \{(2, 1), (3, 4), (1, 2), (4, 3)\}$

   a) Is R a mapping from S into S?
   b) Is R a mapping from S onto S?
   c) Is R a one-to-one mapping from S into S?
   d) Is R a one-to-one mapping from S onto S?

4. Which of the relations described in Exercises 1 through 6 of Section 1-5 are mappings? Of those that are mappings, which are one-to-one?

5. For the function $F = \{(x, y) \mid 2x + 3y = 12\}$, find $F(0)$, $F(1)$, $F(5)$, and $F(-2)$, where F is considered a function from the set of real numbers into itself.

6. Find the image set for the mapping $\{(x, y) \mid y = 3x\}$, considered as a mapping from the set of all integers into itself.

7. Find a one-to-one mapping from the set of real numbers $0 < x < 1$ onto the set of real numbers $0 < x < 3$.

8. Suppose that a particular function F from X into Y is given by describing the ordered pairs belonging to the set F. If the elements in each pair in F are reversed in order, is the set of pairs so formed a function from Y into X? Explain. For what kinds of functions would your answer be different?

9. Prove that the mapping F from $\mathbf{Z}$ into $\mathbf{Z}$ ($\mathbf{Z}$ is the set of all integers) given by $F = \{(x, y) \mid y = x - 5\}$ is a one-to-one mapping from $\mathbf{Z}$ onto $\mathbf{Z}$.

10. Prove that the mapping G from the set of real numbers into itself given by $G = \{(x, y) \mid y = x^2 + 2\}$ is neither one-to-one nor onto.

1-7   BINARY OPERATIONS

The operations of addition, subtraction, multiplication, and division of real numbers are examples of binary operations familiar to every student. Less familiar are the binary operations of intersection and union defined for sets. In combining arithmetic fractions by finding a common denominator, still another binary operation is important—finding the least common multiple (LCM) of two numbers. We will formulate a definition general enough to include all these cases.

> **Definition.** A *binary operation* on a set A is a function from a subset of $A \times A$ into a set B.

In most, but not all, cases the domain of the function is the entire set $A \times A$, and the set B is A itself. To distinguish this special case, we say that the set A is *closed with respect to the binary operation* if the domain of the operation is $A \times A$ and the range is a subset of A. The binary operations mentioned in the first paragraph of this section are examples of the definition. Addition, multiplication, and subtraction can be considered as binary operations on the set of real numbers or on the set of integers, as well as on many other sets of numbers. The first two sets are closed with respect to these operations. Division is an operation on the set of real numbers $\mathbf{R}$, but $\mathbf{R}$ is not closed with respect to division, since the domain of the operation is not all of $\mathbf{R} \times \mathbf{R}$; that is, division by zero is not defined. Division is also an operation on the set of integers, but again the set is not closed with respect to the operation. Division by zero is still not defined, and the division of one integer by another is not always an integer and hence the range of the operation is not a subset of the integers.

To make our definition clear, we will formulate, for comparison, the operation of division for real numbers in set notation and in the usual way. As a function from a subset of $\mathbf{R} \times \mathbf{R}$ into $\mathbf{R}$, the operation of division should be written as a set of pairs whose first elements are elements from $\mathbf{R} \times \mathbf{R}$, and whose second elements are in $\mathbf{R}$. We could write this as follows:

$$\{((a, b), c) \mid a \in \mathbf{R}, 0 \neq b \in \mathbf{R}, \text{ and } c = a \div b\}.$$

Since this notation is very clumsy, we will write division in the usual way, as $a \div b = c$. Similarly, for any operation on a set A, we use a symbol representing the operation as a connective between the elements of the pair in the product set $A \times A$ and equate this to the image element under the mapping which gives the function. For example, the operation of set union is written $A \cup B = C$. Where the operation has no commonly used symbol, we will often use $\circ$ or $*$ to indicate the operation.

Consider the operation $*$ defined on the set of real numbers by

$$a * b = a + b - ab,$$

where the operations of addition, subtraction, and multiplication on the right side are the usual ones. We easily compute $2 * 3 = -1, 5 * 7 = -23$, and $(-3) * 5 = 17$. The set of real numbers is closed with respect to this operation. If we interpreted this operation as an operation on the set of positive integers, the set would not be closed with respect to the operation.

The definition of a binary operation is somewhat abstract, and necessarily so, since it must apply in many different circumstances in the material which follows. Loosely speaking, we may think of a binary operation as a rule by which two elements can be combined to produce a third element in a unique way. The student should reread the definition to satisfy himself that this is a reasonable interpretation.

There are certain standard terms used to distinguish binary operations having special properties. An operation $*$ on the set A is *commutative* if and only if $x * y = y * x$ for every x and y in A for which the operation is defined.

Commutative law for $*$: $x * y = y * x$.

Addition and multiplication for numbers, and intersection and union for sets, are examples of commutative operations. Division, however, is not commutative for numbers, since, example, $7 \div 14 \neq 14 \div 7$.

A binary operation $*$ on a set A is *associative* if $x * (y * z) = (x * y) * z$ for every x, y, and z in A for which the operation is defined.

Associative law for $*$: $x * (y * z) = (x * y) * z$.

Again, addition and multiplication of numbers, and intersection and union for sets, are examples of associative operations. Division of numbers is not associative, since, for example, $(12 \div 3) \div 2 \neq 12 \div (3 \div 2)$. The operation $*$ for numbers, defined above as $a * b = a + b - ab$, is both commutative and associative. Associativity can be proved as follows. For any real numbers x, y, and z,

$$
\begin{aligned}
x * (y * z) &= x * (y + z - yz) \\
&= x + y + z - yz - x(y + z - yz) \\
&= x + y + z - yz - xy - xz + xyz \\
&= x + y + z - xy - xz - yz + xyz.
\end{aligned}
$$

Similarly,

$$(x * y) * z = (x + y - xy) * z$$
$$= x + y - xy + z - (x + y - xy)z$$
$$= x + y - xy + z - xz - yz + xyz$$
$$= x + y + z - xy - xz - yz + xyz.$$

Since both expressions equal the same number, we have shown that $x * (y * z) = (x * y) * z$, and hence that $*$ is associative.

It sometimes happens that a set has two operations of interest and that these operations are related by an identity called the distributive law. Suppose that we refer to these operations as $*$ and $\circ$, defined on a set A. Then $*$ is *left-distributive over* $\circ$ (equivalently, it satisfies the left-distributive law) provided that

$$x * (y \circ z) = (x * y) \circ (x * z)$$

for every x, y, and z in A for which the operations are defined. We define *right-distributive* similarly.

Left-distributive law for $*$ over $\circ$: $x * (y \circ z) = (x * y) \circ (x * z)$.

Right-distributive law for $*$ over $\circ$: $(y \circ z) * x = (y * x) \circ (z * x)$.

For numbers, multiplications is both right- and left-distributive over addition. That is

$$a(b + c) = ab + ac \quad \text{and} \quad (b + c)a = ba + ca.$$

In sets, each of the operations of intersection and union is both right- and left-distributive over the other. That is, for left-distributive, we have

$$X \cap (Y \cup Z) = (X \cap Y) \cup (X \cap Z)$$

and also

$$X \cup (Y \cap Z) = (X \cup Y) \cap (X \cup Z).$$

As a final comment, we note that to prove that the commutative, associative, or distributive laws hold for given operations on a set, it is necessary to prove that the required identity is valid for every combination of elements in the set. This calls for a general proof, using literal representation of arbitrary elements. However, to prove that one of these laws does not hold, it is sufficient to give a single example, using specific elements, in which the identity fails to hold. This is referred to as a proof by *counterexample*.

In addition to the properties which characterize binary operations in relation to the way in which arbitrary elements combine, other equally important properties refer only to special elements in the set. By way of introduction, consider the number zero. Zero is unique among the set of integers because of certain properties it possesses in relation to the operation of addition. We learn, as children, that zero means none of something and, for purposes of counting, this property of the number zero is significant. However, to the mathematician other properties are more important. Zero is that integer with the property that $0 + x = x + 0 = x$ for every integer x. We refer to this property by saying that zero is the *additive identity element* for the set of integers. Clearly, zero is the only additive identity in the set. We may define identity relative to any operation on an arbitrary set.

> **Definition of identity element.** The element e is an *identity element* with respect to the operation $*$ on the set M if and only if $e * x = x * e = x$ for every x in the set M.

From the definition, it follows that the integer 1 is the identity with respect to the operation of multiplication in the set of integers or in any set of numbers which contains 1. To distinguish 1 from the additive identity 0, we refer to 1 as the *multiplicative identity*, rather than to use the longer phrase "identity with respect to multiplication."

Not every operation possesses an identity element in a given set. For example, there is no identity with respect to subtraction in the set of integers, or in any set of numbers. The number 0 might be considered a possibility, since $x - 0 = x$ for every integer x. However, the definition of identity would also require that $0 - x = x$ for all x, which is false. For instance, $0 - 3 = -3$, and $-3 \neq 3$. A little calculation will convince the reader that no other integer fares any better as a candidate for a subtractive identity. This illustration should remind you that to prove a given element e is the identity with respect to an operation $*$ in a set, it is essential to verify that both of the equations $x * e = x$ and $e * x = x$ are satisfied for every x in the set.

Example 1–17. Let $*$ be the operation in the set of real numbers, defined previously by $a * b = a + b - ab$. We will find the identity relative to $*$ and prove that it is the identity. If a number e is to be the identity relative to $*$ then $e * x = x$ for every real number x. In other words $e + x - ex = x$. Then $e(1 - x) = 0$, which implies that $e = 0$, at least if $x \neq 1$. This computation suggests that 0 is the identity with respect to $*$, but a proof that this guess is correct must be based on the definition, as follows.

For every real number x, $0 * x = 0 + x - 0 \cdot x = x$, and $x * 0 = x + 0 - x \cdot 0 = x$. Hence 0 is the identity with respect to $*$ in the set of real numbers.

The reader is familiar with the concept of negative numbers and the way in which these are introduced in the elementary grades. Algebraically, we can describe negative numbers in another way. The *negative*, or *opposite*, of a number x is that number which adds to x to produce 0 as a sum. A similar concept is that of the *reciprocal* of a number. A reciprocal of a number x is that number which when multiplied by x produces 1, the multiplicative identity, as a product. Both ideas are incorporated in the definition of inverse which follows.

> **Definition of inverse.** The element x' is the *inverse* of x relative to the operation $*$ on a set M if and only if $x * x' = x' * x = e$, where e is the identity element relative to the operation $*$ in M.

From this definition we see that the negative of a number is the inverse of the number relative to the operation of addition. We shorten this to the statement that the negative of a number is its *additive inverse*. From the equations $5 + (-5) = 0$ and $(-5) + 5 = 0$ we may deduce that the additive inverse of 5 is -5 and that the additive inverse of -5 is 5. In common notation, the latter is written as $-(-5) = 5$, a familiar result for signed numbers. In this usage the negative sign is a notation for the additive inverse of a number.

Similarly, from the equations $2(\frac{1}{2}) = 1$ and $(\frac{1}{2})2 = 1$ we deduce that the multiplicative inverse of 2 is $1/2$ and the multiplicative inverse of $1/2$ is 2. Just as the word negative is a common term for "additive inverse," the word reciprocal is used as interchangeable with "multiplicative inverse."

Example 1–18. Let us find the inverse relative to the operation $*$ of Example 1–17 for the number 3. If y is to be the inverse of 3 relative to $*$, then at least $3 * y = 0$ must be true since 0 is the identity with respect to $*$. That is, $3 + y - 3y = 0$, or $-2y = -3$, or $y = 3/2$. We prove that $3/2$ is the correct inverse of 3 with the following computations. First, $3 * \frac{3}{2} = 3 + \frac{3}{2} - 3(\frac{3}{2}) = \frac{9}{2} - \frac{9}{2} = 0$, and also $\frac{3}{2} * 3 = \frac{3}{2} + 3 - (\frac{3}{2})3 = \frac{9}{2} - \frac{9}{2} = 0$.

EXERCISES

1. a) Is the set of all integers closed with respect to the operation of subtraction?
   b) Give a numerical counterexample which shows that the set of positive integers is not closed with respect to subtraction.

2. Give numerical counterexamples to show that.
   a) subtraction is not commutative in the set of integers;
   b) subtraction is not associative in the set of integers.

3. Is multiplication left-distributive over subtraction for the set of real numbers? Give some examples illustrating this.

4. Show that division is right-distributive, but not left-distributive, over addition, considering the set of real numbers.

5. Prove or disprove that multiplication is left-distributive over the operation $*$, where $a * b = a + b - ab$ for real numbers.

6. Let the letter m be the symbol for the operation least common multiple (LCM), described in the first paragraph of this section. Find the values of the following (for example, $6\,m\,15 = 30$):
   a) $3\,m\,9$ b) $21\,m\,35$ c) $8\,m\,20$ d) $11\,m\,13$

7. Is the operation m in Exercise 6 commutative? associative? Show that m is not left-distributive over addition.

8. For the set of real numbers, we define two binary operations $\$$ and $\#$ (in terms of ordinary arithmetic operations) as follows:

$$a\,\$\,b = 2ab \quad \text{and} \quad a\,\#\,b = a + 2b.$$

a) Is $ commutative?   If not, give a counterexample.

b) Is # commutative?   If not, give a counterexample.

c) Prove or disprove that $ is associative.

d) Prove or disprove that # is associative.

e) Prove or disprove that $ is left-distributive over # .

f) Prove or disprove that # is left-distributive over $.

9. Is there an identity element for the operation of division in the set of real numbers? Explain.

10. a) Find the inverse relative to the operation $*$ defined in Example 1–17 of the number 5 and prove that your answer is correct.

b) Does the number 1 have an inverse relative to $*$ in the set of real numbers?   Explain.

11. Let $\circ$ be the binary operation in the set $\mathbf{R}$ of real numbers defined by $a \circ b = a + b - 3$.

a) Find the identity with respect to $\circ$ in $\mathbf{R}$, and prove that your answer is correct.

b) Find the inverse of 4 relative to the operation $\circ$ in $\mathbf{R}$ and prove that your answer is correct.

c) Prove that the operation $\circ$ is commutative in $\mathbf{R}$.

d) Prove that the operation $\circ$ is associative in $\mathbf{R}$.

e) Prove by a numerical counterexample that the operation $\circ$ is not left-distributive over the operation $*$ of Example 1-17.

1-8   EQUIVALENCE RELATIONS AND PARTITIONS

A special class of relations, called equivalence relations, is of great importance in mathematics.   The relation of equality is an example of such a relation and, in fact, we may consider the concept of equivalence relation as a generalization of the notion of equality.   Other examples are the relations implied when we say that two triangles are congruent, or that two triangles are similar in plane geometry.

Since an equivalence relation is to be, first of all, a relation as defined in Section 1–5, we have a choice of two notations.   For this reason, we will give two equivalent forms of the definition, one using each of the possible notations. (See Andree [23] and Crouch [28].)   The reader should compare these two definitions to make sure that he understands why they are equivalent.   In the future we will occasionally use the second form, but will more often use the notation of the first form.

Definition (first form).   An *equivalence relation* R in a set A is a relation in A which satisfies the three properties below.

Reflexive property: $a R a$ for all a in A.

Symmetric property: If $a R b$ for some a and b in A, then $b R a$.

Transitive property: If $a R b$ and $b R c$ for some a, b, and c in A, then $a R c$.

Whenever R is an equivalence relation and x and y are elements such that $x R y$ holds, we say that x *is equivalent to y.*

Consider the relation "is similar to" in the set of all triangles in the plane. That is, if x and y are triangles, the statement "x is similar to y" corresponds to the notation $x \mathrel{R} y$ in the definition. The reflexive property requires, in this case, that each triangle in the plane must be similar to itself. The symmetric property requires that if one triangle is similar to a second, then it must follow that the second is similar to the first. Finally, if we have three triangles such that the first is similar to the second and the second is similar to the third, then the transitive property would require that the first be similar to the third. Since these properties are true for similarity, we have verified the fact that the relation "is similar to" is an equivalence relation in the set of all plane triangles.

Suppose that we consider the relation of $\leq$ for the set of real numbers. For any real number a, $a \leq a$, so that $\leq$ has the reflexive property. It is easy to find numbers a and b such that $a \leq b$ but b is not less than or equal to a. For instance $2 \leq 3$, while $3 \leq 2$ is false. Thus $\leq$ does not have the symmetric property and is not an equivalence relation. It is true, however, that $\leq$ has the transitive property. That is, if a, b, and c are numbers such that $a \leq b$ and $b \leq c$, then it follows that $a \leq c$.

The following form of the definition of an equivalence relation makes use of the notation of sets. It is hoped that this statement of the definition may clarify points about which the reader may still be in doubt. The first form is included primarily because of its widespread use in the literature and the second form is included in order to fit the concept into the formal definitions previously given in set notation. In this second form, the notation $(x, y) \in R$ replaces $x \mathrel{R} y$ as used in the first form. Either notation is appropriate in any reference to equivalence relations made in this text.

Definition (second form). An *equivalence relation* R in a set A is a relation in A [that is, a set of ordered pairs (x, y) of elements of A] which satisfies the three properties below.

Reflexive property: $(a, a) \in R$ for all a in R.

Symmetric property: If $(a, b) \in R$ for some a and b in A, then $(b, a) \in R$.

Transitive property: If $(a, b) \in R$ and $(b, c) \in R$ for some a, b, and c in R. then $(a, c) \in R$.

Whenever R is an equivalence relation and x and y are elements such that $(x, y) \in R$, we say that x *is equivalent to* y.

Example 1–19. To illustrate the meaning of the definition, let us consider the problem of defining an equivalence relation in the set $S = \{1, 3, 5, 7\}$ by listing the pairs in the relation. There are, of course, many such relations. For example, the set $R_1 = \{(1, 1), (3, 3), (5, 5), (7, 7)\}$ is an equivalence relation in S. To satisfy the reflexive property, each equivalence relation in S must contain at least these four pairs. The symmetric property is satisfied, since if the first and second elements of any pair in R_1 are interchanged, the resulting pair is again a pair in R_1. Finally the transitive property is trivially satisfied, since no two distinct pairs of the forms (a, b) and (b, c) exist in R_1.

Example 1–20. Let us construct (define) a second, and more interesting, equivalence relation R_2 in the set $S = \{1, 3, 5, 7\}$. Suppose that we begin with the pairs of R_1 and also include the pair $(3, 5)$ in R_2. Then if R_2 is to be an equivalence relation, we must include the pair $(5, 3)$ as well, in order to satisfy the symmetric property. This set would be an equivalence relation as it now stands, but suppose that $(5, 7)$ is included. Then to preserve symmetry, $(7, 5)$ must be added. If we stopped now, R_2 would not satisfy the transitive property, since $(3, 5)$ and $(5, 7)$ belong to R_2 but $(3, 7)$ does not. Therefore we will include $(3, 7)$ and with it $(7, 3)$, to again preserve symmetry. Now

$$R_2 = \{(1, 1), (3, 3), (5, 5), (7, 7), (3, 5), (5, 3), (5, 7), (7, 5), (3, 7), (7, 3)\}$$

is an equivalence relation, although further checking of the transitive property needs to be done to verify this. For instance, $(3, 7)$ and $(7, 5)$ belong to R_2, which requires that $(3, 5)$ must be in R_2, as is the case. Can you find another instance of the transitive property which has not been checked for R_2?

Now suppose that in a given set A we have an equivalence relation denoted by $\sim$. That is, a is equivalent to b whenever $a \sim b$ is a valid statement. Consider the set of all elements x in A which have the property that $a \sim x$ for some fixed element a. This set is the *equivalence set containing* a, and a is called a *representative* for the set. The equivalence set is denoted by $[a]$:

$$[a] = \{x \in A \mid a \sim x\}.$$

Suppose that b and c are any two elements in $[a]$. Then $a \sim b$ and $a \sim c$, by definition. Using the symmetric property, we know that $b \sim a$. Now combining $b \sim a$ with $a \sim c$ by the transitive property, we have established that $b \sim c$. Hence any two elements of the same equivalence set are equivalent. In particular, if $b \sim a$ then $[a] = [b]$; that is, any element of a set will serve as a representative for that set. It is also clear that no element can belong to more than one equivalence set in A. Suppose that $x \in [a]$ and $x \in [b]$. Then, by the above argument, $[x] = [a]$ and $[x] = [b]$. Hence $[a] = [b]$. For any element c in A, we may form $[c]$, so we have shown that each element in A belongs to one and only one of the equivalence sets of A, formed with respect to the equivalence relation $\sim$. In the terminology introduced earlier, every equivalence relation on a set A provides a partition of the set into equivalence sets of elements. We have just proved a result, which we state below as a theorem. This theorem will be referred to in later sections.

Theorem 1–1. Let $\sim$ be an equivalence relation in a set A and let $[a]$ denote the equivalence set of all elements of A equivalent to a, where $a \in A$. Then, for any $a, b \in A$,

1) $[a] = [b]$ if and only if $a \sim b$.
2) If $[a] \neq [b]$ then $[a] \cap [b] = \emptyset$, the empty set.
3) The set of equivalence sets in A forms a partition of A.

Example 1–21. Let us find the equivalence sets for the relations R_1 and R_2 of Examples 1–19 and 1–20.   Since in Example 1–19 each element of S is equivalent only to itself, the four equivalence sets for R_1 are $[1] = \{1\}$, $[3] = \{3\}$, $[5] = \{5\}$, and $[7] = \{7\}$.   In Example 1–20, the element $1 \in S$ is equivalent only to itself, since the only pair involving 1 is the pair $(1, 1)$.   However, each of 3, 5, and 7 is paired with each of the others and hence is equivalent to each of the others in addition to itself.   There are two equivalence sets in S for this relation, $[1] = \{1\}$ and $[3] = \{3, 5, 7\}$.   The latter set could also have been designated $[5]$ or $[7]$ since any of 3, 5, or 7 will serve as a representative of the set.

The converse of statement (3) in the preceding theorem is also true.   That is, if sets X_1, X_2, ... , X_n form a partition of a set A, then they serve to define an equivalence relation R on the set R, where $x \, R \, y$ if and only if x and y belong to the same set X_i for some i.   That this is an equivalence relation is easy to verify.   Any element x is in the same set with itself so that $x \, R \, x$, the reflexive property.   Suppose that $x \, R \, y$, meaning that x and y belong to the same set X_i.   Then y and x are in the same set X_i, so that $y \, R \, x$, the symmetric property.   Finally, if $x \, R \, y$ and $y \, R \, z$, this says that x and y are in the same set and also that y and z are in the same set.   Since in a partition no element is in more than one set, x and z must be in the same set and $x \, R \, z$.   This is the transitive property, and hence R is an equivalence relation.

Example 1–22. As a final example, consider the set of nonnegative integers, $\mathbf{Z}^0 = \{0, 1, 2, 3, \ldots\}$ and define in $\mathbf{Z}^0$ the relation $\sim$, where $a \sim b$ if and only if division of a and b by the integer 5 leaves the same remainder in each case.   For example, $9 \sim 24$, since the division of 9 by 5 leaves a remainder of 4 and division of 24 by 5 leaves a remainder of 4.   This relation has the following equivalence sets, which form a partition of $\mathbf{Z}^0$:

$$[0] = \{0, 5, 10, 15, \ldots\},$$
$$[1] = \{1, 6, 11, 16, \ldots\},$$
$$[2] = \{2, 7, 12, 17, \ldots\},$$
$$[3] = \{3, 8, 13, 18, \ldots\},$$
$$[4] = \{4, 9, 14, 19, \ldots\}.$$

Note that $[0] = [5] = [10] = \ldots$ and that, $[3] = [8] = [13] = \ldots$.   Another notation for this equivalence relation is to write $a \equiv b \pmod 5$ whenever $a \sim b$ as defined above.   We read this as "a is congruent to b modulo 5."   Such congruences are treated more fully in Appendix B.

Example 1–23. Suppose that it is desired to find a relation in the set $T = \{a, b, c\}$ which is reflexive and symmetric but not transitive, and to specify this relation by listing the pairs in the relation.   For the relation to be reflexive, the pairs (a, a), (b, b) and (c, c) must be included.   If we include the pairs (a, b) and (b, c) but omit the pair (a, c), then the relation will fail to be transitive.   Finally, the pairs (b, a)

and (c, b) must be included to satisfy the symmetric property. Hence a suitable answer is the relation

$$R_3 = \{(a, a), (b, b), (c, c), (a, b), (b, c), (b, a), (c, b)\}.$$

EXERCISES

1. Consider the relation "is perpendicular to" as a relation in the set of all lines in a plane. Is this relation reflexive? symmetric? transitive? Explain.

2. Consider the relation $\neq$ as a relation in the set of integers. Show by a counterexample that this relation is not transitive.

3. Consider the relation $\subseteq$ in the collection of all subsets of the set $\mathbf{Z}$ of integers.

   a) Prove this relation is reflexive and transitive.
   b) Prove by a counterexample that the relation is not symmetric.

4. Let S be the set $S = \{1, 2, 3, 4, 5\}$ and consider the relation

$$R = \{(1, 3), (2, 4), (3, 5), (1, 1), (2, 2), (4, 2), (3, 1)\}.$$

Explain why this relation on S has none of the three properties of an equivalence relation.

5. Let S be the set of Exercise 4 and construct an equivalence relation on S by listing pairs of elements of S. Give a relation containing eight or more such pairs.

6. The set S of Exercise 4 has a partition consisting of the sets $\{1, 3, 5\}$ and $\{2, 4\}$. This partition determines an equivalence relation. List the pairs in this relation.

7. Let $T = \{a, b, c, d, e\}$ and let R be the equivalence relation $R = \{(a, a), (b, b), (c, c), (d, d) (e, e), (a, b), (b, a), (a, c), (c, a), (b, c), (c, b), (d, e), (e, d)\}$.

   a) Find the equivalence sets $[a]$ and $[d]$.
   b) Are there any other equivalence sets besides those asked for in (a)?

8. Define the relation R on the set of all integers as follows: $a \, R \, b$ if and only if a and b have a common factor other than ± 1. Is this relation an equivalence relation? Show proof for your answer.

9. Find a relation which is transitive but not reflexive. Specify the set and the relation in the set.

10. Find a relation which is reflexive and symmetric but not transitive. Specify the set and the relation in the set.

11. Let A be the set $\{1, 2, 3, 4\}$. Define, by listing pairs, a relation in A which is

    a) symmetric but not transitive.
    b) transitive but not symmetric.
    c) symmetric and transitive but not reflexive.
    d) reflexive and transitive but not symmetric.
    e) reflexive but neither symmetric nor transitive.
    f) symmetric but neither reflexive nor transitive.
    g) transitive but neither reflexive nor symmetric.

12. Define the relation R in the set $\mathbf{Z}$ of integers by $a \, R \, b$ if and only if $a - b = 3k$ for some integer k.

    a) Prove that R is an equivalence relation in $\mathbf{Z}$.
    b) Determine the three equivalence sets for this relation.

CHAPTER 2

INTEGERS AND RINGS

2-1 THE PRINCIPLE OF MATHEMATICAL INDUCTION

The *natural numbers*, also referred to as the *positive integers* or the *positive whole numbers*, consist of the integers 1, 2, 3, ..., n, ..., the numbers used for counting. When we wish to refer to this set by a single symbol, we will use the notation $\mathbf{Z}^+$. This set has already been mentioned in several examples and problems. It is possible to specify this set by means of axioms, such as Peano's well-known set, but such a treatment is not appropriate at this stage of our development of abstract algebra. For supplementary reading, the student is urged to look up one of the many references on the subject (for instance, Beaumont and Pierce [24]).

We will assume, then, that the elementary properties of the set of natural numbers and of the operations of addition and multiplication in the set are known. However, one of the axioms of the system is not referred to in elementary mathematics and is therefore not as familiar. This axiom can be stated in any of three equivalent ways; we will wish to refer to each of these statements in the future so all three forms will be presented in this section. An axiom of a system needs no proof, but we must choose one form of the statement as our initial assumption and then other forms should be proven equivalent. These proofs of equivalence are rather difficult and will be given only in part. The interested reader may consult other sources for further details or attempt the proofs on his own.

The first form of the axiom is called the *well-ordering principle* (abbreviated WOP) and is stated below.

The Well-Ordering Principle: Every nonempty set of natural numbers contains a least natural number.

By a *least* element of a set S of natural numbers, we mean an element $n \in S$ such that for every x in S either n equals x or n is less than x. This principle is intuitively evident, but it should be pointed out that not all sets possess this property. The set of integers, for example, does not. The set $T = \{3k \mid k \in \mathbf{Z}\}$ is a nonempty set of integers. This set has no least element, since if any number m is a candidate for the honor, it fails to qualify since $m-3$ is another integer in the set and is smaller than m. Similarly, the set of positive real numbers fails to satisfy the WOP. The set $Q = \{x \mid x \text{ is a positive real number less than 10}\}$ is a nonempty set of positive real numbers.   However, for each number $r \in Q$, the number $r/2$ is also in Q and hence Q has no least element.

Be sure to notice that the WOP is a property of Z^+ which refers not just to the set Z^+ itself but to all nonempty subsets of Z^+.   From it we can deduce that Z^+ contains a smallest number, namely the integer 1, but also that every subset of Z^+ which is nonempty has a least element as well.   What this element is depends, of course, on the subset under consideration.   The principle of mathematical induction is equivalent to the WOP in the sense that if either property is assumed to be true, the other may then be derived as a theorem.   One or the other of these principles must be taken as an axiom for Z^+, since neither can be derived from other properties of Z^+.   The value of the principle of induction is that it provides a method of proof which is often easier to use than the WOP.   The statement below is often referred to as the *first principle of mathematical induction*, to distinguish it from a slightly different form which will be introduced at the end of this section.

First principle of mathematical induction: If S is any set of natural numbers which contains the integer 1 and which contains the integer $n + 1$ for every integer n in S, then S contains every positive integer.

Before we give the proof, it might be well to illustrate the meaning of the principle with an example.   Suppose that people are standing in a line of unknown length at the gate of a football stadium awaiting admission.   Two facts are known concerning the people in line: (a) the first person in line holds a ticket, and (b) each person standing immediately behind a person with a ticket also holds a ticket. Thus person number two must have a ticket, since he stands behind number one, who is known to have a ticket.   Similarly, since number three is immediately behind number two, he must have a ticket, etc.   It then seems intuitively clear that every person in line holds a ticket.   This reasoning reflects the content of the principle of mathematical induction.   To be exactly analogous, the line would need to be of infinite length, but the general idea is the same.   We could think of the set S mentioned in the principle of mathematical induction as the set of numbers corresponding to people with tickets.   The given information states that 1 is in the set S and that for each n in S, $n + 1$ is also in S.   Thus we could reason by the principle of mathematical induction that S contains all integers, at least to the number of people in the line.   The principle of mathematical induction is merely a formal statement of a property of Z^+ which we intuitively feel is self-evident.

Theorem 2–1.   The first principle of mathematical induction holds in the set of natural numbers.

Proof.   Assume that a set S of natural numbers has the two properties that $1 \in S$ and $n + 1 \in S$ whenever $n \in S$.   Let F be the set of all natural numbers which are not in S.   To prove the result, we need only show that $F = \varnothing$, so that $S = Z^+$.

Suppose, on the contrary, that $F \neq \emptyset$. By the WOP, F must then contain a smallest integer m. Thus $m \in F$, but $m - 1 \notin F$, since m is the smallest integer in F. Further, $m \neq 1$, since 1 is an element of S, not of F. Since $m - 1 \notin F$, $m - 1$ must be an element in S. (Note that since $m \neq 1$, $m - 1 \neq 0$ and so is a natural number.) Now by the second property of S, since $m - 1$ is in S, $m - 1 + 1 = m$ must also be in S. This means that m is in both S and F, a contradiction. Therefore the assumption that $F \neq \emptyset$ leads to a contradiction and so must be false. That is. $F = \emptyset$ and $S = \mathbf{Z}^+$, as was to be proved.

To illustrate the value of the principle of mathematical induction, we will use it in two ways: first as a means of stating a definition, and second as a method of proof.

Definition of positive integral exponents. If r is any real number, then $r^1 = r$ and $r^{n+1} = r^n \cdot r$ for every natural number n.

To see that this definition actually defines the meaning of positive integral exponents, think of the set S in the principle of mathematical induction as the set of integers n for which r^n is defined. Then $1 \in S$ by the first part of the definition, and for every $n \in S$, $n + 1$ is also in S, by the second part. Applying the principle of mathematical induction, $S = \mathbf{Z}^+$, and we have defined r^n for every n in $\mathbf{Z}^+$. This definition is referred to either as an *inductive definition* or as a *recursive definition*. It is more precise than definitions which describe r^n by stating the number of factors r which are to be multiplied to give r^n. Further, this definition is easier to use in proofs involving exponents, as can be seen from the next example.

The principle of mathematical induction can be used in the proof of many theorems which state a property that is to hold for every natural number n. Suppose we refer to such a property as P_n. We apply the principle of mathematical induction by thinking of S as the set of integers for which the property P_n is true. First, we show that $1 \in S$, or, in other words, that P_1 is true. Here, P_1 represents P_n in the case $n = 1$. Next, we show that whenever an integer k is in the set S, that is, whenever P_k is true, it must follow that $k + 1$ is in S, that is, P_{k+1} is true. Note that we do not attempt to prove that P_k is true directly, but only that P_{k+1} is true in any case where P_k is true. This corresponds exactly to the formulation of the principle of mathematical induction. These two parts of the proof allow us to state by the principle of mathematical induction that every natural number n is in S, or equivalently, that P_n is valid for every natural number m. This completes the proof of the theorem.

As an example of such a proof, let us prove the following theorems:

Theorem 2–2. If a is a real number and m an arbitrary natural number, then $a^{m+n} = a^m a^n$ for every natural number n.

Proof (by induction on n). Suppose that $n = 1$. The theorem reads $a^{m+1} = a^m a^1$ in this case. Since $a^1 = a$ by definition, this statement is identical to the second part of the definition of the meaning of exponents and hence is true. That is, 1 belongs to the set of natural numbers for which the theorem is true. Next, assume that k is a value of n for which the theorem is true. That is, assume that $a^{m+k} = a^m a^k$. (This is called the induction hypothesis.) If each side of this equation is multiplied by a, the result is $a^{m+k}a = (a^m a^k)a$. Using the associative law for numbers, this implies that $a^{m+k}a = a^m(a^k a)$. Now by our definition of exponent, we have that $a^{m+k+1} = a^m a^{k+1}$. This equation shows that the theorem is true when $n = k + 1$, and hence $k + 1$ is in the set of natural numbers for which the theorem holds. By the principle of mathematical induction, the theorem holds for every natural number n.

The step in a proof by induction which is most apt to confuse the student is the induction hypothesis. When the proof reads, "Assume that the theorem is true when $n = k$," the student is tempted to ask, "But how do we know it is true when $n = k$?" Note that the statement of the principle of mathematical induction requires that the integer $n + 1$ (or $k + 1$ if k is used as the generic symbol) belong to the set S *only in the case that n belongs to S*. Our assumption that the theorem holds for $n = k$, then, is simply a way of selecting an arbitrary integer in S to begin the proof of this property. There is, of course, at least one integer in S, the integer 1, as was shown in the first part of the proof.

A slight modification of the principle of mathematical induction is to the case where, instead of stating that $1 \in S$, we have $2 \in S$, or $i \in S$ for some i larger than 1. Then if $n + 1 \in S$ for every $n \in S$, it follows that S contains all natural numbers not less than 2, or not less than i, as the case may be. The proof of this modification is left to the reader. This formulation is useful when a theorem holds only for integers larger than 1 or some other fixed integer. Consider, as an example, the following.

Theorem 2–3. For every natural number n greater than 1, the number of straight lines determined by n points in the plane, no three of which are collinear, is $(n/2)(n - 1)$.

Proof. The number of lines determined by 2 points is 1. Since

$$\frac{2}{2}(2 - 1) = 1,$$

the theorem is true in the case $n = 2$. Assume that k is any integer for which the theorem is true, and consider $k + 1$ points, no three collinear. Excluding any one point, the remaining k points determine $(k/2)(k - 1)$ lines, since the theorem is true for $n = k$. From the excluded point one and only one line can be drawn to each of the remaining k points. Since no three points are collinear, these k lines are distinct. The total number of lines determined by the $k + 1$ points is therefore

$$k + \frac{k}{2}(k - 1) = \tfrac{1}{2}(2k + k(k - 1))$$

$$= \tfrac{1}{2}(k + 1)(k) = \frac{k + 1}{2}[(k + 1) - 1].$$

Comparison with the formula in the theorem shows that the formula holds for the case $n = k + 1$. By the principle of mathematical induction the theorem holds for all natural numbers n.

In these theorems, the first case has been trivial. This is not always true, as one can see in Exercise 10, below.

A common fallacy in problems where a proof by induction should be used is that checking a number of special cases of the theorem constitutes a proof. Example 2–1 is a rather trivial example but it illustrates the fallacy clearly. In many problems it is not this easy to see where the difficulty lies, but the student should always remember that no proof is acceptable which checks only special cases, unless there are only a finite number of cases to consider and every one is checked separately.

Example 2–1. Consider the false theorem that every natural number n is less than 100. Although this theorem is clearly false, since 200 is not less than 100, it is true for each of the integers $1, 2, 3, \ldots, 99$. Thus we could consider, and verify, the theorem for each of these 99 cases, and yet the theorem is false. Clearly a theorem is not proved by considering three cases, or ten, or for that matter any number of cases short of every case that could arise. This example illustrates that to prove that a theorem holds for every natural number the principle of induction is a very useful tool indeed. Many theorems can be proved only by its use, or the use of one of the principles to which it is equivalent.

Example 2–1 illustrates that in a proof by induction the step using the induction hypothesis cannot be dispensed with. We can also illustrate that a proof by induction is not valid if the first step is omitted – that in which we prove a theorem for the case $n = 1$. Consider, for instance, the following example.

Example 2–2. The statement that $2^n = 0$ for every natural number n is clearly false. However, suppose that we attempt a "proof" by induction in which we deliberately omit the first step. Assume that k is an integer for which $2^k = 0$. Then $2^{k+1} = 2^k \cdot k$, by properties of exponents. Since $2^k = 0, 2^k \cdot k = 0$, or, in other words, $2^{k+1} = 0$. We have shown that if the theorem holds for $n = k$ then it must also hold for $n = k + 1$. This illustrates that the omission of the step where the theorem is proved for $n = 1$ is serious and leads to an invalid proof.

We have shown with these examples that each part of the procedure in a proof by induction is essential. The omission of either part will invalidate the proof. In writing an induction proof, we must be careful to follow the procedure outlined, step by step.

We will conclude this section with a statement of the second principle of mathematical induction. No examples of the use of this form of the principle are given here, and none of the exercises require it. It is best for the student to use only the first principle until it becomes very familiar. We include the second principle here because it follows, as does the first principle, from the well-ordering principle, and the proof is so nearly the same that we may safely omit it.   We will use this second form for the first time in Section 2–11.

Second principle of mathematical induction: If S is any set of natural numbers which contains the natural number n whenever it contains all natural numbers $m < n$, then S contains every natural number.

Note that although the number 1 is not specifically mentioned in the second principle, we are still required to show that $1 \in S$ [S always contains all natural numbers smaller than 1, since there are no such numbers (they constitute the empty set)].   Hence, to apply the principle, we must show that $1 \in S$, just as we did in applying the first principle.

EXERCISES

1. Show that replacing the word "least" by "greatest" in the well-ordering principle gives a false theorem for Z^+.

2. Consider the set $S = \{1/n \mid n$ is a natural number$\}$.   Use the well-ordering principle to prove there exists a largest number in S.   What is this largest number?   Is there a smallest number in S?

3. Use the principle of mathematical induction to prove that each of the following holds for every natural number n.

   a) $1 + 2 + 3 + \ldots + n = \dfrac{n}{2}(n + 1)$

   b) $1^2 + 2^2 + 3^2 + \ldots + n^2 = \frac{1}{6}n(n + 1)(2n + 1)$

   c) $2^{-1} + 2^{-2} + 2^{-3} + \ldots + 2^{-n} = 1 - 2^{-n}$

   d) $3 + 3^2 + 3^3 + \ldots + 3^n = \frac{3}{2}(3^n - 1)$

4. (Sum of a finite arithmetic progression.)   Use the principle of mathematical induction to prove that

$$a + (a + d) + (a + 2d) + \ldots + a + (n - 1)\, d = \frac{n}{2}[2a + (n - 1)\, d]$$

   for every natural number n.

5. (Sum of a finite geometric progression.)   Use the principle of mathematical induction to prove that

$$a + ar + ar^2 + \ldots + ar^{n-1} = \frac{a(1 - r^n)}{1 - r}$$

   for every natural number n, where a and r are real numbers.

6. Consider the false theorem that $n^2 - n + 5$ is a prime for every natural number n.   (A prime is an integer p which is not 0, nor ± 1, and which contains no factors other than ± 1 and $\pm p$).   Show that this theorem holds for $n = 1$, $n = 2$, $n = 3$, and $n = 4$, but that it does not hold for $n = 5$.

7. Consider the false theorem that $2 + 4 + 6 + \cdots + 2n = n^2 + n + 100$ for every natural number n.   Show that this theorem does not hold for $n = 1$ but that if it holds for any integer $n = k$, then it also holds for $n = k + 1$.

8. Use the principle of mathematical induction and the definition of exponent to prove that if a is a real number and m is a natural number, then $(a^m)^n = a^{mn}$ for every natural number n.

9. Use the principle of mathematical induction to prove that for every natural number n,

$$1 + \frac{1}{4} + \frac{1}{9} + \cdots + \frac{1}{n^2} \le 2 - \frac{1}{n}.$$

(Here the symbol $a \le b$ means either $a < b$ or $a = b$.)

10. Use the principle of mathematical induction to prove that for every natural number n greater than 2, the sum of the interior angles of a convex polygon of n sides is $(n - 2) \cdot 180°$. (Assume, for the purpose of this exercise, that you know that the sum of the angles in a triangle is $180°$. However, a complete proof should include the proof of this fact.)

11. Prove or disprove that the WOP holds for the set of positive even integers.

2-2 THE INTEGERS

The purpose of this section is to summarize the algebraic properties of the set of integers. We will assume that these properties are known from earlier courses and merely collect them in a form suitable for reference in later sections. The set, referred to as **Z** throughout the text, is the set

$$\mathbf{Z} = \{0, \pm 1, \pm 2, \pm 3, \ldots\}.$$

The set **Z** is described in terms of two binary operations, addition and multiplication. The operations of subtraction and division are later defined in terms of these two basic operations. The first list of properties to be considered are contained in the following theorem. The theorem is not proved since we have not stated axioms for the system on which a proof could be based. The integers contain the natural numbers as a proper subset. All properties of the natural numbers discussed in the preceding section still hold when considered as a subset of the integers.

Theorem 2–4. The set **Z** of integers together with the binary operations of addition and multiplication form a mathematical system in which the following properties hold:

a) **Z** is closed with respect to both addition and multiplication.
b) Addition is associative in **Z**.
c) The number 0 is the additive identity in **Z**.
d) Each element $a \in Z$ has an additive inverse in **Z**, denoted by $-a$.
e) Addition is commutative in **Z**.
f) Multiplication is associative in **Z**.
g) Multiplication is both left-distributive and right-distributive over addition in **Z**.
h) Multiplication is commutative in **Z**.
i) The number 1 is the multiplicative identity in **Z**.
j) If a and b are elements of **Z** such that $ab = 0$, then either $a = 0$ or $b = 0$.

The order in which the properties in Theorem 2–4 are listed is immaterial except that the statement referring to additive identity should precede that referring to additive inverse, since the existence of the latter depends upon the existence of the former.   In a system such as $\mathbf{Z}$ in which the two operations of addition and multiplication are both defined, we commonly refer to the additive identity as the *zero* of the system and to the multiplicative identity as the *unity*.   Similarly, the additive inverse of an element is called its *negative*, and the multiplicative inverse, if one exists, is called the *reciprocal* or merely the *inverse* of the element. In $\mathbf{Z}$ only 1 and -1 have reciprocals in the system.

The final property of $\mathbf{Z}$ listed in the theorem needs further comment.   If, in any system, the product of two nonzero elements is the zero of the system, we say the numbers are *zero divisors*.   We could rephrase property (j) above as the statement that $\mathbf{Z}$ contains no zero divisors.   We will examine a system in the next section which contains zero divisors.   Consequently the fact that $\mathbf{Z}$ has none is worthy of note.

Definition of subtraction.   If a and b are integers, the binary operation of subtraction is denoted by $a - b$ and defined to mean $a + (-b)$.

In words, the definition of subtraction says that to subtract one integer from another, we add the negative of the integer to the other.   All properties of subtraction for integers can be derived from those of addition.   An illustration is contained in the following example.

Example 2–3.   Prove that $3 - 2 = 1$ using addition facts for positive integers, the definition of subtraction, and the properties of Theorem 2–4.

Proof.
$$
\begin{aligned}
3 - 2 &= 3 + (-2) && \text{by definition of subtraction,} \\
&= (1 + 2) + (-2) && \text{an assumed addition fact,} \\
&= 1 + [2 + (-2)] && \text{by the associative law,} \\
&= 1 + 0 && \text{by definition of negative,} \\
&= 1 && \text{since 0 is the additive identity.}
\end{aligned}
$$

The operation of division for integers can also be defined by stating that $a \div b = c$ if and only if $bc = a$.   Thus properties of division depend on those of multiplication.   This operation is less important than subtraction because the set $\mathbf{Z}$ is not closed with respect to division.

Another interesting property, which holds for addition but not for multiplication of integers, deals with the existence of solutions of equations.   Every equation of the form

$$ a + x = b \qquad \text{or} \qquad y + c = d $$

for integers $a, b, c,$ and d has a single solution for x or y among the set of integers. A solution for the first is the integer $b - a$, as may be verified by substitution into the equation.   On the other hand, the equation $3x = 7$ has no solution among the integers.   That is, we can solve equations of this simple type involving addition, but we cannot always solve such equations involving multiplication.

Example 2–4. Solve the equation $7 + x = 3$ in the set **Z**.

Since the negative of 7 is an integer, by property (d) above, we may add -7 to each member of the equation to obtain

$$-7 + (7 + x) = -7 + 3, \quad \text{from which follows}$$
$$(-7 + 7) + x = -7 + 3 \quad \text{by the associative law of addition,}$$
$$0 + x = -7 + 3 \quad \text{by definition of negative,}$$
$$x = -7 + 3 \quad \text{by definition of zero,}$$
$$x = -4 \quad \text{since } -7 + 3 = -4.$$

This solution is checked by substitution of -4 into the given equation.

In working with equations involving integers, two properties known as *cancellation laws* are important:

Cancellation law for addition: If $a + x = b + x$ for integers a, b, and x, then $a = b$.

Cancellation law for multiplication: If $ax = bx$ for integers a, b, and x, and $x \neq 0$, then $a = b$.

We will see that these cancellation laws are not valid in all mathematical systems and therefore it is important to check for them when considering new systems.

The final properties of integers that we will mention here have to do with inequalities.   We say the set of integers forms an *ordered* system.   Other systems like those in Section 2–3 are not ordered.   A mathematical system consisting of a set S with two operations of addition and multiplication is said to be *ordered* if there exists a subset P of S with the properties that (a) P is closed under addition, (b) P is closed under multiplication, and (c) for each nonzero element x of S, either x or the additive inverse of x, but not both, is an element in P.   The set P is called the *positive set* of S.   The positive set in **Z** is merely the set $\mathbf{Z}^+$ of natural numbers. Inequalities are defined for **Z** as follows and similarly for any ordered system.

Definition of inequalities.   If a and b are integers then $a < b$ if and only if $b - a = \mathbf{Z}^+$.   The symbol $<$ is called an *order relation*.   We read "$a < b$" as "a is less than b."

In addition to the symbol "$<$" of the definition, three other symbols are also used.   First, $b > a$ is taken to mean the same as $a < b$.   We read "$b > a$" as "b is greater than a."   The symbol "$a \leq b$" is read "a is less than or equal to b" and means that either $a < b$ or $a = b$.   Similarly, "$b \geq a$" is read "b is greater than or equal to a" and means that either $b > a$ or $b = a$.   Some elementary properties of inequality are listed in the following theorem.

Theorem 2–5.   Let a, b, and c denote integers.
a) If $a < b$, then $a + c < b + c$ and $a - c < b - c$.
b) If $a < b$ and $0 < c$, then $ac < bc$.
c) If $a < b$ and $c < 0$, then $bc < ac$.

Proof. We will prove half of (a) and the part (c), leaving the remaining parts of the proof for the reader. Suppose that $a < b$. Then by definition $b - a = k$ where $k \in \mathbf{Z}^+$. But $b - a = (b + c) - (a + c)$ so that $(b + c) - (a + c)$ is also equal to $k \in \mathbf{Z}^+$. Hence $a + c < b + c$, which is the first part of (a).

Now assume that $a < b$ and $c < 0$. Then $b - a = k \in \mathbf{Z}^+$, as before. Further, since $c < 0$, $c \notin \mathbf{Z}^+$ and by properties of the positive set, $-c \in \mathbf{Z}^+$. Since $\mathbf{Z}^+$ is closed under multiplication $k(-c) \in \mathbf{Z}^+$, or $(b - a)(-c) \in \mathbf{Z}^+$, or $ac - bc \in \mathbf{Z}^+$ But this means that $bc < ac$, which completes the proof of part (c).

Many theorems refer in some way to two integers m and n. In proving the theorem it is often necessary to compare the integers in size and to make a special case for the proof depending upon which is larger. (See Section 2–7 for an example.) It is helpful to know exactly what the possibilities are. The following principle gives us the answer.

Law of trichotomy. For any two integers m and n, one and only one of the following statements is true:

a) $m = n$ b) $m < n$ c) $n < m$

We will not give a formal proof of this intuitively obvious statement. However, it can be thought of as a reformulation of the properties of the positive set $\mathbf{Z}^+$ mentioned earlier. Condition (a) merely gives the possibility that $n - m$ is zero and the remaining conditions state that either $n - m$ is in $\mathbf{Z}^+$ or its negative, $m - n$, is in $\mathbf{Z}^+$. Hence the law of trichotomy is just another way of saying that the integers form an ordered system.

EXERCISES

1. Which of the properties listed in Theorem 2-4 hold in the set of even integers? In the set of negative integers, $\{-1, -2, -3, \ldots\}$? In the set $\mathbf{Z}^+$?

2. Prove, or disprove, that there is an identity element in $\mathbf{Z}$ for the operation of subtraction.

3. Let T be the set of all subsets of a given set S.
   a) What is the identity element for the operation of union in T?
   b) What is the identity element for the operation of intersection in T?
   c) Explain why elements of T (that is, subsets of S) do not have inverses in T relative to either the operation of union or intersection.
   d) Do cancellation laws for union and intersection hold in T? Explain.

4. Prove, by counterexample, that $\mathbf{Z}$ is not closed with respect to division.

5. Prove that if a and b are integers, then $-(a + b) = (-a) + (-b)$.

6. Assume that the addition facts for natural numbers are known, the definition of subtraction is known, and that the properties of $\mathbf{Z}$ given in Theorem 2-4 are known. Then prove, as in Example 2-3, that
   a) $8 - 5 = 3$ and   b) $(-2) + 7 = 5$.

   Use, in addition, the result in Exercise 5, and prove that
   c) $2 - 5 = -3$ and   d) $3 - 7 = -4$.

7. Prove the two parts of Theorem 2-5 not proved in the text.

8. The set **R** of all real numbers has no zero divisors. Explain how this fact is used in solving quadratic equations by the method of factoring.

9. Let $a \circ b$ be defined to mean a^b for integers a and b.

    a) Is $\circ$ commutative in **Z**?

    b) Is $\circ$ associative in **Z**?

    c) Is there an identity in **Z** for the operation $\circ$?

    d) One cancellation law for $\circ$ would read, if $a \circ x = b \circ x$, then $a = b$. Does this law hold in **Z**?

10. Prove that if a, b, and c are integers such that $a < b$ and $b < c$, then it is always the case that $a < c$. (This is the transitive property of inequality.)

2-3   THE INTEGERS MODULO n

The set of integers are an important example of a general mathematical system which we will define in the next section. Before presenting the definition of such systems, it will be helpful to consider other systems which share some, but not all, the properties of the integers. These examples will be new to the reader. Their description will help to focus our attention on significant features shared by seemingly diverse systems and to provide motivation for the classification scheme that is a central topic in the study of modern algebra.

First, we will consider the finite mathematical system known as the set of integers modulo 7. Any other prime integer would serve as well, but the example will be more meaningful if we restrict the discussion to a specific prime. The set, which we will refer to as Z_7, contains seven symbols, as follows:

$$Z_7 = \{0, 1, 2, 3, 4, 5, 6\}.$$

The student should be warned that, while the symbols appear to be integers and behave in some instances like integers, they should be thought of as new symbols whose properties at the moment are completely unknown and must be introduced by definitions. This point of view is one of several which may be used in discussing Z_7.

First, we will define for the set, two binary operations, called addition and multiplication, which will be denoted by the symbols commonly associated with these operations. If we wish Z_7 to be closed with respect to these operations, it is not possible to use ordinary addition and multiplication of integers. For instance, under ordinary addition $4 + 5$ is not an element of the set Z_7. We define the operation of addition in Z_7 to be the ordinary arithmetic sum less the largest multiple of 7 contained in this sum. Thus $4 + 5 = 2$ and $5 + 6 = 4$ in the set Z_7. The result could be considered as the remainder obtained after the ordinary sum is divided by 7, and hence the result is always an element of Z_7. When it is necessary to differentiate between this sum in Z_7 and the ordinary arithmetic sum in the set of integers, we refer to the addition in Z_7 as *addition modulo* 7. Ordinarily, the context will make clear which operation is involved.

Multiplication in Z_7 is defined similarly. That is, the product of two elements of Z_7 is obtained by first multiplying the two integers in the ordinary way, then subtracting the largest multiple of 7 contained in this product. We refer to this multiplication in Z_7 as *multiplication modulo* 7. Clearly, this operation is closed for the set Z_7. As examples, $3 \cdot 5 = 1$ and $4 \cdot 6 = 3$ in Z_7.

In Section 2–2 we assumed that the reader was familiar with the operations of addition and multiplication of integers. Had this not been the case, it would have been difficult to explain fully how computations are performed. However, in a finite system such as Z_7 it is entirely feasible to give briefly all sums and products of elements in the system. This is customarily done with tables of operations like those in Table 2–1. These tables are labeled in the upper left corner with the name of the operation involved. The entries in the body of the table for addition modulo 7 are the values of $a + b$ for all a and b in Z_7. The sum $a + b$ is entered to the right of the symbol a in the left column and directly below the symbol b in the column heading. Thus $3 + 4$ appears in row four opposite the symbol 3 and in column five, underneath the symbol 4. We read that $3 + 4 = 0$. Note that the sum $4 + 3$ is entered separately opposite 4 and under 3. These two sums are the same, but we will study systems in which this is not always the case. It is important, then, to be able to read the table correctly. All other operation tables will be read in this way. The use of these tables will greatly shorten the work of computation necessary for the exercises given in this section.

TABLE 2–1

TABLES OF ADDITION AND MULTIPLICATION MODULO 7 IN Z_7

+	0	1	2	3	4	5	6		·	0	1	2	3	4	5	6
0	0	1	2	3	4	5	6		0	0	0	0	0	0	0	0
1	1	2	3	4	5	6	0		1	0	1	2	3	4	5	6
2	2	3	4	5	6	0	1		2	0	2	4	6	1	3	5
3	3	4	5	6	0	1	2		3	0	3	6	2	5	1	4
4	4	5	6	0	1	2	3		4	0	4	1	5	2	6	3
5	5	6	0	1	2	3	4		5	0	5	3	1	6	4	2
6	6	0	1	2	3	4	5		6	0	6	5	4	3	2	1

Since both addition and multiplication modulo 7 are performed by first taking the ordinary sum or product, the associative, commutative, and distributive laws for integers carry over directly to the new operations. Further, zero is the additive identity in Z_7 and one is the multiplicative identity in Z_7.

In order to appreciate the general definition of negative, or additive inverse, given in Section 1–7, suppose that we consider negatives in Z_7. Recall that x is the negative of y if and only if $x + y = 0$. Thus 2 is the negative of 5 and, conversely, 5 is the negative of 2 in Z_7. This follows from the fact that $5 + 2 = 0$ modulo 7. Similarly, the negative of 1 is 6 and the negative of 3 is 4. We may write that $-5 = 2$, $-3 = 4$, and $-1 = 6$ in the set Z_7.

As before, we may introduce subtraction as the operation of adding the negative of the element to be subtracted. Thus $5 - 3 = 5 + 4 = 2$ in Z_7. Similarly, $1 - 6 = 1 + 1 = 2$ in Z_7. This last example suggests that it would be incorrect to think of 6 as larger than 1. In fact, it can be proved that no order relation, with properties such as $<$ has for the set of integers, can be defined in the set Z_7. This is a significant point of difference between Z and Z_7.

Another point of difference between Z and Z_7 is that division of two elements in Z usually gives a number not in Z, but division may be defined in a reasonable way in Z_7 so that the result is always an element of Z_7. To do this, first consider multiplicative inverses of elements of Z_7. Recall that x is the multiplicative inverse of y in Z_7 if and only if $xy = 1$. (This was formerly stated $xy = yx = 1$. Why is it permissible to omit the middle member of this equation?) Since $2 \cdot 4 = 1$ in Z_7, 2 is the inverse of 4 and, conversely, 4 is the inverse of 2. We might indicate this by writing $\frac{1}{2} = 4$, but a more common notation in abstract algebra is to write $2^{-1} = 4$. This latter notation for multiplicative inverses will be used consistently throughout this text. As examples, $3^{-1} = 5$ and $6^{-1} = 6$ in Z_7. The element 0 has no inverse, but we will discover that in most mathematical systems the additive identity has no multiplicative inverse.

Now the operation of division can be introduced in terms of inverses. We define $a \div b$ to be $a \cdot b^{-1}$ for all a and b in Z_7 for which b^{-1} exists, and $a \div 0$ is not defined. Thus we have that $2 \div 3 = 2 \cdot 5 = 3$ and $3 \div 6 = 3 \cdot 6 = 4$ in Z_7.

Both cancellation laws hold in the set Z_7. We may prove the cancellation law for multiplication as follows. Suppose that $ax = bx$ for a, b, and x in Z_7, and $x \neq 0$. Since $x \neq 0$, x^{-1} is an element of Z_7. Then $(ax)x^{-1} = (bx)x^{-1}$. Using the associative law for multiplication, we have $a(xx^{-1}) = b(xx^{-1})$. But $xx^{-1} = 1$ and $a \cdot 1 = a$ and $b \cdot 1 = b$, so that $a = b$. This completes the proof. Note that although the cancellation law holds in the set Z of integers as well, this method of proof would be impossible, since inverses of integers are not in general integers, and hence could not be used for proofs in Z.

The simple equations mentioned in Section 2–2 can be solved in Z_7. The equation $a + x = b$, where a and b are in Z_7, has the solution $b - a$, and the equation $ax = b$ has the solution ba^{-1}, provided that a is not zero. As numerical examples, we can see by substitution that $x = 6$ is the solution of the equation $3 + x = 2$, and that $x = 3$ is the solution of the equation $3x = 2$. The formulas given above may be used in solving such equations, or the equations may be solved by trial and error, since Z_7 contains only 7 elements as possible solutions.

It is also possible to solve some, but not all, quadratic equations in Z_7. The equation $x^2 = 4$ has 2 and 5 as solutions, which is not surprising when you recall that $5 = -2$. The equation $3x^2 = 6$ has 3 and 4 as solutions. The equation $x^2 = 5$, on the other hand, has no solutions in the set Z_7, as can be shown by substitution of each of the 7 elements in Z_7 into the equation.

Instead of considering Z_7 and operations modulo 7, we could equally well consider $Z_p = \{0, 1, 2, \ldots, p - 1\}$, where p is any prime, and define operations modulo p in an analogous way. If this were done, all the statements of this section would remain valid except the specific numerical examples.   As we will see, this is not the case for Z_n, where n is an integer which is not prime.

For contrast with the preceding system, consider $Z_6 = \{0\ 1, 2, 3, 4, 5\}$, the set of integers modulo 6.   Let the operations of addition and multiplication modulo 6 be defined analogously to the operations in Z_7.   That is, the sum and product modulo 6 are formed from the ordinary sum and product by subtracting the largest multiple of six, which leaves the difference nonnegative.   Thus $3 + 4 = 1, 3 \cdot 5 = 3$, and $3 \cdot 4 = 0$ modulo 6.   Table 2–2 gives addition and multiplication tables modulo 6.

TABLE 2–2

TABLES FOR ADDITION AND MULTIPLICATION MODULO 6 IN Z_6

+	0	1	2	3	4	5			0	1	2	3	4	5
0	0	1	2	3	4	5		0	0	0	0	0	0	0
1	1	2	3	4	5	0		1	0	1	2	3	4	5
2	2	3	4	5	0	1		2	0	2	4	0	2	4
3	3	4	5	0	1	2		3	0	3	0	3	0	3
4	4	5	0	1	2	3		4	0	4	2	0	4	2
5	5	0	1	2	3	4		5	0	5	4	3	2	1

In Z_6, as in Z_7, the commutative, associative, and distributive laws hold for these operations.   Zero is the additive identity, and each element has a negative, just as in Z_7.   Thus $-2 = 4$ and $-1 = 5$ in Z_6.   Subtraction is defined as before.   For example, $2 - 3 = 2 + 3 = 5$, $1 - 4 = 1 + 2 = 3$, and $5 - 2 = 5 + 4 = 3$ in Z_6.   The cancellation law for addition also holds, and it is possible to solve all equations of the form $a + x = b$ for a and b in Z_6.   So as far as addition and subtraction are concerned, Z_6 and Z_7 have the same properties, although, of course, numerical answers differ.

As soon as we consider multiplication, differences become apparent.   The element 1 is the multiplicative identity, but when we look for multiplicative inverses, we find that not every element has an inverse in Z_6.   We note that $1 \cdot 1 = 1$ and $5 \cdot 5 = 1$, so that $1^{-1} = 1$ and $5^{-1} = 5$.   Next, let us examine the products which can be formed with $2 : 2 \cdot 0 = 0$, $2 \cdot 1 = 2$, $2 \cdot 2 = 4$, $2 \cdot 3 = 0$, $2 \cdot 4 = 2$, and $2 \cdot 5 = 4$ modulo 6.   Since there is no element x in Z_6 such that $2x = 1, 2$ has no multiplicative inverse in Z_6.   Similarly, 3 and 4 do not have multiplicative inverses in Z_6.   Note that since $2x = 1$ has no solution in Z_6, not all equations of the form $ax = b$ can be solved.   This is another point of difference between Z_6 and Z_7.

Since division is defined in terms of inverses, we can divide only by 1 or 5 in Z_6.   Division is important in a mathematical system primarily when it is possible to divide by all nonzero elements of the system.   Thus in Z_6 the operation of division is of little value.   It might serve as an example of an operation on a set with a very limited domain, but it has no practical application.

The cancellation law for multiplication fails to hold in Z_6.   As we noted in a preceding paragraph, $2 \cdot 2 = 2 \cdot 5$, and yet $2 \neq 5$. This implies also that factorization is not unique, since 4 may be factored in two ways, as $2 \cdot 2$ and as $2 \cdot 5$.

As a final remark, we note that $2 \cdot 3 = 0$ and yet neither 2 nor 3 is zero. Whenever a product ab is zero and neither a nor b is zero in a mathematical system. we say that a and b are *zero divisors*. In Z_6, 2, 3, and 4 are all zero divisors. The existence, or lack of, zero divisors in a system is of considerable interest. Recall that in the algebra of numbers we solve an equation like

$$(x - 2)(x - 3) = 0$$

by reasoning as follows: Since the product of $x - 2$ and $x - 3$ is zero only if one of the factors is zero, we set each factor separately equal to zero and obtain solutions $x = 2$ and $x = 3$. This technique is available only because in the system of real numbers we have no zero divisors. This method is not valid when we are working with a system such as Z_6. For example, consider this same equation as an equation in Z_6. The equation is satisfied by $x = 5$, for then $x - 2 = 3$ and $x - 3 = 2$ and $3 \cdot 2 = 0$. This illustration points up the fact that methods of factoring and solving equations are not automatic in a mathematical system, but depend on the properties of the system, in particular upon whether or not zero divisors exist in the system.

The preceding remarks raise a question concerning the procedure for solving equations in Z_7 or Z_6. Since factoring and the associated methods we learned in previous courses do not always apply, how can equations be solved in these systems? The best method for solving equations in Z_6, Z_7 and other finite systems is trial and error, as illustrated in the next two examples.

Example 2–5. Solve the equation $2x^2 + 3x + 1 = 0$ in Z_6. Let $f(x)$ denote $2x^2 + 3x + 1$, where operations are modulo 6. Then $f(0) = 0 + 0 + 1 = 1$, $f(1) = 2 \cdot 1^2 + 3 \cdot 1 + 1 = 0$, $f(2) = 2 \cdot 2^2 + 3 \cdot 2 + 1 = 2 \cdot 4 + 3 \cdot 2 + 1 = 2 + 0 + 1 = 3$, $f(3) = 2 \cdot 3^2 + 3 \cdot 3 + 1 = 2 \cdot 3 + 3 \cdot 3 + 1 = 0 + 3 + 1 = 4$, $f(4) = 2 \cdot 4^2 + 3 \cdot 4 + 1 = 2 \cdot 4 + 3 \cdot 4 + 1 = 2 + 0 + 1 = 3$, $f(5) = 2 \cdot 5^2 + 3 \cdot 5 + 1 = 2 \cdot 1 + 3 \cdot 5 + 1 = 2 + 3 + 1 = 0$. From these calculations we see that the solutions of the equation are $x = 1$ and $x = 5$, and no others.

Example 2–6. Solve the equation $x^2 = 2$ in Z_7. If we let $g(x) = x^2$, then in Z_7, $g(0) = 0$, $g(1) = 1$, $g(2) = 4$, $g(3) = 2$, $g(4) = 2$, $g(5) = 4$, and $g(6) = 1$. Hence $x = 3$ and $x = 4$ are the solutions of $x^2 = 2$ in Z_7.

We can generalize the definitions of the two preceding systems as follows. Let $Z_n = \{0, 1, 2, \ldots, n - 1\}$ and refer to this set as the set of integers modulo n for an arbitrary natural number n. Operations of addition and multiplication modulo n are defined analogously to the special cases for 7 and 6 just described. That is, addition modulo n is the operation in Z_n defined by first performing ordinary addition and then subtracting the largest multiple of n contained in the result. Multiplication modulo n is performed in a similar way. When n is a prime, a system similar to Z_7 is obtained in which inverses for nonzero elements exist, there are no zero divisors, division by nonzero elements is always possible, etc. If, however, n is not prime, then Z_n resembles Z_6. Some elements fail to have inverses, factorization is not unique, zero divisors exist, etc.

All systems Z_n share some properties with the set $\mathbf{Z}$ of integers and these properties form the basis of the definition of a class of systems called *rings*, which is the subject of the next section.

EXERCISES

1. Evaluate the following numerical expressions in Z_7, using arithmetic modulo 7.

   a) $3 - 6$

   b) $1 - 5$

   c) $2 \cdot 5 + 4 \cdot 3$

   d) $3 \div 6$

   e) $2 \div 5$

   f) $2 \cdot 3^{-1} + 5 \cdot 4^{-1}$

2. Find all solutions to the following equations in Z_7, where all operations are modulo 7.

   a) $x - 3 = 6$

   b) $2 - x = 5$

   c) $5x = 4$

   d) $3x + 2 = 5$

   e) $x^2 = 1$

   f) $3x^2 = 6$

   g) $x^3 = 6$

   h) $x^2 + 2x + 6 = 0$

   i) $x^2 + x + 2 = 0$

   j) $(x - 4)^2 = 4$

3. Evaluate in Z_6:

   a) $3 - 4$

   b) $1 - 3$

   c) $-2 + 5$

   d) $-3 - 4$

   e) $3(1 - 5)$

   f) $3 \cdot 1 - 3 \cdot 5$

4. Find all solutions to the following equations in Z_6, where all operations are modulo 6.

   a) $x^2 + x = 0$

   b) $x^2 = 2$

   c) $2x^2 + x + 3 = 0$

   d $4x^2 + 5x + 2 = 0$

5. Show that 3 and 4 have no multiplicative inverses in the set Z_6.

6. Prove that the cancellation law for addition holds in Z_6, using the fact that each element of Z_6 has a negative in Z_6.

7. a) Prove the cancellation law for multiplication holds in Z_7, using the fact that every nonzero element in Z_7 has a multiplicative inverse in Z_7.

   b) Prove, using the cancellation law for multiplication, that Z_7 has no zero divisors.

8. a) Factor 3 in two different ways in Z_6 neither involving the factor 1.

   b) Compare the set of elements in Z_6 which can be factored in more than one way with the set of zero divisors in Z_6.

   c) How is the set of zero divisors in Z_6 related to the set of elements with multiplicative inverses?

   d) Give an example, other than the one in the text, to show that the cancellation law for multiplication does not hold in Z_6.

9. Consider that $Z_5 = \{0, 1, 2, 3, 4\}$, with addition and multiplication defined modulo 5 (multiples of 5 are subtracted in forming sums and products). Evaluate the following expressions in Z_5.

   a) $3 - 4$

   b) $1 - 3$

   c) $2 \div 4$

   d) $3 \div 2$

10. Solve the following equations in Z_5, or show that they have no solutions.   All operations are modulo 5.

   a) $x - 3 = 2$ b) $2 - x = 4$
   c) $3x = 4$ d) $2x = 3$
   e) $4x = 2$ f) $x^2 = 4$
   g) $x^2 = 3$ h) $x^2 + 4x + 2 = 0$

2-4   RINGS AND INTEGRAL DOMAINS

In discussing the set **Z** of integers and the operations of addition and multiplication, we have verified a number of properties which hold in many other mathematical systems as well.   It is convenient to classify systems according to their properties. This is helpful in several ways.   The most obvious value is that it enables us to prove general theorems valid for all systems having similar characteristics and thus avoid the necessity of reproducing proofs for each new system.

   The first mathematical systems we will investigate are called rings.   In regard to the definition of a ring, two operations are involved, which will usually be referred to as addition and multiplication.   Actually, it is not important that these operations be written as $+$ and $\cdot$, or that they even resemble the operations of addition and multiplication of numbers.   They could just as easily be written $*$ and $\circ$, or in any other way, so long as the corresponding conditions are satisfied. We will also adopt the convention of referring to the additive identity as zero (denoted **0**), additive inverses as negatives, the multiplicative identity as unity (denoted **1**), and multiplicative inverses simply as inverses.   This will help avoid any confusion in distinguishing between the two operations in an unfamiliar situation.

   Definition. A *ring* is a set R of elements on which are defined two binary operations, written as $+$ and $\cdot$, satisfying the following conditions:

   1) R is closed with respect to addition.
   2) Addition is associative in R.
   3) R contains a zero element.
   4) For each element a in R, there exists a negative $-a$ in the set R.
   5) Addition is commutative in R.
   6) R is closed with respect to multiplication.
   7) Multiplication in associative in R.
   8) Multiplication is left- and right-distributive over addition.

   As examples, the set **Z** of integers, the set Z_7 of integers modulo 7, the set Z_6 of integers modulo 6, and the sets Z_n of integers modulo n for each natural number n, are all rings.   The properties of these sets which establish the fact that they are rings have been previously discussed.   For example, properties (a) through (g) of Theorem 2–4 show that **Z** is a ring.   The set **R** of all real numbers is another example of a ring, although we have not verified this fact.

A ring is called a *commutative ring* if and only if the operation of multiplication is commutative. All of the preceding examples of a ring are commutative. A ring is a *ring with unity* if and only if there is a multiplicative identity (unity element) in the ring.

A ring is an *integral domain* if and only if it is a commutative ring with unity in which there are no zero divisors. The set Z of integers and the set Z_7 of integers modulo 7 are integral domains, but Z_6 is not an integral domain.

If a ring S is a subset of a ring R and has the same operations, then we call S a *subring* of R. The set of even integers is a subring of the set of all integers. (See Exercise 2 of this section.) This ring of even integers is an example of a ring with no unity element. We can state that Z_7 is *not* a subring of the ring of integers. We might consider Z_7 a subset of Z, since the symbols look the same, but addition and multiplication are defined differently in Z_7 than in Z. In any ring R the zero element alone is a subring, called the zero ring.

If a subset S of a ring R is being checked to determine whether or not the set is a ring, and hence a subring of R, it is helpful to notice that several properties need not be checked. Properties (2), (5), (7), and (8) all hold in S by virtue of the fact that they are known to hold in R. We sometimes speak of such properties as *inherited* properties. For example, the associative law of addition holds for every triple of elements of R by definition of a ring. Then this property must hold for every triple of elements in S, since each element of S is also an element of R. The remaining properties must be checked since they could conceivably hold in the set R as a whole and still fail to hold in some subset of R.

Example 2-7. Prove that the set $S = \{a + b\sqrt{2} \,|\, a \text{ and } b \in Z\}$ is a ring. If we assume the fact stated, but not proved, in the text that the set R of all real numbers forms a ring, then we need only show that S is a subring of R. This means we only need to verify properties (1), (3), (4), and (6). Note that the definition of S states that a number is in S if and only if it can be expressed in the form $a + b\sqrt{2}$ where a and b are integers. To verify property (1), suppose that $a + b\sqrt{2}$ and $c + d\sqrt{2}$ are any elements in S. Then the sum is $(a + c) + (b + d)\sqrt{2}$. Since Z is closed under addition, $a + c$ and $b + d$ are integers and hence this sum is another element of S. The zero real number is, of course, the number 0 and can be written as $0 + 0\sqrt{2}$ which shows that S contains a zero, satisfying property (2). If $a + b\sqrt{2}$ is any element of S then it has a negative which can be written as $(-a) + (-b)\sqrt{2}$. But if a and b are integers, then so are $(-a)$ and $(-b)$, and hence each element in S has a negative in S, which is property (4). Finally, whenever $a + b\sqrt{2}$ and $c + d\sqrt{2}$ are elements in S, the product is the number $(ac + 2bd) + (ad + bc)\sqrt{2}$. By closure properties of Z, the numbers $ac + 2bd$ and $ad + bc$ are both in Z so the product of two elements of S is always an element of S. This establishes property (6), and completes the proof that S is a ring.

In addition to the examples already presented, let us consider two more examples of rings. The second of these examples will only have meaning if you have previously taken a course in calculus. It is included to illustrate the fact that there are applications in calculus for the ideas we are discussing here.   A final important example of rings is the subject of the next section.

Example 2–8. Let $R = \{w, x, y, z\}$ and let addition and multiplication be defined by the following tables.   As in Section 2–5, the sum $x + y$, for instance, appears in the row opposite x and the column headed y.   We note that $x + y = z$.   Similarly, $wz = w$ and $xz = z$.

+	w	x	y	z
w	w	x	y	z
x	x	w	z	y
y	y	z	w	x
z	z	y	x	w

·	w	x	y	z
w	w	w	w	w
x	w	x	y	z
y	w	w	w	w
z	w	x	y	z

We will not show proof that this set is a ring.   Many of the conditions are obviously satisfied, but checking associativity and distributivity would require checking each possible combination of elements-64 cases for each law—and will be omitted.   The reader should check several cases for each law.   This ring is not commutative, since, for example, $yz = w$ while $zy = y$.

Example 2–9. Let S denote the set of all functions f such that $f \colon I \to \mathbf{R}$, where I is the interval $0 \le x \le 1$ and $\mathbf{R}$ is the set of real numbers, and such that each function f in S is continuous.   Then define the operations of addition and multiplication for two functions f and g in S by

$$(f + g)(x) = f(x) + g(x) \quad \text{and} \quad fg(x) = f(x)g(x),$$

for each $x \in I$.   Since the sum and product of continuous functions are continuous, both operations are closed on S.   The remaining properties of a ring will not be proved, but should be checked by the reader.   Note that this ring is commutative and has for its unity element the function u defined by $u(x) = 1$ for $0 \le x \le 1$.

EXERCISES

1. Which of the following are rings with respect to addition and multiplication of numbers?

   a) $\{a + bi \,|\, a$ and b are integers and $i^2 = -1\}$.
   b) $\{a + b\sqrt{3} \,|\, a$ and b are rational numbers$\}$.
   c) $\{a + b\sqrt[3]{2} \,|\, a$ and b are rational numbers$\}$.
   d) $\{5m \,|\, m$ is an integer$\}$.   e) $\{m/2 \,|\, m$ is an integer$\}$.
   f) $\{m/2^n \,|\, m$ and n are integers$\}$.

2. Prove that the even integers form a commutative ring under ordinary addition and multiplication, but not an integral domain.

3. Let $Z_n = \{0, 1, 2, \ldots, n\text{-}1\}$ with the operations of addition and multiplication modulo n.

   a) Prove that Z_n is a ring for any integer n greater than 0.
   b) Prove that Z_n is not an integral domain if n is not prime.

4. Prove that the set consisting of the zero element alone is a subring of the ring of integers.

5. For the ring R of Example 2-8, what is the zero element? Is there a unity element? Are there zero divisors? Check each of the associative and distributive laws in three special cases for this ring.

6. For the ring S of Example 2-9, what is the zero element? Show that the ring has zero divisors. Find the sum and product of the functions f and g in S if $f(x) = x^2 + 3$ and $g(x) = 2 - 3x^2$, for $x \in I$.

7. Prove or disprove that the set $T = \{a\ b\}$ is a ring with operations given by the following tables.

+	a	b		·	a	b
a	a	b		a	a	a
b	b	a		b	a	b

8. Consider that $Z_6 = \{0, 1, 2, 3, 4, 5\}$, with the operation of addition modulo 6 and "multiplication" defined by $x \odot y = y$ for every x and y in Z_6. Prove or disprove that this set is a ring.

9. If A and B are subrings of a ring R, show that $A \cap B$ is a subring of R.

10. Let T be the set $\{0, \pm 3, \pm 6, \pm 9, \ldots\}$ consisting of integers which are multiples of 3, and let F be the set $\{0, \pm 5, \pm 10, \pm 15, \ldots\}$ consisting of integers which are multiples of 5. Then both T and F are subrings of Z.

    a) What is the set $T \cap F$?
    b) Is the set $T \cap F$ a subring of Z?
    c) What is the set $T \cup F$?
    d) Prove by counterexample that $T \cup F$ is not a subring of Z.

2-5 TWO-BY-TWO MATRICES*

A final example of a ring is the set of *two-by-two matrices*. We include the example because of its practical importance in other branches of mathematics, and for the excellent example it provides of a ring which is not commutative. For simplicity, we have not chosen to discuss the more general ring of n-by-n matrices for arbitrary n, but all remarks apply with obvious changes in the more general case. Matrix theory is important as a tool in handling simultaneous linear equations or inequalities and in many other areas in advanced mathematics courses.

A *two-by-two-matrix* is an array of four elements, which we will assume in this section are real numbers, represented by the following notation.

$$\text{General two-by-two matrix:} \quad \begin{pmatrix} a & b \\ c & d \end{pmatrix}.$$

We will usually abbreviate "two-by-two" to the symbol 2×2. It should be

---

* Section 2–5 may be omitted without loss of continuity.

pointed out for the student who has worked with determinants that whereas
a determinant represents a single number, the value of the determinant, a matrix
is an *array* of numbers and has no numerical value.   In this notation, the numbers
a and *b* are said to form the *first row*, while *c* and *d* form the *second row*.   The
numbers *a* and *c* form the *first column* and *b* and *d* the *second column*.   In addition, we say that *a* and *d* form the *principal diagonal* of the matrix.   The symbol
2×2 reflects the fact that the matrix has two rows and two columns.   In general,
an $m \times n$ matrix would be an array of elements having *m* rows and *n* columns.

Matrices arise naturally in many practical situations.   For instance, any
page from a book of tables contains a matrix of some size.   As a practical example, suppose that two books, one on calculus and one on algebra, are sold
both new and used in a certain bookstore.   The matrix of prices might be indicated
as follows (entries are in dollars):

$$\begin{array}{cc} New & Used \end{array}$$
$$\begin{array}{c} \text{Calculus} \\ \text{Algebra} \end{array} \begin{pmatrix} 8.95 & 5.50 \\ 6.75 & 4.50 \end{pmatrix}.$$

We say that the 2×2 matrices *A* and *B* are *equal* if and only if each of the
elements in the first equals the corresponding element of the second.   That is,

$$\begin{pmatrix} a & b \\ c & d \end{pmatrix} = \begin{pmatrix} w & x \\ y & z \end{pmatrix}$$

if and only if $a = w$, $b = x$, $c = y$, and $d = z$.

Let us refer to the set of all 2×2 matrices with real numbers as elements
as the set *M*, at least throughout this section.   As a binary operation on the set
M, we define the *sum* of matrices *A* and *B* to be the matrix obtained by adding
the corresponding elements of *A* and *B*.   This sum is written $A + B$.   As an
example,

$$\begin{pmatrix} 1 & 5 \\ 3 & 0 \end{pmatrix} + \begin{pmatrix} 2 & 8 \\ 9 & 4 \end{pmatrix} = \begin{pmatrix} 3 & 13 \\ 12 & 4 \end{pmatrix}.$$

Addition is clearly commutative.   To show that the addition of matrices is associative, consider the following proof using arbitrary 2×2 matrices:

$$\begin{pmatrix} a & b \\ c & d \end{pmatrix} + \left[\begin{pmatrix} e & f \\ g & h \end{pmatrix} + \begin{pmatrix} i & j \\ k & m \end{pmatrix} \right]$$

$$= \begin{pmatrix} a & b \\ c & d \end{pmatrix} + \begin{pmatrix} e+i & f+j \\ g+k & h+m \end{pmatrix} \qquad \text{by definition of matrix addition,}$$

$$= \begin{pmatrix} a+(e+i) & b+(f+j) \\ c+(g+k) & d+(h+m) \end{pmatrix} \qquad \text{by definition of matrix addition,}$$

$$= \begin{pmatrix} (a+e)+i & (b+f)+j \\ (c+g)+k & (d+h)+m \end{pmatrix} \qquad \begin{array}{l} \text{by the associative law for} \\ \text{addition of numbers,} \end{array}$$

$$= \begin{pmatrix} a+e & b+f \\ c+g & d+h \end{pmatrix} + \begin{pmatrix} i & j \\ k & m \end{pmatrix} \qquad \text{by definition of matrix addition,}$$

$$= \left[\begin{pmatrix} a & b \\ c & d \end{pmatrix} + \begin{pmatrix} e & f \\ g & h \end{pmatrix} \right] + \begin{pmatrix} i & j \\ k & m \end{pmatrix} \qquad \text{by definition of matrix addition.}$$

This establishes the associative law for the addition of 2×2 matrices. We included this proof to illustrate the method, but will omit general proofs for most other laws in this section. The student should check other laws in several special cases.

The zero element (additive identity) in M is the matrix

$$\begin{pmatrix} 0 & 0 \\ 0 & 0 \end{pmatrix},$$

as can be seen from the fact that adding this matrix to any element of M leaves the element unchanged. We denote the zero matrix by 0. The negative of

$$\begin{pmatrix} a & b \\ c & d \end{pmatrix}$$

is the matrix

$$\begin{pmatrix} -a & -b \\ -c & -d \end{pmatrix}.$$

(Can you verify this?) The notation for the negative of a matrix A is the standard symbol $-A$. Subtraction is defined, as usual, to be the addition of the negative. That is, if A and B represent 2×2 matrices, $A - B = A + (-B)$.

In order to provide motivation for the definition of multiplication, we turn to a problem from analytic geometry. In addition to furnishing a reason for our definition, this example illustrates one of the important applications for matrices. In Euclidean geometry as well as in other geometries, matrix methods are invaluable in the study of transformations.

In analytic geometry, transformations of coordinates in the plane are considered for the purpose of simplifying equations of curves. Rotations of coordinates take the form

$$x' = ex + fy \qquad \text{and} \qquad y' = gx + hy,$$

with certain restrictions upon the real numbers e, f, g, and h. Once the form of the equations is understood, one can identify a rotation by simply specifying the matrix B formed from the constants, namely,

$$B = \begin{pmatrix} e & f \\ g & h \end{pmatrix}.$$

Now suppose that a second rotation is to follow the first and is given by

$$x'' = ax' + by' \qquad \text{and} \qquad y'' = cx' + dy'.$$

This rotation corresponds to the matrix

$$R = \begin{pmatrix} a & b \\ c & d \end{pmatrix}.$$

To obtain a single rotation equivalent to the sequence of the two rotations indicated above, we can substitute the first set of equations directly into the second set of equations and collect terms as follows:

$$x'' = a(ex + fy) + b(gx + hy) = (ae + bg)x + (af + bh)y,$$
$$y'' = c(ex + fy) + d(gx + hy) = (ce + dg)x + (cf + dh)y.$$

This rotation is associated with the matrix

$$C = \begin{pmatrix} ae + bg & af + bh \\ ce + dg & cf + dh \end{pmatrix}.$$

The rotations above with matrices A and B, as well as all transformations in geometry, are mappings. The rotations have the added property of being one-to-one. The product of these two mappings is as follows: If α is the rotation with matrix A, and β is the rotation with matrix B, the product $\alpha\beta$ is defined to be the mapping resulting from first performing the rotation β and then performing α upon the result. Thus if P is any point, we represent the image of P under β as $\beta(P)$ in the usual functional notation. Then $(\alpha\beta)(P)$ is defined to be $\alpha(\beta(P))$. The matrix of $\alpha\beta$ is the matrix C given in the preceding paragraph. Using this example for our guide, we will define the product of the matrices A and B to be C, as summarized in the following definition.

Definition. If

$$A = \begin{pmatrix} a & b \\ c & d \end{pmatrix} \quad \text{and} \quad B = \begin{pmatrix} e & f \\ g & h \end{pmatrix},$$

then the *product* of A and B is given by

$$\begin{pmatrix} a & b \\ c & d \end{pmatrix}\begin{pmatrix} e & f \\ g & h \end{pmatrix} = \begin{pmatrix} ae + bg & af + bh \\ ce + dg & cf + dh \end{pmatrix}.$$

The notion of a matrix was first invented in order to treat problems of the type illustrated by our example. It was natural, then, to define the product of two matrices in a way which fitted in with this application. Much of mathematics is developed in a similar way. From a real problem in physics, economics, another branch of mathematics, or some other area of endeavor, an idea for a useful mathematical model (mathematical system) arises. The definitions and structure given the model are motivated by the properties of elements in the original problem. It often happens that such a model is later found to have a much wider field of application than the problem which led to its invention.

An easy way to remember the above definition is to note that the element in row i, column j, in the product is obtained by multiplying the elements of row

i of the left factor by the corresponding elements of column j from the right factor and adding the results. This is true for i and j each equal to 1 or 2. A little practice will make this operation easy to perform.

Multiplication in the set M of 2×2 matrices is associative, but not commutative. Some examples illustrating associativity are contained in the exercises. To show that multiplication is not commutative, we need only consider the following example:

$$\begin{pmatrix} 1 & 2 \\ 3 & 4 \end{pmatrix}\begin{pmatrix} 2 & 0 \\ 3 & -1 \end{pmatrix} = \begin{pmatrix} 8 & -2 \\ 18 & -4 \end{pmatrix},$$

whereas

$$\begin{pmatrix} 2 & 0 \\ 3 & -1 \end{pmatrix}\begin{pmatrix} 1 & 2 \\ 3 & 4 \end{pmatrix} = \begin{pmatrix} 2 & 4 \\ 0 & 2 \end{pmatrix}.$$

The left- and right-distributive laws of multiplication over addition hold in M. Again, we will illustrate this with examples in the exercises and omit the proof.

The unity element of M (multiplicative identity element) is the matrix

$$I = \begin{pmatrix} 1 & 0 \\ 0 & 1 \end{pmatrix}.$$

(By actual multiplication, check the fact that $IA = AI = A$ for an arbitrary matrix A in M.) When we consider multiplicative inverses, we find that in some cases inverses exist and in other cases they do not exist. For the matrices

$$X = \begin{pmatrix} 2 & 3 \\ 1 & 2 \end{pmatrix} \quad \text{and} \quad Y = \begin{pmatrix} 2 & -3 \\ -1 & 2 \end{pmatrix}$$

we find that $XY = YX = I$, so that $Y = X^{-1}$ and $X = Y^{-1}$. However, for the matrix

$$Z = \begin{pmatrix} 3 & 6 \\ 2 & 4 \end{pmatrix}$$

no inverse exists. It can be shown that a matrix

$$\begin{pmatrix} a & b \\ c & d \end{pmatrix}$$

has an inverse if and only if $ad - cb \neq 0$. The reader is encouraged to find such a method for 2×2 matrices, in the cases where an inverse exists, before reading further.

As was the case in Z_6, we find that M contains zero divisors. For example,

$$\begin{pmatrix} 1 & 2 \\ 3 & 6 \end{pmatrix}\begin{pmatrix} -2 & 6 \\ 1 & -3 \end{pmatrix} = \begin{pmatrix} 0 & 0 \\ 0 & 0 \end{pmatrix}.$$

Because of the existence of zero divisors, there is no valid cancellation law for multiplication in M. Similarly, not all equations of the form $AX = B$ can be solved in M.

EXERCISES

1. Given the matrices

$$A = \begin{pmatrix} 2 & -3 \\ 1 & 5 \end{pmatrix} \quad \text{and} \quad B = \begin{pmatrix} 3 & -2 \\ 0 & 4 \end{pmatrix},$$

find (a) $A + B$, (b) AB, (c) BA, (d) $5A$, (e) $3B$, (f) $A - B$, (g) $B - A$.

2. Given the matrices

$$X = \begin{pmatrix} 5 & 1 \\ 0 & 2 \end{pmatrix}, \quad Y = \begin{pmatrix} -2 & 0 \\ 1 & -3 \end{pmatrix}, \quad \text{and} \quad Z = \begin{pmatrix} 3 & 1 \\ 2 & 7 \end{pmatrix},$$

find (a) $X(YZ)$, (b) $(XY)Z$, (c) $X(Y + Z)$, (d) $XY + XZ$, (e) $(X + Y)Z$, (f) $XZ + YZ$.

3. Construct an example (other than that in Exercise 2) to illustrate the associative law in M.

4. Construct examples (other than that in Exercise 2) to illustrate each of the left- and right-distributive laws in M.

5. Find an instance of zero divisors in M other than that in the text.

6. Show by example that the cancellation law for multiplication does not hold in M.

7. Given the two rotations

$$\begin{cases} x' = y, \\ y' = -x, \end{cases} \quad \text{and} \quad \begin{cases} x'' = \tfrac{1}{2}x' + \dfrac{\sqrt{3}}{2}y', \\ y'' = -\dfrac{\sqrt{3}}{2}x' + \tfrac{1}{2}y', \end{cases}$$

find x'' in terms of x and y (a) by direct substitution, and (b) by multiplying the matrices associated with the two rotations to find the matrix of the combined rotation.

8. Prove that I is the identity with respect to multiplication for the set M.

9. Describe the effect on the matrix

$$A = \begin{pmatrix} a & b \\ c & d \end{pmatrix}$$

of multiplication by the matrix

$$kI = \begin{pmatrix} k & 0 \\ 0 & k \end{pmatrix}.$$

Consider both the products $(kI)A$ and $A(kI)$.

10. Describe the effect on the matrix

$$A = \begin{pmatrix} a & b \\ c & d \end{pmatrix}$$

of multiplying on the left by each of the following matrices:

a) $\begin{pmatrix} 0 & 1 \\ 1 & 0 \end{pmatrix}$,   b) $\begin{pmatrix} 2 & 0 \\ 0 & 3 \end{pmatrix}$,   c) $\begin{pmatrix} 1 & 0 \\ 2 & 1 \end{pmatrix}$,   d) $\begin{pmatrix} 1 & 3 \\ 0 & 1 \end{pmatrix}$.

Try to formulate a general statement of these effects.

2-6 ELEMENTARY THEOREMS ABOUT RINGS

The concept of a ring has been introduced in order that general theorems may be derived for a large class of mathematical systems at once. In this section we will consider several results concerning the operations of addition and multiplication, many of which have already been proved for the set of integers, the ring of 2×2 matrices, and the rings Z_6 and Z_7. However, these proofs could replace the earlier proofs and will serve for many other systems to be considered at a later time.

We say an element with given properties is *unique* in the set, if it is the only element in the set having these properties. Condition (3) in the definition of a ring requires the existence of a zero element and condition (4) states that each element in a ring has a negative in the ring. No mention of uniqueness of these elements appears in the definition. The next theorem states that these elements are unique and certain others are unique if they exist at all.

Theorem 2–6. If R is a ring, then

a) the zero of R is unique,
b) for each element a in R, the negative of a is a unique element in R,
c) if R has a unity element it is unique, and
d) if an element a in R has an inverse in R it is unique.

Proof. a) Suppose that z and z' both have the property required of the zero element in a ring R; namely, that for every a in R, $z + a = a + z = a$ and $z' + a = a + z' = a$. Then, on the one hand, $z + z' = z'$, since z is a zero of R. On the other hand, $z + z' = z$, since z' is also a zero of R. Therefore, $z' = z$, which proves the zero of R is unique. In the future we will denote this unique zero by $\mathbf{0}$.

b) Now assume that n and n' are each negatives of an element a in R. That is, $n + a = a + n = \mathbf{0}$ and $n' + a = a + n' = \mathbf{0}$. Then,

$$\begin{aligned}
n &= n + \mathbf{0} & & \text{by definition of zero,} \\
&= n + (a + n') & & \text{by definition of negative,} \\
&= (n + a) + n' & & \text{by the associative law of addition,} \\
&= \mathbf{0} + n' & & \text{by definition of negative,} \\
&= n' & & \text{by definition of zero.}
\end{aligned}$$

Hence $n = n'$, proving that the negative of an element is unique.

The proofs of parts (c) and (d) are similar, and left for the reader.

It is convenient to have an easily recognizable symbol for the zero of a ring and for the unity element, whenever it exists.   From now on, we will denote the zero of a ring by the symbol **0** and the unity element, when it exists, by **1**.   The use of bold-face type will distinguish between these elements and the integers 0 and 1 which may also be referred to in the same context.

The following example is an interesting one which will be helpful in understanding what is meant when we say that the unity of a ring is unique.

Example 2–10.   Consider the subset $S = \{0, 2, 4, 6, 8\}$ of Z_{10}, with addition and multiplication modulo 10.   Notice, in this subset that $0 \cdot 6 = 0, 2 \cdot 6 = 2, 4 \cdot 6 = 4, 6 \cdot 6 = 6$, and $8 \cdot 6 = 8$.   Since multiplication is commutative, 6 is a unity element for this ring S.   But S is a subring of Z_{10} which has 1 for its unity.   Does this contradict our statement that a ring has only one unity?   No, because 6 acts as unity only in S.   For example, $7 \cdot 6 = 2$ in Z_{10}, so that 6 is *not* a unity for Z_{10}. That is, a subring may have a unity different from that of the ring.   However, in this case, the unity of the subring will not be a unity for the entire ring.   Further, the unity of the entire ring cannot be an element in the subring or else the subring would then be a ring with two different unity elements, which is impossible.

In the examples of rings we have considered, the cancellation law of addition has always held, but the cancellation law of multiplication held in some rings, but not in others.   The next theorem, then, contains all we can expect in the way of cancellation laws for rings.

Theorem 2–7. (Cancellation law for addition)   If R is a ring and a, b, c are elements in R such that $a + c = b + c$, then $a = b$.

Proof.   Suppose that a, b, and c are elements of the ring R and that $a + c = b + c$. By definition of a ring, $-c \in R$ and hence $(a + c) + (-c) = (b + c) + (-c)$.   By the associative law of addition, $a + [c + (-c)] = b + [c + (-c)]$, or $a + \mathbf{0} = b + \mathbf{0}$ and therefore $a = b$, as we were to prove.

We have noted in our examples that multiplication by zero always gives zero as a result.   We state this in the following theorem.

Theorem 2–8.   If R is a ring and $a \in R$ then $a \cdot \mathbf{0} = \mathbf{0} \cdot a = \mathbf{0}$.

Proof.   Let $a \in R$, a ring with $\mathbf{0}$ as its zero element.   Then $a \cdot \mathbf{0} + a \cdot a = a(\mathbf{0} + a) = a \cdot a = \mathbf{0} + a \cdot a$.   Hence, $a \cdot \mathbf{0} + a \cdot a = \mathbf{0} + a \cdot a$, and by the cancellation law of addition, $a \cdot \mathbf{0} = \mathbf{0}$.   The other half of the theorem is proved similarly.

In the next theorem, which deals with negatives, be sure to notice how the fact that an element in a ring has a unique negative is used in the proof.

Theorem 2–9.   Let R be a ring with elements a and b in R.   Then (a) $-(-a) = a$, (b) $a(-b) = (-a)b = -(ab)$, (c) $(-a)(-b) = ab$, and (d) $-(a + b) = (-a) + (-b)$.

Proof.   a) If $a \in R$, a ring, then by definition of a ring, $-a \in R$.   The definition of negative requires that $a + (-a) = (-a) + a = \mathbf{0}$.   These two equations also imply that a is a negative for $-a$, by definition. Since each element has a unique negative in R we may conclude that $-(-a) = a$.

b) Next, for $a, b \in R$, $-b$, ab, and $-(ab)$ are in R by definition of a ring, and

$$
\begin{aligned}
a(-b) &= 0 + a(-b) &&\text{by definition of zero,}\\
&= [-(ab) + ab] + a(-b) &&\text{by definition of negative,}\\
&= -(ab) + [ab + a(-b)] &&\text{by the associative law of addition,}\\
&= -(ab) + a[b + (-b)] &&\text{by the distributive property,}\\
&= -(ab) + a \cdot 0 &&\text{by definition of negative,}\\
&= -(ab) + 0 &&\text{by theorem 2–8,}\\
&= -(ab) &&\text{by definition of zero.}
\end{aligned}
$$

Therefore $a(-b) = -(ab)$. The other half of part (b) can be proved in a similar way.

c) For $a, b \in R$, $(-a)(-b) = -[a(-b)] = -[-(ab)] = ab$. Here the reasons for each step are an earlier part of this theorem.

Part (d) is proved by showing that $(a + b) + [(-a) + (-b)] = 0$. (See Exercise 5, Section 2–2, where the same theorem was mentioned for integers.) The details are left for the reader.

There are other elementary properties of rings which we will not state formally as theorems. For example, every equation $a + x = b$ or $y + a = b$ has a unique solution if a and b are elements of any ring. Direct substitution verifies that $x = (-a) + b$ is a solution of the first and that $y = b + (-a)$ is a solution of the second. Uniqueness can be proved by an application of the cancellation law. On the other hand, equations such as $ax = b$ or $ya = b$ may have solutions in a ring, or not, depending on the ring. All such equations have solutions in the rings Z_p for p a prime but not, in all cases, in the other rings we have discussed. The equation $7x = 5$, for example, has no solutions in $\mathbf{Z}$.

The associative law of addition provides a means of regrouping a sum of three terms, each representing an element in a ring. This law can be extended to allow regrouping of four, five, or more terms, as well. The next example ilustrates how this can be done in a special case.

Example 2–11. Prove that $((a + b) + (c + d)) + e = a + (b + (c + (d + e)))$, where $a, b, c, d, e \in R$, a ring.

Proof.
$$
\begin{aligned}
((a + b) + (c + d)) + e &= (a + b) + ((c + d) + e)\\
&= (a + b) + (c + (d + e))\\
&= a + (b + (c + (d + e))).
\end{aligned}
$$

The reason for each step is the associative law of addition. Notice that in the first step $a + b$ and $c + d$ were each considered as names for single elements of R. In the third step $(c + (d + e))$ was considered as a single element. In each case this allowed us to use the associative law which applies to just three elements as a tool for regrouping a sum containing five elements.

Once the method of Example 2–11 is understood it is customary to change the grouping symbols in a sum of arbitrary length without explaining each in-termediate step. In fact, when no special grouping is considered important, it is common to write a sum with no grouping symbols at all. The value of the sum is independent of the grouping or association used so we frequently omit parentheses entirely. For example, the sum $a + b + c + d$ could be interpreted as $(a + b) + (c + d)$ or as $a + (b + (c + d))$, and either would be correct.

Similarly, the associative law of multiplication, the commutative laws of ad-dition and multiplication, and the distributive laws can be generalized. The proofs of these laws are tedious in spite of the fact that the laws are reasonably self-evident. For this reason, we omit the proofs. The easiest to prove, the generalized distributive law, is included as an exercise and the others are proved in an appendix. In this section we will state the theorems but give no proof. The proofs of the theorems do not require all the properties of rings, and are stated in terms of the most general conditions under which they hold.

Theorem 2–10. (Generalized associative law) Let S be a set which is closed with respect to an associative binary operation of addition (or multiplication). Then the sum (or product) of n elements $a_1, a_2, ..., a_n$ in S, taken in that order, is a unique element of S independent of the way in which grouping symbols such as parentheses are inserted into the sum (or product).

Theorem 2–11. (Generalized commutative law) Let S be a set which is closed with respect to a binary operation of addition (or multiplication) which is both associative and commutative. Then the sum (or product) of n elements of S is a unique element of S independent of the order in which the elements of the sum (or product) are written.

Theorem 2–12. (Generalized distributive law) If S is a set closed with respect to addition and multiplication, if addition is associative and multiplication is left-distributive over addition, then $x(a_1 + a_2 + \cdots + a_n) = xa_1 + xa_2 + \cdots + xa_n$, where $x, a_1, a_2, \ldots, a_n$ are any elements of S. A similar statement holds for the right-distributive law.

EXERCISES

1. Solve each of the following equations in Z_6, in Z_7, and finally in Z.

   a) $2 + x = 5$ b) $x - 3 = 1$ c) $5 + x = 3$
   d) $3 - x = 5$ e) $x - 4 = 2$

2. Solve the following equations in the ring of 2×2 matrices and check your solution.

   a) $\begin{pmatrix} 2 & 1 \\ -3 & 4 \end{pmatrix} + X = \begin{pmatrix} 3 & 7 \\ 1 & 5 \end{pmatrix}$ b) $X - \begin{pmatrix} 2 & 5 \\ 3 & -1 \end{pmatrix} = \begin{pmatrix} 4 & 2 \\ 3 & 1 \end{pmatrix}$

   c) $\begin{pmatrix} 7 & 1 \\ 5 & 4 \end{pmatrix} - X = \begin{pmatrix} 2 & 1 \\ 7 & 6 \end{pmatrix}$

3. Simplify each of the following by removing all parentheses or other grouping symbols. Assume that all letters represent elements of an arbitrary ring.

  a) $a - [b - c(d + e)]$ b) $a - [b(c - d) - e(f - g)]$

  In the following proofs be sure to use only the definition of a ring and the theorems and results we have proved previously. Give a justification for each step of your proof.

4. a) Prove that if a ring has a unity then it is unique.

  b) Prove that if an element a in a ring R has an inverse in R then this inverse is unique.

5. Prove that $0 \cdot a = 0$ for every element a in a ring R.

6. Prove that $(-a)b = -(ab)$ for every pair of elements a and b in a ring R.

7. Prove that $a(b - c) = ab - ac$ and that $(b - c)a = ba - ca$ for any a, b, and c in a ring R.

8. Prove that the following hold for arbitrary elements of a ring R.

  a) $(x + y)(z + w) = (xz + xw) + (yz + yw)$
  b) $(a + b)(c - d) = (ac + bc) - (ad + bd)$

9. Prove that in a ring with unity having at least two elements, $0 \neq 1$.

10. Prove Theorem 2-12 by induction on n. Begin the proof with the case $n = 2$, which is exactly property (8) of the definition of a ring and hence needs no further proof.

2-7   COEFFICIENTS AND EXPONENTS

Integral coefficients and exponents for elements in rings mean the same for general rings as for real numbers, with the exception that negative exponents have meaning only when inverses exist. The main purpose of this section is not, then, to present anything new, but rather to present a familiar topic in a more precise manner than is customary at the time a student first encounters these notions. We will treat coefficients and exponents simultaneously to emphasize the basic similarities between them, one referring to addition and the other to multiplication.

  Consider a ring R which may or may not have further properties such as commutativity or the possession of a unity element. First, we will formulate an inductive definition of positive integral exponents and coefficients.

  Definition. If x is an element of the ring R, then

  a) $1 \cdot x = x$ and $x^1 = x$, where 1 is the natural number 1.

  b) $(n + 1)x = nx + x$ and $x^{n+1} = x^n x$ for every natural number n greater than or equal to 1.

  In the expression nx, n is a *coefficient* of x, and in the expression x^n, n is an *exponent*. Note that some confusion could result in interpretation of this definition. If R has a unity element **1**, then $\mathbf{1} \cdot x = x$. This definition, however, concerns the integer 1 rather than the unity element of the ring. Until now no meaning has been attached to the product of an integer and a ring element. In dealing with number systems this distinction is not necessary, since integral coefficients also belong to the set of numbers being considered. However, if A is a matrix,

$2A$ does not represent the product of two matrices, but means $A + A$, according to the foregoing definition.

Next, we will state the basic theorem concerning positive integral exponents. Note the close analogy between properties of coefficients and those of exponents.

Theorem 2–13. Let a and b be elements in an arbitrary ring R, and let m be a natural number. Then, for every natural number n,

a) $n \cdot 0 = 0$ $(0 \in R)$ and $1^n = 1$ $(1 \in R)$. The latter is valid in any case where R is a ring with unity.

b) $n(a + b) = na + nb$ and $(ab)^n = a^n b^n$. The latter holds if and only if $ab = ba$.

c) $(m + n)a = ma + na$ and $a^{m+n} = a^m a^n$

d) $(nm)a = n(ma)$ and $(a^m)^n = a^{mn}$

The proof of each part of this theorem can best be done by induction on n. We will give the proof of only two parts and leave the rest, which can be proved in a similar manner, for the reader.

To prove that $(m + n)a = ma + na$, we consider first the case where $n = 1$. The theorem reads, in this case, $(m + 1)a = ma + a$, which is merely the second part of the definition of coefficient and hence is valid. Next, we assume that $(m + k)a = ma + ka$ for some integer k, and we will prove that $[m + (k + 1)]a = ma + (k + 1)a$.

$$
\begin{aligned}
[m + (k + 1)]a &= [(m + k) + 1]a && \text{by associativity in } \mathbf{Z}^+, \\
&= (m + k)a + a && \text{by definition of coefficient,} \\
&= (ma + ka) + a && \text{by our induction hypothesis,} \\
&= ma + (ka + a) && \text{by associativity in } R, \\
&= ma + (k + 1)a && \text{by definition of coefficient.}
\end{aligned}
$$

From the assumption that the theorem is valid for the integer k, we have proved that it is valid for the integer $k + 1$. By the principle of mathematical induction, the theorem holds for every natural number n.

To prove that $(a^m)^n = a^{mn}$, we consider first the case $n = 1$. The theorem reads, in this case, $(a^m)^1 = a^{m \cdot 1}$. Since $m \cdot 1 = m$, this is merely the first statement of the definition of exponent and hence is valid. Now assume that $(a^m)^k = a^{mk}$ for some integer k. We will prove that $(a^m)^{k+1} = a^{m(k+1)}$.

$$
\begin{aligned}
(a^m)^{k+1} &= (a^m)^k a^m && \text{by definition of exponent,} \\
&= a^{mk} a^m && \text{by our induction hypothesis,} \\
&= a^{mk+m} && \text{by (c) of this theorem,} \\
&= a^{m(k+1)} && \text{by the distributive law in } \mathbf{Z}.
\end{aligned}
$$

Thus the theorem is valid for the integer $k + 1$ whenever it is valid for the integer k. By the principle of mathematical induction the theorem is valid for every natural number n.

It is important to remember that in Theorem 2–13 the symbols n and m represent natural numbers, whereas a and b are elements of a ring. The statement $n(a + b)$ $= na + nb$ looks like the distributive law in the ring R, but it is not. The symbol n is not an element of R and the equation does not refer to multiplication in R but to a property of coefficients.

A second important fact that is evident from this theorem is that the concepts of coefficient and exponent are closely related. The only difference is that coefficients are used in connection with addition, whereas exponents relate to multiplication. Thus $3a$ is a short notation for $a + a + a$, while a^3 is a short notation for $a \cdot a \cdot a$. If this relationship is kept in mind it will be easier to remember both sets of properties.

Now we need to extend the definition to include 0 and negative integers, whenever this is possible.

Definition. If x is an element of the ring R, then

a) $0 \cdot x = \mathbf{0}$, where 0 is the integer 0 and $\mathbf{0}$ is the zero element of R.

b) $x^0 = \mathbf{1}$, the unity of R, if R is a ring with unity. But x^0 is not defined if R has no unity.

c) $(-n)x = n(-x)$ for every natural number n.

d) $x^{-n} = (x^{-1})^n$, if x^{-1} exists in R. But x^{-n} is not defined if x^{-1} does not exist.

Note that here, as before, we have used different type to distinguish between integers and ring elements. That is, 0 is the integer zero and $\mathbf{0}$ is the additive identity of the ring. Similarly, 1 is the integer one, while $\mathbf{1}$ is the unity element of the ring.

In the proof of the next theorem, we make use of the fact that in an arbitrary ring with unity $\mathbf{1}$, $\mathbf{1}^m = \mathbf{1}$ for every natural number m. While this may seem obvious, it cannot be used without proof. The proof is by induction on m. If $m = 1$, the equation reads $\mathbf{1}^1 = \mathbf{1}$. Since this is merely the statement of the definition, (part a), for the element $\mathbf{1}$ in a ring, the equation is valid in this case. Now assume, as the induction hypothesis, that $\mathbf{1}^k = \mathbf{1}$ for an integer k. Since $\mathbf{1}^{k+1} = \mathbf{1}^k \cdot \mathbf{1}$ by definition (part b), and since $\mathbf{1}^k = \mathbf{1}$ and $\mathbf{1} \cdot \mathbf{1} = \mathbf{1}$, we have that $\mathbf{1}^{k+1} = \mathbf{1}$. Hence whenever the equation is valid for $m = k$ it is also valid for $m = k + 1$. By the principle of mathematical induction, $\mathbf{1}^m = \mathbf{1}$ for every natural number m.

Theorem 2–14. The properties of coefficients and exponents stated for positive integers in Theorem 2–13 hold for negative integers or combinations of positive and negative integers in all cases where the quantities involved are defined.

These properties can be derived directly from the definition and from Theorem 2–13. To illustrate the technique, we will prove that $a^{m+n} = a^m a^n$ in the case $n = -k$ is a negative integer and a is an element of a ring R. We assume for this proof that $1 \in R$ and a^{-1} exists. Otherwise no proof is needed, because the expressions are not defined. For the proof we will consider the three possible cases, in the light of the law of trichotomy.

First, assume that $k = m$, that is, $n = -m$. Then

$$
\begin{aligned}
a^{m+n} &= a^{m-k} && \text{replacing } n \text{ by its equal, } -k, \\
&= a^0 && \text{since } k = m, \\
&= 1 && \text{by definition of } a^0, \\
&= 1^m && \text{by the statements preceding the theorem,} \\
&= (aa^{-1})^m && \text{since } aa^{-1} = 1, \text{ by definition of } a^{-1}, \\
&= a^m(a^{-1})^m && \text{by Theorem 2–13 (b), since } aa^{-1} = a^{-1}a, \\
&= a^m a^{-m} && \text{by definition of negative exponent,} \\
&= a^m a^n && \text{since } n = -m.
\end{aligned}
$$

Next suppose that $k > m$, then $k = m + t$ for some natural number t. We still are using the fact that $n = -k$. Then

$$
\begin{aligned}
a^{m+n} &= a^{m-k} && \text{replacing } n \text{ by } -k, \\
&= a^{-t} && \text{since } k = m + t, \\
&= (a^{-1})^t && \text{by definition of negative exponent,} \\
&= 1(a^{-1})^t && \text{since } 1 \text{ is the unity of } R, \\
&= (aa^{-1})^m(a^{-1})^t && \text{since } aa^{-1} = 1, \\
&= [a^m(a^{-1})^m](a^{-1})^t && \text{by Theorem 2–13 (b) since } aa^{-1} = a^{-1}a, \\
&= a^m[(a^{-1})^m(a^{-1})^t] && \text{by the associative law in } R, \\
&= a^m(a^{-1})^{m+t} && \text{by Theorem 2–13 (c) for natural numbers } m, t, \\
&= a^m(a^{-1})^k && \text{since } k = m + t, \\
&= a^m a^{-k} && \text{by definition of negative exponent,} \\
&= a^m a^n && \text{replacing } -k \text{ by its equal, } n.
\end{aligned}
$$

Finally, if $k < m$, then $m = k + s$ for some natural number s, and

$$
\begin{aligned}
a^{m+n} &= a^{m-k} && \text{replacing } n \text{ by } -k, \\
&= a^s && \text{since } m - k = s, \\
&= a^s(1) && \text{since } 1 \text{ is the unity in } R, \\
&= a^s(1^k) && \text{from our proof that } 1^k = 1, \text{ above,} \\
&= a^s(aa^{-1})^k && \text{since } aa^{-1} = 1, \\
&= a^s[a^k(a^{-1})^k] && \text{by Theorem 2–13 (b) since } aa^{-1} = a^{-1}a, \\
&= (a^s a^k)(a^{-1})^k && \text{by the associative law in } R, \\
&= a^{s+k}(a^{-1})^k && \text{by Theorem 2–13 (c) for natural numbers } s, k, \\
&= a^{s+k} a^{-k} && \text{by definition of negative exponent,} \\
&= a^m a^n && \text{since } s + k = m \text{ and } -k = n.
\end{aligned}
$$

In this proof and the proofs of the other properties, the idea is to transform the expression so that the properties of positive exponents (or coefficients) can be applied. None of the proofs is difficult, but they are long, and it is felt that this example is sufficient to illustrate the method.

The following example presents an unfamiliar situation involving exponents. It is included to help fix in mind the precise statement of the definitions.

Example 2–12. Consider the set of real numbers with an operation of "multiplication" given by $a * b = a + b - ab$ for every a, b. Suppose we try to find x^{-2} if x is the real number 3, where exponents are interpreted in terms of the operation $*$. Since $x^{-2} = (x^{-1})^2$ by the definition, we need to find 3^{-1}. Further, 3^{-1} is defined as the number y such that $3 * y$ is the identity. In Example 1–17 in Section 1–7, the identity for this operation was found to be the number 0, since $0 * a = a * 0 = a$ for every real number a. Therefore the inverse of 3 will be the number y such that $3 * y = 0$. Hence $3 + y - 3y = 0$, or $y(1 - 3) = -3$, or $y = \frac{3}{2}$. That is, $3^{-1} = \frac{3}{2}$ in this system. Hence $3^{-2} = (3^{-1})^2 = (\frac{3}{2})^2 = \frac{3}{2} * \frac{3}{2} = \frac{3}{4}$, the desired answer.

EXERCISES

1. Assume that R is the ring Z_6 with operations modulo 6. Compute each of the following for the element $a = 3 \in R$.

   a) $3a$ b) $10a$ c) a^3 d) a^7 e) $(-5)a$ f) $(-10)a$

2. Assume that R is the ring Z_7 with operations modulo 7. Compute each of the following for the element $a = 5 \in R$.

   a) $3a$ b) $10a$ c) a^3 d) a^7
   e) $(-5)a$ f) $(-10)a$ g) a^{-2} h) a^{-5}

3. Assume that R is the ring of 2×2 matrices with the usual matrix operations. Compute each of the following for the element

$$a = \begin{pmatrix} 1 & 3 \\ 2 & -4 \end{pmatrix} \in R. \quad \text{Note that} \quad a^{-1} = \begin{pmatrix} 2/5 & 3/10 \\ 1/5 & -1/10 \end{pmatrix}.$$

   a) $3a$ b) $10a$ c) a^3 d) a^4
   e) $(-3)a$ f) $(-10)a$ g) a^{-2} h) a^{-3}

4. If 0 is the additive indentity of a ring R, prove by induction that $n \cdot 0 = 0$ for every natural number n.

5. Prove that if R is a ring, $a \in R$, and m is a natural number that $(-m)a = -(ma)$. [*Hint:* Show that $ma + (-m)a = 0$. Be sure to remember that m is a coefficient and not a ring element].

6. Prove the statement that $(nm)a = n(ma)$ in Theorem 2–13.

7. Prove the statement that $a^{m+n} = a^m a^n$ in Theorem 2–13.

8. Let R be a ring with unity, not necessarily commutative. Suppose that a and b are elements of R such that a^{-1} and b^{-1} both exist in R. Prove that $(ab)^{-1}$ exists in R by proving that $(ab)^{-1} = b^{-1}a^{-1}$.
   [*Hint:* Prove that $(ab)(b^{-1}a^{-1})$ and $(b^{-1}a^{-1})(ab)$ both equal the unity of R.]

9. Prove that if a and b are elements of a commutative ring R with unity, such that a^{-1} and b^{-1} exist in R, then $(ab)^n = a^n b^n$ for every negative integer n. Use the result in Exercise 8 in this proof, but do not use induction.

10. Prove that if a is any element of a ring R and m is a natural number, then $(m + n)a = ma + na$ for every negative integer n.

11. Discuss the possibility of assigning a meaning to fractional exponents for elements in a ring. In particular, find all elements a in Z_7 for which $a^{1/2}$ could be reasonably defined. Are there elements for which this is not possible? Why?

12. Consider the operation of "addition" in the set of integers defined by $a \oplus b = a + b - 1$. (Compare this with Example 2-12.)

   a) Find $3x$ for $x = 5$, where 3 is interpreted as a coefficient defined relative to the operation $\oplus$.
   b) Find the identity for this operation.
   c) Find the inverse of 5 with respect to this operation.
   d) Evaluate $(-3)x$ for $x = 5$, where -3 is considered a coefficient defined relative to the operation $\oplus$.

2-8 DIVISIBILITY AND PRIMES

We have noted that the set of integers is not closed for the operation of division, since the domain of the operation is not the entire set $\mathbf{Z} \times \mathbf{Z}$ and the range includes numbers other than integers. However, it is possible in certain cases to divide one integer by another, and many properties of the integers depend on whether or not this is the case. In order to discuss divisibility, we need another definition.

Definition of divisor. An integer b *divides* the integer a if and only if there exists an integer c such that $a = bc$. In this case we say that b is a *divisor of a* (also a *factor of a*) and that a is a *multiple* of b. We write this as $b \mid a$.

We note immediately that $b \mid 0$ (read "b divides 0"), since $b \cdot 0 = 0$ for every integer b. Similarly, for every integer b, $\pm 1 \mid b$ and $\pm b \mid b$. If we consider "divides" as a relation, we see by the above remark that this relation is reflexive. It is not symmetric, since $2 \mid 4$ but $4 \nmid 2$. (The symbol is read "does not divide.") The relation is transitive, since if $a \mid b$ and $b \mid c$, then $b = ax$ and $c = by$ for integers x and y. Hence $c = by = (ax)y = a(xy)$, which shows that $a \mid c$.

Another immediate consequence of the definition is the fact that if $b \mid a$ for positive integers a and b, then $b \leq a$. Suppose that $b \mid a$. Then $a = bc$ for some positive integer c. Now $1 \leq c$, and upon multiplying by b, we have that $b \leq bc = a$.

Integers a and b are *associates* if and only if $a \mid b$ and $b \mid a$. For any integer a, a and $-a$ are associates. In Exercise 2 of this section you will be asked to prove that there are no other associates of a.

Definition of prime. A nonzero integer p is a *prime* if and only if it is neither 1 nor -1 and has no divisors other than ± 1 and $\pm p$.

As examples, $2, -3, 97$, and 8191 are primes. One of the reasons for discussing primes is the fact, to be proved later, that every positive integer larger than 1 is uniquely expressible as a product of prime factors. This is useful in constructing proofs of theorems in many branches of mathematics.

Before proving the fundamental factorization theorem, we need to investigate the division of integers more thoroughly.   While it is not true that each integer is a divisor of every other, problems involving division with arbitrary integers are commonly introduced early in the elementary grades.   Such problems are "solved" by finding a quotient and remainder as an answer.   We will make this process more precise, as indicated in the following theorem.

> **Division algorithm.**   If m and n are integers with $m \neq 0$, then there exist unique integers q and r such that $n = mq + r$ where $0 \leq r < |m|$.

We refer to q as the *quotient* and r as the *remainder* in the division of n by m We will prove the theorem in the case n and m are both natural numbers.   If $n = 0$, then $q = 0$ and $r = 0$ satisfy the theorem.   The examples will show how to treat cases where m or n or both are negative.

The proof depends on the well-ordering principle (WOP).   Let S be the set of all natural numbers of the form $n - mt$, for arbitrary integers t.   Since $n = n - m \cdot 0$, the set S is nonempty.   By the WOP S contains a least integer $s_0 = n - mq_0$, where q_0 is some specific value of t.   By the law of trichotomy, $m < s_0$, $m = s_0$, or $s_0 < m$.   Suppose that $m > s_0$.   Then $s_0 - m$ is a natural number and

$$s_0 - m = n - mq_0 - m = n - m(q_0 + 1).$$

That is, $s_0 - m \in S$ and $s_0 - m < s_0$, which contradicts the statement that s_0 was the smallest integer in S.   Therefore, $s_0 \leq m$.   Suppose next that $s_0 = m$.   Then

$$n = mq_0 + s_0 = mq_0 + m = (q_0 + 1)m + 0.$$

In this case, we let $q_0 + 1 = q$ and $0 = r$ to give the q and r required by the theorem.   Finally, if $s_0 < m$, we have completed the proof, since $q = q_0$ and $r = s_0$ satisfy the requirements of the theorem.

To prove uniqueness, assume that $n = mq + r = mq' + r'$, where q, r, q', and r' are nonnegative integers, $0 \leq r < m$, and $0 \leq r' < m$.   Assume for convenience that $r \leq r'$.   (If $r' < r$, we need only multiply the following equation by -1, and the argument is valid.)   Then $m(q - q') = r' - r$ and $0 \leq r' - r < m$.   Unless $r' - r = q - q' = 0$, this is a contradiction of an earlier result.   (If $b \mid a$ for positive integers a and b, then $b \leq a$.)   Hence $r' - r = 0$ and $q - q' = 0$ or, equivalently, $r' = r$ and $q' = q$.   This shows that p and q are unique, and completes the proof.

Example 2–13.   If $n = 59$ and $m = -14$, find the quotient q and the remainder r when n is divided by m.   Find the q and r which satisfy the conditions of the division algorithm.   Express n in the form $mq + r$.

First we perform a usual long division, ignoring the sign of m.

$$
\begin{array}{r}
4 \\
\overline{14)59} \\
56 \\
\overline{3}
\end{array}
$$

Thus $59 = 14(4) + 3$. Since m is negative, we can modify this by inspection to give $59 = (-14)(-4) + 8$. Then $q = -4$, and $r = 3$. Note that $0 \le 3 < |-14|$.

Example 2–14. If $n = -79$ and $m = 11$, find the quotient q and the remainder r when n is divided by m. Find q and r satisfying the conditions of the division algorithm and express n in the form $mq + r$.

First, by long division, ignoring signs, we determine that $79 = 11(7) + 2$. Since $n = -79$, we may multiply through by -1, giving $-79 = 11(-7) - 2$. However, the remainder r of -2 does not satisfy the condition $0 \le r < |m|$. Adding and subtracting 11 (the value of m) to the right of this equation gives $-79 = 11(-7) - 11 + 11 - 2 = 11(-8) + 9$. Since $0 \le 9 < 11$, we see that the correct quotient is -8 and the remainder is 9.

This is admittedly not the way a student would ordinarily think of the solution to this problem. Although long division involving negatives is not ordinarily taught in school, the tendency would be to accept -7 as quotient and -2 as remainder. In order for the quotient and remainder to be unique, it is necessary to specify a single procedure as the correct one. We will always use the answer which satisfies the conditions stated in the division algorithm. The fact that the quotient and remainder are unique, and not subject to the whim of the person performing the division, is important in theoretical work. It is not just a trick to force students into getting identical answers in order to help the paper grading, but is useful in proving theorems about integers, as we shall see.

EXERCISES

1. Find (a) all divisors of 24, (b) all multiples of -5, and (c) all primes p such that $-10 < p < 30$. (All are to be found within the set $\mathbf{Z}$ of integers.)

2. Prove that the only associate of the integer a is $-a$. [*Hint:* If a and b are positive integers and $b \mid a$, then $b \le a$.]

3. For each of the following pairs of values of m and n, find the quotient q and the remainder r in the division of n by m, and express n in the form $n = qm + r$. Do this so that the conditions of the division algorithm are satisfied.

   a) $n = 57, m = 3$ b) $n = 7, m = 38$ c) $n = 39, m = 23$
   d) $n = -13, m = 5$ e) $n = 126, m = -11$ f) $n = -46, m = -7$
   g) $n = -125, m = 23$ h) $n = 0, m = 6$ i) $n = -235, m = -17$

4. Find a prime larger than 400 and different from any example in the text.

5. Show that 4307 is not a prime.

6. Prove that if $x = y + z$ and if d divides any two of x, y, and z, then d divides the third.

7. Let S be the set of all divisors of 40 and let T be the set of all divisors of 36.

   a) Determine the sets S and T.
   b) Find $S \cap T$, he set of common divisors of 40 and 36.
   c) Find the largest number in $S \cap T$, called the greatest common divisor of 40 and 36.

8. Let U be the set of all multiples of 6 and V be the set of all multiples of 4.

   a) Determine the sets U and V.
   b) Find $U \cap V$, the set of common multiples of 6 and 4.
   c) Find the smallest positive integer in $U \cap V$, called the least common multiple of 4 and 6.

9. Use the method of Exercise 7 to find the greatest common divisor of 396 and 504.

10. Show that if a divides the product bc, for integers a, b, and c, it does not follow that a must divide either b or c separately. Can you suggest a restriction on a, b, or c so that if $a \mid bc$, and if ab, then it must follow that $a \nmid c$?

2-9 GREATEST COMMON DIVISOR AND EUCLID'S ALGORITHM

The notion of a common divisor for two or more integers is of importance in combining or simplifying fractions and in many other practical problems in mathematics.

> **Definition of greatest common divisor.** A *greatest common divisor* (GCD) of two integers a and b (not both zero) is a positive integer d such that
>
> a) $d \mid a$ and $d \mid b$, and
> b) if, for an integer c, $c \mid a$ and $c \mid b$, then $c \mid d$.
>
> We will denote such a divisor by $d = D(a, b)$.

The definition does not assert that such a divisor exists, or that it is unique when it does exist. The following theorem establishes these facts. There are more elegant ways to prove the theorem than the method employed here. This method was chosen because it is *constructive*; that is, it provides a method by which the GCD can be computed in specific cases.

> **Theorem 2-15.** Every pair of integers a and b, not both zero, has a unique GCD $D(a, b)$ which can be expressed in the form $D(a, b) = ma + nb$ for some integers m and n.

Since it follows directly from the definition that $D(a, b) = D(|a|, |b|)$, it is sufficient to consider the case where a and b are both nonnegative.

If $a = b$, then $D(a, b) = a = b$ and no proof is required. Suppose, then, that $b < a$. (This assumption does not effect the generality of the proof, but amounts only to naming the smaller of the integers b and the larger a.) By the division algorithm, there exist unique integers q_1 and r_1 such that

$$a = q_1 b + r_1 \qquad \text{where } 0 \leq r_1 < b.$$

Next, we divide by r_1 and obtain, according to the division algorithm,

$$b = q_2 r_1 + r_2 \qquad \text{where } 0 \leq r_2 < r_1.$$

We continue this process for as long as the remainder is nonzero. At each step, the divisor of the preceding step is divided by the remainder at that step to produce a new quotient and remainder.   We can tabulate the results as follows.

$$a = q_1 b + r_1 \qquad\qquad \text{where } 0 \le r_1 < b,$$
$$b = q_2 r_1 + r_2 \qquad\qquad \text{where } 0 \le r_2 < r_1,$$
$$r_1 = q_3 r_2 + r_3 \qquad\qquad \text{where } 0 \le r_3 < r_2,$$

(1)
$$\vdots$$

$$r_{i-3} = q_{i-1} r_{i-2} + r_{i-1} \qquad \text{where } 0 \le r_{i-1} < r_{i-2},$$
$$r_{i-2} = q_i r_{i-1} + r_i \qquad\qquad \text{where } 0 \le r_i < r_{i-1},$$
$$r_{i-1} = q_{i+1} r_i + 0.$$

This process must terminate with a remainder of zero, as shown, because of the inequalities $b > r_1 > r_2 > \cdots$ Since only finitely many integers lie between 0 and b, some r must be zero.   Now if $r_{i+1} = 0$, as indicated, $r_i \mid r_{i-1}$ by the last equation of the system (1).   By the preceding equation $r_i \mid r_{i-2}$, since it divides both r_i and r_{i-1}.   (See Exercise 6 of Section 2–8.)   Working back through the equations (1) in this way, we see that $r_i \mid r_j$ for each $j < i$.   Finally, $r_i \mid b$, and from the first equation, it follows that $r_i \mid a$.   Hence r_i is a divisor of both a and b.   Now suppose that c divides both a and b.   By the first equation of (1), $c \mid r_1$.   Proceeding as before, $c \mid r_j$ for each $j \le i$.   In particular, $c \mid r_i$.   Therefore, $r_i = D(a, b)$, the GCD of a and b.

Uniqueness follows from the uniqueness of each of the r_j, for $j \le i$, or it can be proved directly.

That $D(a, b)$ can be expressed in the form $D(a, b) = ma + nb$ for integers m and n also follows from the system of equations (1).   Beginning with the second from the last equation, $r_i = r_{i-2} - q_i r_{i-1}$.   Solving the preceding equation for r_{i-1} and substituting, we obtain

$$r_i = r_{i-2} - q_i (r_{i-3} - q_{i-1} r_{i-2}).$$

Continuing in this way, we can eliminate each r_j for $j < i$, leaving the desired expression $r_i = ma + nb$ for some m and n.

The expression $ma + nb$ is called a *linear combination* of a and b.

Example 2–15.   To illustrate the procedure followed in the theorem, consider the integers 26 and 118.   We desire to find $D(26, 118)$ and express it as a linear combination of 26 and 118, that is, as $26m + 118n$ for some integers m and n. The following are equations (1) for this numerical example:

$$118 = 4(26) + 14,$$
$$26 = 1(14) + 12,$$
$$14 = 1(12) + 2,$$
$$12 = 6(2) + 0.$$

Hence $2 = D(26, 118)$.   Further, from the next-to-last equation,

$$2 = 14 - 12.$$

But since $12 = 26 - 14$, by the second equation, we have that

$$2 = 14 - (26 - 14)$$
$$= 2(14) - 26.$$

Now, from the first equation, $14 = 118 - 4(26)$, so that

$$2 = 2[118 - 4(26)] - 26$$
$$= 2(118) - 9(26).$$

The integers m and n required to express $D(26, 118)$ as a linear combination of 26 and 118 are therefore -9 and 2, respectively. The only difficulty here is in recognizing which simplifications should be performed and which should be avoided in the numerical work. A general rule is to collect coefficients of the integers corresponding to each of the remainders and to a and b, but not to simplify further. This permits the elimination of each remainder in turn and the recognition of the coefficients of a and b required.

Example 2–16. If $m \mid n$, then $D(m, n) = |m|$, and it is not necessary to employ the algorithm. The correct linear combination can be chosen by inspection. For instance, $D(-11, 33) = 11$ and $11 = (-1)(-11) + 0(33)$.

The process of successive division represented by equations (1) in the proof of the theorem is referred to as *Euclid's algorithm*. The name arises from the fact that this process for finding the GCD of two integers is described early in Book VII of Euclid's *Elements*, although it was probably known much earlier than this.

Two integers a and b are *relatively prime* if and only if their GCD is 1. Thus 9 and 16 are relatively prime, although clearly neither is a prime integer. The condition that integers be relatively prime can also be stated as the condition that they have no common factors except ± 1.

In the special case of relatively prime integers, the theorem can be stated in the form of the following corollary. This corollary is frequently used in mathematical proofs in many areas of mathematics. (See, for example, the proof of Theorem 2–16, Section 2–10.)

Corollary. If a and b are relatively prime integers, then there exist integers m and n such that $1 = ma + nb$.

Example 2–17. Express 1 as a linear combination of the relatively prime integers 8 and 27. Employing Euclid's algorithm, we find that

$$27 = 3(8) + 3,$$
$$8 = 2(3) + 2,$$
$$3 = 1(2) + 1,$$
$$2 = 2(1) + 0.$$

Hence

$$1 = 3 - 1(2) = 3 - 1[8 - 2(3)] = 3(3) - (8) = 3[27 - 3(8)] - (8)$$
$$= 3(27) - 10(8).$$

The expression $1 = 3(27) - 10(8)$ is the desired result.

The definition of GCD can be extended, by induction, to finite sets of integers, but this will be left as an exercise.

EXERCISES

1. Reduce the following fractions to lowest terms.

   a) 360/405   b) 1037/2379   c) 3880/18,333   d) 4949/7081

2. Find each of the GCD's $D(a, b)$ indicated below, and find integers m and n such that $D(a, b) = ma + nb$ in each case.

   a) $D(17,629)$ b) $D(91,259)$ c) $D(-120, 168)$
   d) $D(168, 896)$ e) $D(96, 133)$ f) $D(110, -273)$

3. Without using Euclid's algorithm, prove that $D(a, b)$ is unique.

4. Prove that if n is a positive integer, $D(na, nb) = n[D(a,b)]$ for all integers a and b, not both zero.

5. Write a definition for the GCD of three integers, no two of which are zero.

6. Find the GCD of the three integers 994, 1065, and 2485.

2-10   UNIQUE FACTORIZATION THEOREM

A significant fact about the set of integers, as we mentioned earlier, is the uniqueness of factorization. This property is not characteristic of all rings, as examples for Z_6 demonstrated. Matrices also fail to factor into unique factors. The student can readily check this fact by constructing counterexamples. The existence of zero divisors in a system is closely related to the uniqueness of factorization but does not serve as a suitable necessary and sufficient condition. Rather than attempt to establish such conditions, we will prove the unique factorization theorem separately in the two systems where the property is most significant for elementary mathematics, the ring of integers and the ring of polynomials over a field (Chapter 7). Two preliminary results are useful for constructing the proof in the case of the integers.

Theorem 2–16. If the integer a divides the product bc of integers b and c, and if a and b are relatively prime, then a divides c.

Suppose that a and b are relatively prime. Then by Theorem 2–15, there exist integers m and n such that $1 = ma + nb$. Multiplying by c, we have that $c = cma + nbc$. Now it is assumed that $a \mid bc$, so that $bc = ka$ for some integer k. Substituting this into the above equation gives

$$c = cma + nka = (cm + nk)a$$

and hence $a \mid c$ as we were to prove.

Corollary. If the prime p divides the product $a_1 a_2 \ldots a_n$, where each a_i is an integer for $i = 1, 2, \ldots, n$, then p divides at least one a_i.

The proof will be by induction on n. If $n = 1$ the result is valid, since it reduces to the statement that if $p \mid a_1$ then $p \mid a_1$. Suppose, as the induction hypothesis, that the result is true for all products of n factors, and assume that $p = a_1 a_2 \cdots a_n a_{n+1}$. Denote by b the product $a_1 a_2 \cdots a_n$. Then $p \mid b a_{n+1}$. If $p \mid a_{n+1}$, the theorem is satisfied. If $p \nmid a_{n+1}$ then, since p is prime, p and a_{n+1} are relatively prime and by Theorem 2–16, $p \mid b$. Since b is a product of n factors, the induction hypothesis applies and $p \mid a_i$ for at least one $i \le n$. So in either case $p \mid a_i$ for at least one $i \le n + 1$, and by the principle of mathematical induction the theorem is valid for all positive integers n.

Two remarks should be made concerning the fundamental theorem which follows. First, while the theorem is stated only for positive integers in order to simplify the proof, it extends readily to negative integers. Any negative integer k may be written as $k = -t$ for the positive integer t. The theorem may then be applied to t. The second remark concerns the word "product." An integer may be a prime, in which case we consider it as a product of one prime, itself. This enables us to state the theorem in the following simplified form.

Theorem 2–17 (the unique factorization theorem). Every integer $n > 1$ can be expressed uniquely as a product of positive primes except for the order in which the factors occur.

We will first prove that the factorization can be made in at least one way. This proof will use the second principle of mathematical induction. The reader should note in the proof the reasons why this principle is more readily applicable than the first principle. If $n = 2$, no proof is needed, since 2 is prime and we have agreed to interpret this as a product of one prime. Assume, as our induction hypothesis, that the theorem is valid for all integers k such that $2 \le k < n$ and consider the integer n. If n is prime, we have finished the proof. If n is not prime, then $n = ab$ for integers a and b each greater than 1 and less than n. By our induction hypothesis, a and b can be written as products of positive primes, $a = p_1 p_2 \cdots p_r$ and $b = q_1 q_2 \cdots q_s$. Then $n = ab = p_1 p_2 \cdots p_r q_1 q_2 \cdots q_s$ is a product of positive primes. By the second principle of mathematical induction, every positive integer larger than 1 can be factored into prime factors in at least one way.

To prove that the factorization is unique, we will use the first principle of mathematical induction to prove the following statement: If a positive integer m can be factored in any way as a product of n prime factors, then it can be factored into prime factors in no other way. Suppose that $n = 1$, then m is a prime and has no other factors, by the definition of a prime. Suppose that the result is valid for the case of n factors, and consider an integer m which can be factored as $m = p_1 p_2 \cdots p_{n+1}$, where $p_1, \cdots, p_{n+1}$ are primes. If $m = q_1 q_2 \cdots q_s$ for primes $q_1, q_2, \ldots, q_s$, we need to show that each $p_i = q_j$ for some j and that $n + 1 = s$. Thus $p_1 \mid m$ and hence $p_1 \mid q_1 q_2 \cdots q_s$. By the corollary to Theorem 2–15, $p_1 \mid q_j$

for some $j \leq s$. Since p_1 and q_j are both positive primes, $p_1 = q_j$. Now $p_2 p_3 \cdots p_{n+1}$ is a product of n primes and equals

$$q_1 q_2 \cdots q_{j-1} q_{j+1} \cdots q_s.$$

By our induction hypothesis, a product of n primes can be factored in no other way. Therefore, the product of q's must contain prime factors identical to those in the product of p's. That is, m can be factored in only one way. By the first principle of mathematical induction, the factorization into prime factors is unique for every possible number of factors. This completes the proof.

A method for finding the greatest common divisor of two integers by the use of Euclid's algorithm was suggested in Section 2–9. An alternative method is now available, using the unique factorization theorem. If two or more integers are factored into prime factors, their GCD can be found by inspection as the product of those prime factors common to all the integers. In simple cases, this method is often more practical than the previous method.

The *least common multiple* (LCM) of two or more integers is defined as a positive integer m such that each of the given integers divides m, and if k is any integer such that each of the given integers divides k, then m divides k. The LCM of a set of integers can also be found by inspection of the prime factors of the given integers. The LCM is the product of all factors appearing in any integer, each factor repeated the maximum number of times it appears in any one of the given integers. Thus $48 = 2^4 \cdot 3$ and $54 = 3^3 \cdot 2$ have $2^4 \cdot 3^3 = 432$ as LCM.

EXERCISES

1. Factor each of the following integers into prime factors.
   a) 432   b) 2310   c) 97   d) 8259
2. Factor the real number 10 in two ways, using real numbers as factors. (These factors will not all be integers.)
3. There are no primes in the system of real numbers, since each nonzero number divides every real number. Show that in the set of real numbers (a) $2 \mid 3$, (b) $2 \mid 10$, and (c) $5 \mid \sqrt[3]{7}$.
4. Factor the matrix
$$\begin{pmatrix} 3 & 4 \\ 5 & 6 \end{pmatrix}$$
   in two ways as a product of 2×2 matrices.
5. Unique factorization of polynomials will be discussed later. From your knowledge of high school algebra, try to formulate such a theorem for polynomials. Take into account the fact that, for instance, $x - 3 = \frac{1}{3}(3x - 9)$.
6. Use the method of prime factors to find the GCD and the LCM of each of the following sets of numbers.
   a) 45 and 75   b) 2310 and 273   c) 99, 231, and 792
7. Show that if integers m and n exist such that $am + bn = 1$ for integers a and b, then a and b are relatively prime. (This is the converse of part of the theorem in Section 2-9.)
8. Prove that if $D(a, b) = 1$, then $D(a^n, b) = 1$ for every positive integer n.

CHAPTER 3

OTHER NUMBER SYSTEMS

3-1 THE RATIONAL NUMBERS

Rational numbers are customarily written as fractions, quotients of two integers. For several reasons we will use another notation to introduce rational numbers. First, the fraction notation suggests an indicated division and at the outset we will not define division. We prefer to avoid the use of fractional notation until such time as division is introduced. A second, and more general, objection to the familiar notation is that with this notation it is difficult to indicate clearly which properties of the rationals are to be considered as definition and which properties are to be proved from known properties of the integers. This distinction is made easier by the use of a notation which does not suggest to the reader that he already knows the familiar properties of rational numbers. Finally, the notation we will use helps to clarify familiar properties of fractions. For example, the precise meaning of the statement that $\frac{4}{8} = \frac{1}{2}$ is reflected in our notation, and will be made clear by our definitions.

It is important that both the prospective teacher and the future mathematician have a through understanding of the number systems which form the basis for so much of the mathematics taught at all levels. Much of the material in our development would not be suitable for classroom use in the high school. However, the insight and understanding gained in a detailed study of the rational numbers are essential background for effective teaching.

Our point of view, then, will be that the integers are known and that from them we will construct a new system whose properties must be carefully established by formal proof. Our notation will help to emphasize that we assume nothing beyond the definition about this new system. We will show, in the next section, that this new system is actually an extension of the set of integers.

Definition 1. Let S be the set of all ordered pairs (a, b) of integers in which the second element is nonzero.

$$S = \{(a, b) \mid a, b \in \mathbf{Z} \text{ and } b \neq 0\}.$$

Define the relation $\sim$ on the set S by $(a, b) \sim (c, d)$ if and only if $ad = bc$.

This definition represents the first step in the construction of the rational numbers from the integers. We have not yet defined a rational number. Before we can do that we need to investigate the properties of the relation we have defined on S. As examples, we note that $(2, 3) \sim (4, 6)$ since $2 \cdot 6 = 3 \cdot 4 = 12$ and $(-3, 1) \sim (3 \, -1)$ since $(-3)(-1) = 1 \cdot 3 = 3$.

Theorem 3–1. The relation $\sim$ is an equivalence relation in the set S.

Proof. First, if $(a, b) \in S$, then $(a, b) \sim (a, b)$, since $ab = ba$ by the commutative property of multiplication in $\mathbf{Z}$. Hence the reflexive property of $\sim$ has been established.

We will leave the proof of the symmetric property for the reader and prove that the transitive property holds. If $(a, b) \sim (c, d)$ and $(c, d) \sim (e, f)$ for (a, b), (c, d), and (e, f) in S, then, by definition, $ad = bc$ and $cf = de$. Multiplying, we obtain $(ad)(cf) = (bc)(de)$. By the generalized commutative property $(af)(cd) = (be)(cd)$. Now $d \neq 0$ by definition of S and if $c \neq 0$ then $cd \neq 0$ and it follows from the cancellation law that $af = be$. Hence $(a, b) \sim (e, f)$ by definition of $\sim$. However, if $c = 0$ then from $ad = bc$ we can deduce that $a = 0$, since $d \neq 0$. Also we deduce from $cf = de$ that $e = 0$. Then (a, b) is the pair $(0, b)$ and (e, f) is $(0, f)$. But in this case $(a, b) \sim (e, f)$ since $0 \cdot f = b \cdot 0 = 0$. We have proved that in either case $(a, b) \sim (e, f)$ and therefore the transitive property holds. This completes the proof that $\sim$ is an equivalence relation in S.

This equivalence relation partitions S into equivalence sets. As usual, we denote by $[a, b]$ an equivalence set containing the pair (a, b).

Definition 2. The set of *rational numbers* is the set $\mathbf{Q}$ of all equivalence sets in S relative to the relation $\sim$.

$$\mathbf{Q} = \{[a, b] \,|\, (a, b) \in S\}$$

Note that a rational number is not a pair (a, b) of integers, but an equivalence set of such pairs. For example $[1, 2]$ is a rational number where $[1, 2] = \{(1, 2),$ $(2, 4), (-3, -6), (45, 90), \ldots\}$. This notation is not precise, in that only a few elements of the set of equivalent pairs are listed. Can you name other pairs in the set $[1, 2]$? This rational number $[1, 2]$ can be expressed alternately as $[2, 4]$, $[-3, -6]$, and in many other ways. If this does not seem clear, it would be well to review the section on equivalence relations and equivalence sets before proceeding.

In any new system the meaning of equality is important. Equality of elements in $\mathbf{Q}$ means equality of sets, which we have already defined. Since various names for the same element (set) in $\mathbf{Q}$ exist, as we have pointed out, we state the condition that two names represent the same set in the following theorem. The theorem stated is a property of equivalence relations, and the proof is a direct consequence of Theorem 1–1 of Chapter 1.

Theorem 3–2. If $[a, b]$ and $[c, d]$ are two elements of $\mathbf{Q}$, then $[a, b] = [c, d]$ if and only if $ad = bc$.

The next step in the process of constructing the rational numbers is to define suitable binary operations of addition and multiplication in Q. Before we do this, let us consider some of the difficulties that are inherent in the problem. For example, suppose that we decided to define addition in Q by $[a, b] + [c, d] = [a + c, b + d]$. There are two difficulties with this seemingly natural definition. First, although b and d are nonzero, it is quite possible that $b + d = 0$. In this case the notation $[a + c, b + d]$ does not represent an element of Q, since every pair in S has a second element which is nonzero. Thus Q would not be closed relative to this operation, an undesirable situation. There is another difficulty which is more subtle but equally serious. The rational numbers $[1, 2]$ and $[2, 4]$ are equal and yet if they are each added to $[3, 1]$, different answers are obtained. That is, $[1, 2] + [3, 1] = [4, 3]$ while $[2, 4] + [3, 1] = [5, 5]$. Now, $[4, 3] \neq [5, 5]$ since $4 \cdot 5 \neq 3 \cdot 5$. This definition gives results which depend on the name used for a particular number and not on the number itself. We refer to this by saying that the operation is not *well defined*. This is just a way of emphasizing the fact that we have not really defined a binary operation. The number assigned as the sum of two numbers is not unique. The following definition describes the essential property of binary operations which we have violated in this example.

Definition 3. The operation $*$ in a set T is *well defined* provided that, whenever $a = a'$ and $b = b'$ for elements a, b, a', and b' in T, then $a * b = a' * b'$.

Our example used a special case covered by the definition in which b and b' were identical. Hence the definition of our example will not serve as a suitable definition of addition. We now proceed with a more appropriate definition of operations in Q.

Definition 4. Addition and multiplication in the set Q of rational numbers are defined by the following equations:

$$[a, b] + [c, d] = [ad + bc, bd],$$
$$[a, b] [c, d] = [ac, bd].$$

The student will gain insight into the properties of fractions by associating, in his mind, the set $[a, b]$ with the fraction a/b in the statements that follow. He should remember, however, that we will not formally justify this association until the next section.

The definitions of addition and multiplication in Q depend on operations with the representatives used to express the equivalence sets. It is necessary to justify that these operations are well defined. That is, we must verify that the sum or product of two rational numbers depends only upon the numbers themselves and not upon the representation used in writing them. The following example illustrates this notion, but of course does not constitute a proof.

Example 3–1. By our definitions, $[2, 5] = [4, 10]$ and $[-3, 2] = [9, -6]$. Adding, we see that $[2, 5] + [-3, 2] = [-11, 10]$ while $[4, 10] + [9, -6] =$

$[66, -60]$.   Although these two answers look different, $[-11, 10] = [66, -60]$, since $(-11)(-60) = (10)(66)$.   Similarly, $[2, 5][-3, 2] = [-6, 10]$ and $[4, 10]$ $[9, -6] = [36, -60]$.   Again, the results are the same although expressed in terms of different representatives.   Thus $[-6, 10] = [36, -60]$, since $(-6)(-60)$ $= (10)(36)$.

Theorem 3-3.   Addition and multiplication of rational numbers are well defined operations and the set of rational numbers is closed with respect to both operations.

To prove this theorem, suppose that $[a, b]$ and $[c, d]$ are any two elements of **Q**.   Then $b \neq 0$ and $d \neq 0$ from the definition of elements of **Q**.   Since there are no zero divisors in the set of integers, $bd \neq 0$, so that $[ad + bc, bd]$ and $[ac, bd]$ are both elements of **Q**.   Note that the domain of both operations is the entire set **Q** × **Q**.   Thus **Q** is closed with respect to addition and multiplication.

Now suppose that $[a, b] = [a', b']$ and that $[c, d] = [c', d]$.   This means that

1) $$ab' = ba' \quad \text{and} \quad cd' = dc'.$$

Now

$$[a, b] + [c, d] = [ad + bc, bd]$$

and

$$[a', b'] + [c', d'] = [a'd' + b'c', b'd'].$$

To show that addition is well defined, we need to prove that

$$[ad + bc, bd] = [a'd' + b'c', b'd'].$$

Multiplying the first of equations (1) by dd', we obtain $ab'dd' = ba'dd'$.   Multiplying the second of equations (1) by bb', we obtain $cd'bb' = dc'bb'$.   Adding these two equations gives

2) $$ab'dd' + cd'bb' = ba'dd' + dc'bb'.$$

Factoring the terms in (2) leads to

3) $$(ad + bc)b'd' = (a'd' + b'c')bd.$$

Here we have used properties such as the commutative, associative, and distributive laws for integers to obtain (3).   Now by the definition of equality, equation (3) is just the condition that $[ad + bc, bd] = [a'd' + b'c', b'd']$.   This completes the proof that addition is well defined.

The proof that multiplication is well defined will be left for the reader.   The method is similar to the proof for addition.   The main step in proving equality of the two products considered follows by multiplying the equations (1).

This completes the description of the set of rational numbers.   Remember that each rational number is a *set* containing many pairs of integers.   If this idea seems difficult to you, it is primarily because it is new.   Some modern elementary texts use exactly this approach in presenting rational numbers in the seventh or eighth grades. The following example illustrates some of the computations with rational numbers which follow from our definitions.

Example 3–2. If $x = [2, 3]$ and $y = [-5, 2]$ let us find $x + y$, xy, x^2 and $3y$, where 2 is an exponent and 3 is a coefficient.

$x + y = [2, 3] + [-5, 2] = [2 \cdot 2 + 3(-5), 3 \cdot 2] = [-11, 6]$,
$xy = [2, 3][-5, 2] = [-10, 6]$, $x^2 = [2, 3][2, 3] = [4, 9]$,   and
$3y = [-5, 2] + [-5, 2] + [-5, 2] = [-20, 4] + [-5, 2] = [-60, 8]$.

EXERCISES

1. Perform the indicated operations in **Q**.

   a) $[3, 2][2, 5]$ b) $[2, 5][3, 2]$
   c) $[3, 2] + [2, 5]$ d) $[2, 5] + [3, 2]$
   e) $[4, 7] + [0, 3]$ f) $[4, 7][3, 3]$
   g) $[1, 2]([3, 5] + [4, 3])$ h) $[1, 2][3, 5] + [1, 2][4, 3]$

   i) Prove that your answers to (e) and (f) are each equal to $[4, 7]$. What does this suggest?
   j) Prove that your answers to (g) and (h) are equal to each other. What does this suggest?

2. Use the definitions of coefficient and exponent from Section 2-7 to find the following elements of **Q**.

   a) $2[5, 3]$ b) $5[-2, 3]$ c) $[3, 4]^3$
   d) $[2, -5]^4$ e) $3([2, -1] + [1, -2])$ f) $[2, 3]^2[2, 3]^3$

3. Let the "operation" $*$ be defined in **Q** by $[a, b] * [c, d] = [a - c, bd]$. Prove by counter-example that $*$ is not well defined.

4. Let the "operation" $\circ$ be defined in **Q** by $[a, b] \circ [c, d] = [ac, b - d]$. Prove by counter-examples that **Q** is not closed with respect to $\circ$ and that $\circ$ is not well defined.

5. Complete the proof of Theorem 3-1 by proving that the symmetric property of $\sim$ holds in S.

6. Complete the proof of Theorem 3-3 by proving that multiplication is well defined in **Q**.

7. Prove that multiplication is commutative in **Q**.

8. Prove that addition is commutative in **Q**.

9. a) Prove that if m is the LCM of b and d then $[a, b] + [c, d] = [x, m]$ for some integer x.
   b) If in part (a), $m = b'b$ and $m = d'd$, determine x in terms of a, c, b' and d'.

10. An error sometimes found in students' work goes as follows:
    $[2, 3] \neq [3, 5]$ and $[3, 4] \neq [5, 6]$. But $[2, 3][3, 4] = [3, 5][5, 6]$ and hence multiplication is not well defined in **Q**. Discuss this incorrect proof and point out why this is not a correct application of the definition of the term well defined.

3-2   PROPERTIES OF RATIONAL NUMBERS

We defined the set of rational numbers in the previous section. Now we wish to classify the system in terms of its algebraic properties. We will first find that the system is a commutative ring with unity and no zero divisors. The proof of two of the required properties were assigned as exercises in the last section and several other properties were suggested by the numerical examples. In addition to the ring properties, we will establish one further property which will lead to the definition of a *field*. Before we begin, we can establish one elementary property of rational numbers which will be useful in our proofs.

Theorem 3–4. If $[a, b]$ is any element of **Q**, then $[a, b] = [ax, bx]$ for every nonzero integer x.

This follows from the definition of equality and from the commutative law of multiplication in **Z**, since all that is required for equality is that $axb = bxa$.

We will use Theorem 3–4 in several of the following proofs. In words, this theorem states that a rational number is not changed if both the first and second elements of the pair are multiplied by a nonzero integer. This can be recognized as a familiar property of fractions.

Theorem 3–5. The set **Q** of rational numbers with the operations of addition and multiplication defined above is a commutative ring with unity.

We have already shown in Theorem 3–3 that **Q** is closed with respect to both operations.

Associativity of addition can be proved as follows. Assume that $[a, b]$, $[c, d]$, and $[e, f]$ are any three elements of **Q**. Then

$$
\begin{aligned}
[a, b] + ([c, d] + [e, f]) &= [a, b] + [cf + de, df] \\
&= [adf + bcf + bde, bdf] \\
&= [ad + bc, bd] + [e, f] \\
&= ([a, b] + [c, d]) + [e, f].
\end{aligned}
$$

Each step in this proof depends upon the definition of addition in **Q**, or upon properties of **Z**, or both. The reader should supply these reasons to be sure he clearly understands the steps.

The zero element of **Q** is the set $[0, b]$ for any integer $b \neq 0$. Note that $[0, b] = [0, x]$ for any integer $x \neq 0$. That the set $[0, b]$ is the zero set can be justified by considering the following, where $[c, d]$ is any element of **Q**:

$$
\begin{aligned}
[0, b] + [c, d] &= [0 \cdot d + bc, bd] \\
&= [bc, bd] \\
&= [c, d].
\end{aligned}
$$

It is also true that $[c, d] + [0, b] = [c, d]$. This can be proved directly, as above, or will follow from the commutativity of addition, mentioned later.

The negative of an arbitrary element $[a, b]$ in **Q** is the element $[-a, b]$, since

$$
[a, b] + [-a, b] = [ab - ab, bb] = [0, bb],
$$

the zero set of Q. We can also write the negative of $[a, b]$ as $[a, -b]$, since by Theorem 3-4, $[a, -b] = [-a, b]$.

Addition in Q is commutative, as the student may readily verify. The associativity of multiplication follows directly from associativity of the integers.

The left-distributive law of multiplication over addition is proved by considering three arbitrary elements, $[a, b]$, $[c, d]$, and $[e, f]$, in Q:

$$[a, b]([c, d] + [e, f]) = [a, b][cf + de, df]$$
$$= [acf + ade, bdf]$$
$$= [acbf + bdae, b^2df]$$
$$= [ac, bd] + [ae, bf]$$
$$= [a, b][c, d] + [a, b][e, f]$$

Again, the student should supply reasons for each step. Note that at one step we used the property derived earlier, that the set is not changed if both first and second elements of the pair are multiplied by the same nonzero integer, in this case the integer b. Since multiplication is clearly commutative, there is no need to establish the right-distributive law. We have shown, then, that Q is a commutative ring.

The ring Q has a unity element $[1, 1]$. Note that $[1, 1] = [a, a]$ for every nonzero integer a. To show that $[1, 1]$ is the unity element of Q, consider an arbitrary element $[c, d]$ in Q. Then $[1, 1][c, d] = [c, d] = [c, d][1, 1]$. This completes the proof of Theorem 3-5.

Theorem 3-6. Q has no zero divisors and every nonzero element of Q has an inverse.

To prove that Q has no zero divisors, suppose that $[a, b][c, d] = [0, x]$ for some $x \neq 0$. That is, we assume that the product of two elements of Q is zero. Then $[ac, bd] = [0, x]$, and from the definition of equality, $acx = bd \cdot 0 = 0$. Since $x \neq 0$ and Q has no zero divisors, either a or c must be zero, and hence either $[a, b]$ or $[c, d]$ is the zero element of Q.

To show that every nonzero element of Q has a multiplicative inverse, suppose that $[a, b]$ is not the zero of Q. Then $a \neq 0$ and $[b, a]$ is an element of Q.

$$[a, b][b, a] = [ab, ba] = [ab, ab].$$

But $[ab, ab]$ is the unity element of Q so that $[b, a]$ is the inverse of $[a, b]$. We write $[b, a] = [a, b]^{-1}$.

These properties of Q given in Theorem 3-6 serve to classify Q as a field, an algebraic structure to be considered in more detail in Chapter 5. To be specific, and for ease of future reference, the definition of a field is included here.

Definition. A *field* is a commutative ring with unity element in which every nonzero element has a multiplicative inverse.

This definition does not specifically require that a field have no zero divisors.

However, from the fact that every nonzero element has a multiplicative inverse, it is easy to prove that there can be no zero divisors in a field.

Since $\mathbf{Q}$ is a ring, subtraction is defined as usual to be the result of adding the negative of the element to be subtracted.   Thus

$$[a, b] - [c, d] = [a, b] + [-c, d] = [ad - bc, bd].$$

In $\mathbf{Q}$, as in every field, division by nonzero elements may be defined in terms of multiplication by the inverse.   That is, $[a, b] \div [c, d]$ where $c \neq 0$ is defined as $[a, b][c, d]^{-1} = [a, b][d, c]$.   This is the familiar rule of inverting the divisor and multiplying, commonly used in manipulating fractions.   The validity of the rule depends on the definition of the operation of division and the fact that we proved the inverse of $[a, b]$ to be $[b, a]$ if $a \neq 0$.   The definitions of integral coefficients and integral exponents in Section 2–7 apply to $\mathbf{Q}$ as to any ring.

Example 3–3. The following computations are included as illustrations of the definitions of coefficients and exponents, considered for the ring $\mathbf{Q}$ of rational numbers.

$$-2[4, 3] = 2(-[4, 3]) = 2[-4, 3] = [-4, 3] + [-4, 3] = [-24, 9],$$

which can be written as $[-8, 3]$.

$$[-2, 3]^{-2} = ([-2, 3]^{-1})^2 = [3, -2]^2 = [3, -2][3, -2] = [9, 4].$$

These computations can be shortened, but rules for manipulating rational numbers have not been derived.   We can apply the definitions directly until further properties are established by proof.   Among the short cuts referred to are such rules as the one for adding "fractions with a common denominator."   In our notation this rule would read as follows:

$$[a, b] + [c, b] = [a + c, b].$$

Can you prove that this rule holds in $\mathbf{Q}$?

As an exercise, the student should prove that the cancellation laws for addition and multiplication hold in $\mathbf{Q}$ and that equations of the form $a + x = b$ and $cx = d$, for $c \neq 0$, can be solved in $\mathbf{Q}$.   The solutions are of the form indicated earlier for other systems in which these solutions exist.

EXERCISES

1. Use the definitions of exponents and coefficients given in Section 2-7 to evaluate the following as elements in $\mathbf{Q}$.

a) $3[2, 5]$

b) $[2, 3]^2$

c) $-2[-2, 3]$

d) $-3[4, 7]$

e) $[3, 5]^{-2}$

f) $[-2, 3]^{-3}$

g) $0[3, 4]$

h) $[5, 7]^0$

i) $[17, 17]^{20}$

2. Solve each of the following equations in Q or show that they have no solution.

a) $[3, 1] + X = [7, 11]$ b) $[3, -2] + X = [2, 7]$

c) $[3, 5] - X = [7, 2]$ d) $3[4, -3] + X = 2[3, 2]$

e) $[3, 5]X = [4, 7]$ f) $[4, 6]X = [0, 2]$

g) $[0, 5]X = [2, 3]$ h) $X \div [2, 7] = [5, 3]$

In the following proofs give all details with reasons for each step. Use the $[\ ]$ notation for elements of Q.

3. Prove the associative law of multiplication in Q.

4. Prove the right-distributive law of multiplication over addition for Q, either directly from the properties of integers or from the left-distributive law and the commutativity of multiplication.

5. Prove that equations of the form $a + x = b$, where a and b are in Q, have solutions in Q.

6. Prove that equations of the form $cx = d$, where $c \neq 0$ and c and d are in Q, have solutions in Q.

7. Prove that $[a, b] + [c, b] = [a + c, b]$, the property referred to in the next-to-last paragraph of this section.

8. Prove the cancellation law of addition in Q, namely that if $a + x = b + x$ for a, b, x in Q, then $a = b$.

9. Prove the cancellation law of multiplication in Q, namely, that if $ax = bx$ for $x \neq 0$ then $a = b$.

10. Prove that a field has no zero divisors.

*11. Prove that in any ring the cancellation law for multiplication is equivalent to the fact that the ring has no zero divisors. Do this by showing that if we assume either property is true, the other can be proved as a theorem.

*12. Among the rings Z_n of integers modulo n, for various integers n, some are fields and some are not.

a) Prove, by counterexample, that Z_n is not a field if n is not a prime.

b) Prove that Z_p is a field if p is a prime. Remember that all properties of a field except the existence of inverses have been previously proved.

3-3   THE INTEGERS AS A SUBSET OF THE RATIONAL NUMBERS

The relation between the integers and the rational numbers has not been specifically pointed out in the preceding section. While the definition of the rationals depended on properties of integers, the student would not likely suspect that the integers are essentially a subset of the set of rational numbers. We propose to clarify the situation in this section. To do this we need to define a new concept which we will illustrate first with an example.

Consider the set $S = \{a, b, c\}$ with operations of multiplication and addition defined in S by the following tables.

---

* An asterisk before a problem indicates that the problem is more difficult than most.

+	a	b	c
a	b	c	a
b	c	a	b
c	a	b	c

·	a	b	c
a	a	b	c
b	b	a	c
c	c	c	c

One can check that S, with the operations defined by the tables, forms a ring and in fact a field.   The zero of the ring is c and the unity is a.   If we were to change the name of the element c to 0, change the name of a to 1 and change the name of b to 2, the tables would become the tables for the ring Z_3 of integers modulo 3. That is, the only difference between the rings S and Z_3 is the name by which we refer to the elements.   They have identical algebraic properties.   For example, in S, $b^2 = a$ while the counterpart of b, in Z_3, namely 2, has the property that $2^2 = 1$ and 1 is the counterpart of a.   From this we deduce that the inverse of b in S is b and correspondingly the inverse of 2 in Z_3 is 2.   When the situation described here exits between two systems, we say that the systems are *isomorphic*.

The process of "renaming" elements of a ring does not sound very mathematical. We need to formulate this idea in precise mathematical terminology.   This is accomplished by the following definition.

Definition of isomorphism.   A mapping φ from a ring R onto a ring S is an *isomorphism* from R onto S if and only if φ is a one-to-one mapping such that for all elements a and b in R

1) $\varphi(a + b) = \varphi(a) + \varphi(b)$ and   2) $\varphi(ab) = \varphi(a)\varphi(b)$.

If an isomorphism from R onto S exists then we say that R is *isomorphic* to S.

In this definition the mapping φ provides the "renaming" of elements.   For each $a \in R$, $\varphi(a)$ is an element of S which we can visualize as a new name for the element a.   The two conditions formulate the idea that the algebraic properties of the two systems are identical.   When we require that $\varphi(a + b) = \varphi(a) + \varphi(b)$ we are stating that the sum of two elements of R corresponds to the sum of the corresponding elements of S.   That is, it really does not matter whether we perform the addition in R indicated by $a + b$ or in S as indicated by $\varphi(a) + \varphi(b)$ since the results correspond under the renaming process given by the mapping φ.   We refer to condition (1) by saying that φ *preserves addition* and to (2) by saying that φ *preserves multiplication*.

The isomorphism we described between S and Z_3 can be written in the notation of mappings as $\varphi(c) = 0$, $\varphi(a) = 1$, and $\varphi(b) = 2$.   Note that the mapping is a one-to-one mapping of S onto Z_3.   The fact that this mapping preserves both addition and multiplication is proved by checking our earlier comment that with the indicated change of name the tables for S become the tables for Z_3.   For example, $\varphi(a + b) = \varphi(c) = 0$ while $\varphi(a) + \varphi(b) = 1 + 2 = 0$.   Here the sum $a + b$ was obtained from the addition table for S and the sum $1 + 2$ was determined by definition of addition in Z_3.

Now we return to the discussion of the rational numbers. Let I be the set of all equivalence sets in $\mathbf{Z}$ which can be represented by a pair having the integer 1 as second element. That is,

$$I = \{[n, 1] \mid n \text{ is any integer}\}.$$

We now define the mapping φ of I into $\mathbf{Z}$ by $\varphi([n, 1]) = n$. Clearly, this is a one-to-one mapping of I onto $\mathbf{Z}$, since for each integer n there is exactly one set $[n, 1]$, and conversely.

We will show that the mapping φ preserves the operations of addition and multiplication. Let $[n, 1]$ and $[m, 1]$ be any two elements of I. Then

$$\varphi([n, 1] + [m, 1]) = \varphi([n + m, 1])$$
$$= n + m$$
$$= \varphi([n, 1]) + \varphi([m, 1]).$$

The justification for the first equality is the definition of addition in $\mathbf{Q}$; for the second and third equalities it is the definition of the mapping φ. Similarly,

$$\varphi([n, 1][m, 1]) = \varphi([nm, 1])$$
$$= nm$$
$$= \varphi([n, 1])\varphi([m, 1]).$$

This discussion has proved the following theorem.

Theorem 3–7. The subset $I = \{[n, 1] \mid n \text{ is an integer}\}$ of the set $\mathbf{Q}$ of rational numbers is isomorphic to the set $\mathbf{Z}$ of integers. The isomorphism φ is given by $\varphi([n, 1]) = n$ for all $[n, 1] \in I$.

The usual notation for integers and rational numbers is introduced in the following way. We agree to write any set in $\mathbf{Q}$ of the form $[n, 1]$ simply as n. Further, any set $[a, b]$ in $\mathbf{Q}$ will written in the future as a/b and will be called a *fraction*. This convention permits us to write an integer n in the alternative form $n/1$ whenever this is convenient.

In order to justify the dual use of a fraction for representing a rational number and also for representing a division of two integers, consider the problem of dividing an integer m by the integer $n \neq 0$. The integers m and n may be written in the form $[m, 1]$ and $[n, 1]$ according to our notational convention. Then by our definition of division in the preceding section,

$$m \div n = [m, 1] \div [n, 1] = [m, 1][1, n] = [m, n].$$

The result of dividing m by n, then, is the rational number $[m, n]$, which we have agreed to write as m/n, and the distinction between the notations is that $m \div n$ represents an instance of the binary operation $\div$ while m/n is the rational number representing the result of that division. In common usage, this distinction is lost and the two symbols are often used interchangeably. It is important, however, to recognize the distinction and to understand the precise meaning of each symbol.

In adopting the notation a/b to replace the more cumbersome notation $[a, b]$, we omit the symbol which suggests the fact that a rational number is an equivalence set of elements. For the understanding of rational numbers it is important that this fact be kept in mind. When we state that $\frac{1}{2} = \frac{2}{4}$, we are using the fact that $\frac{1}{2}$ and $\frac{1}{4}$ are elements of the same equivalence set and hence either symbol can be used as a representative for the set. When we proved that $[ax, bx] = [a, b]$ for any nonzero integer x, we derived the familiar rule that permits the multiplication or division of numerator and denominator in a fraction by the same nonzero integer. The standard methods of adding, subtracting, and simplifying fractions are all based on this fundamental identity.

EXERCISES

1. Prove that $\frac{1}{2} + \frac{1}{3} = \frac{5}{6}$ using the set notation for rational numbers. (For instance, $\frac{1}{3} = [1, 3]$.) Give detailed reasons for each step.

2. Prove in detail, using set notation, how to add $a/b + e/f$ if the GCD of b and f is d. Let $b = b'd$ and $f = f'd$. Use the common denominator $b'f'd$.

3. Derive the rule for division of fractions which states, "To divide one fraction by another, invert the divisor and multiply." Use set notation.

4. Prove that a fraction is not changed when numerator and denominator are divided by the same nonzero integer. Use set notation.

5. Refer to Exercise 7 at the end of Section 2-4. Prove that the ring T of this exercise is isomorphic to Z_2. Specify a mapping from T onto Z_2 and prove it has the properties required of an isomorphism. You only have two choices of mappings but one choice will not work.

*6. Prove that if the construction of Section 3-1 which defined the rational numbers were repeated, using the set E of even integers instead of the set of all integers, the result would have been a system isomorphic to **Q**.

*7. Prove that if an integral domain D has only a finite number of elements, then D is a field.

3-4   RATIONAL NUMBERS AND RATIONAL POINTS ON A LINE

In developing the number systems used in elementary mathematics, the most difficult step is probably the extension of the rational numbers to the system of real numbers. From the various methods available, we have chosen a method which associates the real numbers with points on a line. The approach used here will be partly intuitive, but should be readily understood and can be made more rigorous in advanced courses. In order to prepare the student for this extension, we will first discuss the rational points on a line and two methods by which the correspondence between rational numbers and rational points can be established.

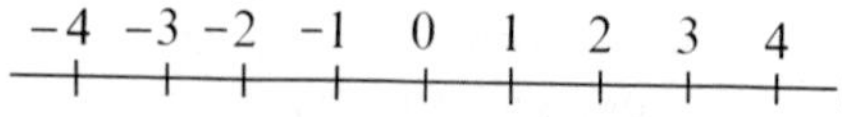

Fig. 3–1.   Points on a line.

First, we will consider the problem of constructing, by straightedge and compass, the points on a line associated with rational numbers. Consider any line l, as in Fig. 3–1, with two arbitrary points chosen as reference points. We associate the numbers 0 and 1 with these points and refer to the numbers as the *coordinates* of the points. The point with coordinate 0 is referred to as the *origin*, and the point with coordinate 1 as the unit point. Customarily, the unit point is taken to the right of the origin, but this is not essential. Using the distance from the origin to the unit point as radius, we may lay off at equal intervals points with coordinates $2, 3, \ldots$ to the right of the unit point, and points with coordinates $-1, -2, \ldots$ to the left of the origin. Thus we may construct a point on line l for each integer, positive or negative.

To construct the point corresponding to the rational number p/q, we may first divide the distance from the origin to the unit point into q equal segments of length $1/q$, using the familiar construction from plane geometry involving similar triangles. Then we lay off p segments of length $1/q$, to the right of the origin when $pq > 0$, and to the left of the origin when $pq < 0$. This serves, theoretically, to assign a point on the line to each rational number. The rational number is termed the coordinate of the associated point. As a practical method, this procedure has its shortcomings, since accurate construction is impossible for all but the simplest cases. However, it should be clear that it is possible to conceive of such a process which does associate points on the line with each rational number.

It is easy to show that there are points on the line that do not correspond to any rational number. For instance, suppose that we construct a right triangle, with each leg 1 unit long (the distance from the origin to the unit point). The hypotenuse is then $\sqrt{2}$ units long, and we can construct the point on line l that is $\sqrt{2}$ units to the right of the origin. This is not one of the points with a rational coordinate. Suppose that $\sqrt{2} = p/q$, where p and q are relatively prime integers, that is, p/q is a rational number expressed in "lowest terms." Then $2 = p^2/q^2$ or $2q^2 = p^2$. That is, 2 divides p^2, and since 2 is prime, by the corollary to Theorem 3–11 of Section 3–11, 2 divides p; hence $p = 2k$ for some integer k. Upon substitution we have $2q^2 = (2k)^2 = 4k^2$. The cancellation law implies that $q^2 = 2k^2$. Hence, by the argument above, 2 divides q. Since $2 \,|\, p$ and $2 \,|\, q$, this is a contradiction of the assumption that p and q are relatively prime. Hence, $\sqrt{2}$ cannot be a rational number. This illustrates the fact that points exist on the line which do not have rational coordinates. We introduce real numbers in the next section to provide coordinates for all points on the line.

In spite of the fact that there are points on the line which do not have rational coordinates, there are no intervals, or segments, of the line which are completely free of rational points. To make this clear, we need to extend the notion of order, defined for integers, to the set of rational numbers. We say that the rational number p/q is *positive*, and write $p/q > 0$, if the integer $pq > 0$. The set of all positive rational numbers will be designated as $\mathbf{Q}_p$. We need to show that $\mathbf{Q}_p$ is well defined. That is, since any rational number p/q may be expressed in many ways (for instance $p/q = 2p/2q$), we need to show that the designation of being positive does not depend upon the form used. To establish this, we consider p/q in the notation $[p, q]$. Suppose that $[p, q] = [r, s]$ and that $pq > 0$. We need to show that $rs > 0$, as well. Since $[p, q] = [r, s]$, we have that $ps = rq$. Since neither p nor s is zero, ps is nonzero. Then $(ps)^2 = rqps > 0$. Now since $pq > 0$ and $(pq)(rs) > 0$, it follows that $rs > 0$, as was to be proved.

Next we define inequalities for rational numbers. If r and s are rational numbers, $r < s$ if and only if $s - r$ is positive. The student should check to see that, for the case where r and s are integers, this definition coincides with the earlier definition of $<$.

The properties of inequalities given in Section 2–2 for integers are valid for the rational numbers as well. We restate the properties in the following theorem.

Theorem 3–8. For rational numbers $a, b,$ and c:
$$\text{If } a < b, \text{ then } a \pm c < b \pm c.$$
$$\text{If } a < b \text{ and } 0 < c, \text{ then } ac < bc.$$
$$\text{If } a < b \text{ and } c < 0, \text{ then } bc < ac.$$

b) (*Law of trichotomy*): For any two rational numbers, m and n, either $m < n$, $m = n$, or $n < m$.

The proof follows from the definition and from properties of integers. We will prove two parts of the theorem as examples and leave the remaining parts as exercises for the reader.

First, we prove that if $a < b$, then $a + c < b + c$ for rational numbers $a, b,$ and c. If $a < b$, then $b - a \in \mathbf{Q}_p$ by definition. But

$$b - a = b - a + 0 = b - a + (c - c) = (b + c) - (a + c).$$

Hence $(b + c) - (a + c) \in \mathbf{Q}_p$ and, by definition, $a + c < b + c$.

Now suppose that $a < b$ and $0 < c$. This part of the proof depends upon the expression of $a, b,$ and c in terms of integers. Let $a = m/n$, $b = p/q$, and $c = s/t$. Then

$$bc - ac = \frac{psnt - qtms}{qtnt}.$$

To prove that $ac < bc$, we need to prove that $bc - ac \in \mathbf{Q}_p$, or that the integer $qtnt(psnt - qtms) > 0$ in order to satisfy the definition of $\mathbf{Q}_p$. To do this, first consider $b - a$, an element of $\mathbf{Q}_p$ since it is given that $a < b$. Thus

$$b - a = \frac{p}{q} - \frac{m}{n} = \frac{pn - qm}{qn}$$

is an element of $\mathbf{Q}_p$, and therefore $qn(pn - qm) > 0$. This inequality involves only the integers $m, n, p,$ and q, so we may use known properties of integers in continuing the proof. Now $t^2 > 0$ and $sr > 0$, since $c = s/t$ is positive. We may multiply the preceding inequality by t^2st. Hence $qtnt(psnt - msqt) > 0$, which is the condition needed to prove that $ac < bc$, as shown above. Other parts of the theorem are proved in a similar manner.

Next, a rational number t is *between* the rational numbers r and s if either $r < t < s$ or $s < t < r$. The following theorem states a property of rational numbers referred to as the *density property*. Because of this property, we say that the set of rational numbers is a *dense set* and that the set of points with rational coordinates is dense in the line l.

Theorem 3–9. Between any two distinct rational numbers there is another rational number.

To prove this theorem, consider the rational numbers r and s, where for convenience we assume that $r < s$. Then we will show that $(r + s)/2$ is between r and s. Since $r < s$, $r + r < r + s$ and hence $r < (r + s)/2$, using Theorem 3–8. Similarly, $r + s < s + s$, and $(r + s)/2 < s$. Together, these statements imply that $r < (r + s)/2 < s$, which completes the proof. This theorem can be extended by introduction to show that between any two rational numbers there exist n other rational numbers for any positive integer n.

This theorem proves the contention made earlier that no interval of the line is free of rational points, but only for the case where the interval has end points which are rational. The theorem is true for arbitrary intervals, but the proof is not given here.

So far, we have shown that each rational number may be associated with a point on a given line and that there is at least one point on this line not associated with any rational number. In the next section we will provide a method of identifying all points on a line, which leads in a natural way to a definition of real numbers.

EXERCISES

1. Using a straightedge and compass, construct the points on a line l which have the coordinates given below. Select two fixed points (origin and unit point) as reference points, as indicated in the text.

   a) $\frac{1}{2}$ b) $\frac{2}{3}$ c) $-\frac{9}{4}$ d) $-\frac{16}{5}$

2. Find a point with a coordinate that is not a rational number, other than $\sqrt{2}$, and prove that this coordinate is not rational.

3. Write out the proof of Theorem 3-8, except for the parts proved in the text.

4. Prove that if $r < s$ for positive rational numbers r and s, then $1/s < 1/r$.

5. Prove that for rational numbers r and s such that $r < s$, there exist n rational numbers $x_1 x_2, \cdots, x_n$ such that $r < x_1 < x_2 < \cdots < x_n < s$ for every natural number n.

3-5   DECIMAL REPRESENTATION AND THE REAL NUMBER SYSTEM

Every reader is familiar with the decimal representation of rational numbers. The decimal expression in the number $r = 5.27$, for instance, means that $r = 5 + 2\left(\frac{1}{10}\right) + 7\left(\frac{1}{10}\right)^2$. Again, $\frac{1}{3}$ may be written as $\frac{1}{3} = 0.3333...$, which means that

$$\tfrac{1}{3} = 3\left(\tfrac{1}{10}\right) + 3\left(\tfrac{1}{10}\right)^2 + 3\left(\tfrac{1}{10}\right)^3 + \cdots$$

Thus we are familiar with two types of decimals—those which can be written with a finite number of digits, called *terminating decimals*, and those which require an infinite sequence of digits, called *infinite decimals*.

In practice, the method of finding the decimal representation for a rational number is to perform a long division to obtain as many digits as are required for a particular application. We may show, formally, that this is always possible by applying the division algorithm. If m/n is a positive rational number, there exist nonnegative integers q and r such that $m = qn + r$, where $r < n$. We refer to q as the *integral part* of m/n. From this equation, $m/n = q + r/n$. Next, we consider $10r$ and n and find integers q_1 and r_1, with $r_1 < n$, such that $10r = q_1 n = q_1 n + r_1$, from which $r/n = q_1(1/10) + r_1/10n$. Substitution gives $m/n = q + q_1(1/10) + r_1/10n$. Applying the algorithm to $10r_1$ and n, we find integers q_2 and r_2 such that $10r_1 = q_2 n + r_2$, from which

$$r_1/10n = q_2(1/10)^2 + r_2/100n$$

Now,

$$m/n = q + q_1(1/10) + q_2(1/10)^2 + r_2/100n.$$

Continuing in this way, we may construct as many terms in the decimal representation of m/n as we like. We would write m/n as $q + 0.q_1 q_2 q_3 \ldots$, where q is the integral part of m/n and $q_1, q_2, \ldots$ are the digits in the decimal part of m/n. In some cases $r_i = 0$ for some i, resulting in a terminating decimal, and in other cases no r_i is zero, which leads to an infinite decimal. Note that since each $r_i < n$, $10r_i < 10n$, and hence each $q_i < 10$, for $i = 1, 2, 3, \ldots$ We may express every decimal as an infinite decimal simply by adding to any terminating decimal a sequence of zeros. Thus $2.5000 \ldots = 2.5$. For convenience, we will consider every decimal as an infinite decimal.

A decimal such as $0.213575757 \ldots$ is termed a *repeating decimal*. That is, a repeating decimal is one which, except for certain initial digits, contains only a finite set of digits in a given order, repeated throughout the remainder of the sequence of digits. Every positive rational number is given by a repeating decimal, allowing the possibility of repetition of zeros in the terminating case. To establish this, one need only consider the possible remainders, $r_1, r_2, r_3, \ldots$ obtained in converting m/n into decimal form. Each remainder is, by the division algorithm, less than n. Hence at most n of these remainders can be different after the first step which determines the integral part of m/n. After at most $n + 1$ steps we encounter a remainder equal to one of the preceding remainders and from this point on, the sequence of quotients and remainders must repeat the preceding sequence, and hence produce a repeating decimal.

The converse is also true; namely, that every repeating decimal equals a positive rational number. The general proof is complicated by notational difficulties, so we will first illustrate the fact by an example.

Example 3–4. Suppose that

$$r = 3.12753753753 \ldots$$

Multiplying by 1000, we obtain

$$1000r = 3127.53753753\ldots$$

Subtracting these equations gives

$$999r = 3124.41.$$

Now we multiply by 100 and divide by 99,900 to obtain

$$r = \frac{312441}{99900} = \frac{104147}{33300},$$

which is a rational number.

In the general case, consider a number s in the form

$$s = q + 0.a_1 a_2 \ldots a_k b_1 b_2 \ldots b_n b_1 b_2 \ldots b_n \ldots,$$

where q is the integral part, each a_i, as well as each b_j, is a digit in the decimal part, and $b_1 b_2 \ldots b_n$ repeats. Then, upon multiplying by 10^{n+k}, we have

$$10^{n+k}s = 10^{n+k}q + a_1 \ldots a_k b_1 \ldots b_n b_1 \ldots b_n \ldots$$

Upon subtracting $10^k s$ from this expression, we have

$$10^{n+k}s - 10^k s = 10^{n+k}q - 10^k q + a_1 \ldots a_k b_1 \ldots b_n - a_1 \ldots a_k.$$

Solving for s gives

$$s = \frac{10^{n+k}q - 10^k q + a_1 \ldots a_k b_1 \ldots b_n - a_1 \ldots a_k}{10^{n+k} - 10^k}$$

which is the quotient of two integers, and hence is rational.

Thus we have shown that the set of positive rational numbers is given by the set of repeating decimals. We extend this in a similar way to the set of negative rational numbers, prefixing a negative sign to the repeating decimals which correspond to negative rational numbers. The number zero corresponds to the repeating decimal composed entirely of zeros. This establishes a one-to-one correspondence between the set of all rational numbers and the set of all positive, negative, and zero repeating decimals, exclusive of those which repeat the digit 9. Such a decimal may always be replaced by one terminating in zeros. Thus $6.7999\ldots = 6.8000\ldots$, and $3.124999\ldots = 3.125000\ldots$

Example 3–5. We will prove, as an illustration, that $3.999\ldots = 4.000\ldots$ A general proof could be given, but the example will illustrate the principle. Let $s = 3.999\ldots$ Then $10s = 39.999\ldots$ and $10s - s = 36.000\ldots$ In other words, $9s = 36$, or $s = 4$. Thus we have proved that $3.999\ldots = 4.000\ldots$

We define the set of *positive real numbers* to be the set of all positive infinite decimals. This includes the terminating decimals, since we allow the use of zeros in the decimal representation. The infinite repeating decimals correspond to rational numbers, and the nonrepeating decimals correspond to irrational numbers such as $\sqrt{2}$. To see that there are other irrational numbers, consider first the rational number $0.252525\ldots$ We may construct an irrational number by inserting the digit 3 after the first 5, two digits 3 after the second 5, three digits 3 after the third 5, etc.   This gives the decimal $0.253253325333\ldots$, which clearly does not repeat.   Obviously, an irrational number can be constructed in a similar way from any given rational number.   Hence it is clear that there exist many irrational numbers.

To associate the real numbers with points on a line, we proceed as follows: The points with integers as coordinates are selected as in Section 3–4.   Each unit interval, for instance, the interval between the points with coordinates n and $n + 1$, is divided into 10 equal parts labeled $0, 1, 2, \ldots, 9$.   Each such part is divided again into 10 parts and numbered $0, 1, 2, \ldots, 9$.   In turn, each of the new intervals is subdivided into 10 parts, and the process is continued indefinitely.   Let a real number r be written as $r = q + 0.a_1a_2a_3\ldots$, where q is the integral part and $a_1, a_2, a_3, \ldots$ are the successive digits in the decimal part of r. To select the point corresponding to this number, we first choose a sequence of intervals.   The interval q to $q + 1$ (that is, the interval between points with these coordinates) is selected as the first interval.   The second interval is chosen as part a_1 of the 10 subintervals into which the first interval is divided.   The third interval is part a_2 of the next smaller set of intervals into which the second chosen interval is divided.   Continuing this process, we select an infinite set of intervals, each a subinterval of the preceding one.   The lengths of these intervals are, respectively, the numbers of the set $\{1, \frac{1}{10}, \frac{1}{100}, \ldots\}$.   Such a sequence of intervals is an example of a *nested set of intervals*.   In general, a nested set of intervals is a sequence of intervals, each included in the preceding, whose lengths approach zero as a limit.   (We have not defined limit in this text, but the reader is referred to any elementary calculus text.   In our case, the condition is satisfied.)   The following principle is equivalent to several other theorems in analysis, one of which is taken as an axiom.   We will assume this without proof.

Axiom.   In any given nested set of intervals there exists one and only one point lying on every interval.

Because of this axiom, the sequence of intervals selected in the preceding paragraph determines a unique point, that point which belongs to every interval of the sequence.   This point is given the number r as its coordinate.   It can be proved that for rational numbers, this point is identical to the point assigned to the number r by the constructive method of Section 3–4.

Conversely, suppose that P is any point on a line l; for the moment we assume that P is to the right of the origin.   Assume further that the line has been divided into intervals and subintervals as described in preceding paragraphs.   We will describe a process by which P is associated with a real number p that will be the coordinate of point P as presented above.   If P lies between two points with integers as coordinates, say q and $q + 1$, we say that P *belongs* to this interval and write q as the integral part of the real number p. If, on the other hand, P is a point with integral coordinate q, we say that P belongs to the interval from q to $q + 1$, and again assign q as the integral part of the number p. Next consider the 10 parts into which the interval from q to $q + 1$ is divided. If P is a division point of such an interval, we say that P belongs to the interval on the right of P. Otherwise, P is within some interval, and we say that P belongs to this interval. If the number of this interval is a_1 (recall that the possible numbers are $0, 1, \ldots, 9$), we assign a_1 as the first digit in the decimal part of p. Continuing in this way, we obtain a sequence of numbers $a_1, a_2, a_3, \ldots$ corresponding to a nested set of intervals to which the point P belongs. Since one and only one point belongs to each such set of intervals, P is the point with coordinate $p = q + 0.a_1a_2a_3 \ldots$, as defined in the preceding paragraph. Thus each point on the line to the right of the origin corresponds to a positive real number, and conversely each positive real number corresponds to a point on the line to the right of the origin.

In a similar way we extend this correspondence to the set of all real numbers and all points on the line by matching the negative real numbers with points on the line to the left of the origin.

To complete our description of the real numbers as a mathematical system, it would be necessary to define addition and multiplication of real numbers and to derive the formal properties of the system. This can be done but the notational difficulties encountered are severe, and it is felt that in a first course it will be excusable to omit these definitions and proofs. The reader is encouraged to consult other sources, such as Beaumont and Pierce [24], for further details.

Without formal definition, we assert that the familiar rules of elementary arithmetic hold for operations with real numbers expressed in decimal form. It is, of course, impossible to carry out the addition or multiplication of infinite decimals, but as many digits of the sum or product as are desired can be obtained by using a sufficient number of digits from the given decimals. For instance, suppose that $\frac{4}{3} = 1.3333\ldots$ and $\frac{2}{7} = 0.285714285714\ldots$ are to be multiplied in decimal form. We obtain the product $0.38095\ldots$ to five decimal places by using six-decimal digits in each of the expressions for $\frac{4}{3}$ and $\frac{2}{7}$. If more digits are desired in the answer, we need to use more than six decimal digits in the factors. Since the exact number of digits needed depends primarily upon the integral parts of the two numbers, no general rule may be given.

It can be shown that the real numbers form a field, and that the order relation mentioned for rational numbers can be extended to an order relation for the real numbers. These properties will be discussed in the next section.

While our treatment of the real numbers in incomplete, it is hoped that the presentation given here in connection with the points on a line will help develop an intuitive appreciation for the system. Other developments lead more readily to formal derivation of the properties of the real number system, but require either considerably more algebraic background or a knowledge of some rather deep theorems of analysis.

EXERCISES

1. Convert each of the following rational numbers into an infinite repeating decimal.

   a) $\frac{3}{8}$ b) $\frac{1}{2}$ c) $\frac{73}{7}$ d) $\frac{11}{9}$

2. Convert each of the following repeating decimals into the form p/q, where p and q are integers.

   a) 2.4444 ...   b) 3.125125125 ...   c) 52.717171 ...
   d) 7.123412341234 ...   e) 0.23157157157 ...   f) 3.26518051805180 ...

3. Use the method of successive subdivision to locate the points having each of the following coordinates.

   a) 2.15000 ...   b) -1.27000 ...   c) 3.213000 ...

4. Construct the point with coordinate $\sqrt{2}$, and use the method of subdivision to determine the decimal representation $\sqrt{2}$ as accurately as possible from your graph.

5. Use the facts that $\pi = 3.1415926536$ and $e = 2.7182818285$, approximately, to find $\pi + e$ and $\pi \cdot e$ correct to five decimal places.

6. Determine, by listing the end points of each interval, the first five of the sequence of nested intervals to which the number π belongs.

7. Show that $2.1999 \ldots = 2.20000 \ldots$ by converting each to a rational number in the form m/n for m and n integers.

3-6   PROPERTIES OF THE REAL NUMBER SYSTEM

In this section we will adopt a new point of view, and consider the real numbers in terms of axioms which define the system rather than as an extension of the system of rational numbers. In order to make the axioms clear, we need two new definitions.

Definition 1. A field F is *ordered* if and only if it contains a set of elements F_p, called the set of positive elements of F, having the following properties.

a) F_p is closed under addition and multiplication. That is, the sum or product of any two elements in F_p is also in F_p.

b) For every element r in F, $r = 0$, $r \in F_p$, or $-r \in F_p$.

In an ordered field F, with a set of positive elements F_p, inequalities are defined as follows. For elements r and s in F, $r < s$ if and only if $s - r \in F_p$. Further, $r \leq s$ if either $r < s$ or $r = s$.

The rational numbers are an example of an ordered field. The set of positive elements is $\mathbf{Q}_p$, where $\mathbf{Q}_p = \{x \mid x \in \mathbf{Q} \text{ and } x > 0\}$, as defined in Section 3–4. The properties required in the definition can easily be shown to be equivalent to the properties for inequalities given for the rational numbers in Section 3–4. To obtain this equivalence one need only recall that $r < s$ means that $s - r$ is positive. From these remarks, it is clear that Theorem 3–8 of Section 3–4 holds for every ordered field.

We could have proved that the real numbers, as defined in terms of infinite decimals, constitute an ordered field. It can also be shown that the ordering of the real numbers is such that $r < s$, for real numbers r and s, if and only if r is the coordinate of a point on the real line which lies to the left of the point with co-ordinate s. That is, the ordering of real numbers corresponds directly to the natural left-right ordering of points on the real line. This is true provided, of course, that the unit point is chosen to the right of the origin.

Definition 2. A set S of elements in an ordered field is said to have an *upper bound* if and only if there exists an element b in the field such that $x \leq b$ for every $x \in S$. If a set S has an upper bound, we say that S is *bounded*, or more specifically, *bounded from above*. An upper bound b is a *least upper bound* (ab-breviated lub) of the set S if and only if b is an upper bound and every upper bound b' of S satisfies $b \leq b'$.

Intuitively, a lub is the smallest upper bound for the set. It is not true that every bounded set in an arbitrary ordered field has a lub in the field. The field of rational numbers is ordered but does not have this property. The following definition distinguishes ordered fields with this property.

Definition 3. An ordered field F is *complete* if and only if every nonempty set S in F which is bounded from above has a lub in F.

The rational numbers do not constitute a complete ordered field. Consider, for example, the set S of all rational numbers which are less than $\sqrt{2}$. Then S is a bounded set, since 10 is certainly an upper bound for S. The set S is non-empty, since $1 \in S$. One lub for S is $\sqrt{2}$, which is not a rational number. To show that S has no lub in the set of rational numbers, we need only to show that $\sqrt{2}$ is the only lub for S. If any number r is a lub of S, then $r \leq \sqrt{2}$ by the defi-nition, applied to the lub r and the upper bound $\sqrt{2}$. Similarly, $\sqrt{2} \leq r$ by the definition, applied to the lub $\sqrt{2}$ and the upper bound r. Together, these in-equalities imply that $r = \sqrt{2}$. In a similar way we can show that whenever a set has a lub in an ordered field, this lub is unique.

Every real number can be thought of as a lub of some set of rational numbers. Although this set is not unique, we may always construct one such set from the infinite decimal which represents the number. Rather than consider the general case, we will use an example which illustrates the method. For the number $\pi = 3.14159\ldots$, we can let $S = \{3, 3.1, 3.14, 3.141, 3.1415, \ldots\}$, where the suc-cessive rational numbers in the set are formed by taking successive decimal approximations of π. Then S clearly is bounded. For instance, 4 is an upper bound. Since the field of real numbers is complete, S has a real number as a lub. This lub is called π, and in the approach to real numbers based on the definition in this section, this lub is defined to be the meaning of the decimal $3.14159\ldots$ Similarly, every infinite decimal would be defined in the axiomatic treatment of the real numbers as the least upper bound of the set of rational numbers formed from successive decimal approximations.

We now state the definition that could have served as a starting point in the discussion of the real number system. The definition is included to emphasize that there is no single best method for describing the system; rather, there are several methods, each having its own merit. In the following definition, each of the properties that define a field, as well as each of the explicitly stated properties, is an axiom of the real number system. From these axioms all the familiar properties of numbers could be developed. The derivations (not given here) are not so readily followed as the constructive methods we have employed in building up the system from the simpler systems of integers and rational numbers.

Definition 4. The elements of a complete ordered field are called *real numbers* and the field is the *real number field*.

In order to make this definition meaningful, it is necessary to prove that any two complete ordered fields are isomorphic. Then we would be sure that there is only one field of real numbers and not several. We will not give this proof, since we have already described the real numbers in another way.

We have described two of many methods by which real numbers may be defined. The first method is to use infinite decimals as the basic definition, and it is followed by the proof that the set has the properties of a complete ordered field, a proof we omitted. The other approach is to begin with the definition of the real numbers as a complete ordered field. In this treatment, as we have seen, infinite decimals can then be introduced in terms of least upper bounds of sets. For further details the student is urged to consult other references that use one or the other of these approaches. Birkhoff and Maclane [25] use the second approach in their book, while Lightstone [38] uses the first.

A third method of defining real numbers, that of employing the theory of the Dedekind cut, is in many ways the best constructive method for extending the rational numbers to the real numbers. This method allows the derivation of the properties of a complete ordered field in a reasonably direct way. The student will find this treatment in McCoy [39] or Beaumont and Pierce [24]. The book, *What Is Mathematics* [27], by Courant and Robbins, discusses in a general way and compares several methods of describing the real numbers.

The reader will certainly have noticed that although we give a rather thorough treatment of the integers and the rational numbers, our treatment of real numbers has been considerably less complete. The reason for this is that the difficulties encountered in giving a thorough treatment of the real numbers are much greater than those involved in the earlier systems. In fact, the difficulties are so great that it took mathematicians centuries to develop a satisfactory treatment. An idea of the problems that arose in this connection can be found from books such as Kline's *Mathematics: A Cultural Approach* [37]. To profit from a complete treatment of the real numbers, a student should have a much more extensive background in algebra and analysis than has been assumed for this chapter. We have tried to include enough material to provide the background for teaching at the high school level without getting hopelessly involved in abstract mathematics. The reader should accept this material as an introduction, to be followed by further reading at a later time.

EXERCISES

1. Prove that the field of rational numbers is an ordered field.

2. Prove that Theorem 3-8 of Section 3-4 holds for every ordered field.

3. Prove that if a lub for a set S exists, in an ordered field, then it is unique.

4. Specify a set of rational numbers which has no lub among the rational numbers. What real number is the lub for the set?

5. Find the lub for each of the following sets.
   a) $\{x \mid x \text{ is a negative integer}\}$
   b) $\{3, -2, 5, 10, -7, 0\}$
   c) $\{1/n \mid n \text{ is a nonzero integer}\}$
   d) $\{y \mid y + |2 - x| = 0, \text{ where } x \text{ is a real number}\}$
   e) $\{x \mid x = 5 - 2y - y^2, \text{ where } y \text{ is a real number}\}$
   f) $\{x \mid x = 5 - 2y - y^2, \text{ where } y \text{ is an integer}\}$

6. Look up the discussion of real numbers in some book on algebra, number theory, or analysis, such as the references mentioned in the text, and write a brief report of your findings.

3-7   THE FIELD OF COMPLEX NUMBERS

In describing the various number systems, we began with the natural numbers, and by a succession of extensions considered the integers, the rational numbers, and the real numbers. A final extension to the set of complex numbers is to be considered in this section. One might justify these extensions by considering the problem of solving equations of various types and the number systems required to guarantee the existence of solutions. The general equation of the form $a + x = b$ for a and b natural numbers can always be solved if we allow integers as solutions, but not if we restrict the solutions to natural numbers. The equation $cx = d$ for c and d integers does not always have an integral solution but always has a solution in the field of rational numbers. To solve equations of the form $x^2 = r$ for r a positive rational number, we need to consider the real number system. Finally, the real numbers are not sufficient to solve quadratic equations with real coefficients, and a further extension is required. For instance, the solution of the equation $x^2 + 1 = 0$ is not a real number. With the introduction of the complex numbers, however, the process terminates. It can be shown that every polynomial equation with complex coefficients has only complex numbers as solutions. The precise meaning of "polynomial" equation has not yet been specified in this text, but the reader is familiar with such equations from elementary algebra. Regarding the property of solving equations mentioned above, we refer to the complex numbers as being an *algebraically closed* field. The complex numbers will be the first field considered here that is algebraically closed.

Definition 5. The *complex number system* is the set **C** of all pairs (a, b) where a and b are real numbers with operations of addition and multiplication defined by

$$(a, b) + (c, d) = (a + c, b + d),$$

$$(a, b)(c, d) = (ac - bd, ad + bc).$$

In connection with this definition, it is to be understood that $(a, b) = (c, d)$ if and only if $a = c$ and $b = d$. Further, the operations within the parentheses used to define the sum and product of complex numbers are the operations for real numbers. In the complex number (a, b), a is called the *real part* of (a, b) and b is called the *imaginary part* of (a, b).

The complex numbers may be represented graphically by letting the pair (a, b) signifying a complex number correspond to the point in the cartesian coordinate plane having coordinates (a, b). We refer to this plane, whose points are interpreted as complex numbers, as the *complex plane*. The points which lie on the x-axis are points of the form $(a, 0)$, representing complex numbers whose imaginary parts are zero. We will show later that these are the real numbers, and because of this, the x-axis in the complex plane is referred to as the *real axis*. The points lying on the y-axis are of the form $(0, b)$, representing complex numbers whose real part is zero. This axis is referred to as the *imaginary axis*, and the corresponding numbers are referred to as *pure imaginary numbers*. The words "real" and "imaginary" as used here are unfortunate choices in that they suggest an unjustified distinction between the two types of numbers. Imaginary numbers are just as realistic as real numbers, and are valuable practical concepts in such applied fields as electrical engineering. In fact, imaginary numbers are used in advanced courses in defining and working with such practical functions as the elementary trigonometric functions, $\sin x$ and $\cos x$.

Theorem 3–10. The set of complex numbers forms a field.

Closure and commutativity for addition and multiplication are apparent from the definition and properties of the real numbers. Likewise, the associative law of addition is an immediate consequence of the associative law for real numbers.

The pair $(0, 0)$ is the additive identity, or zero, element of **C**. The negative of the complex number (a, b) is the number $(-a, -b)$, since

$$(a, b) + (-a, -b) = (0, 0).$$

The associative law of multiplication is not self-evident, so the proof will be given. Let $(a, b), (c, d)$ and (e, f) represent any three complex numbers. Then,

$$\begin{aligned}(a, b)[(c, d)(e, f)] &= (a, b)(ce - df, cf + de) \\ &= (ace - adf - bcf - bde, acf + ade + bce - bdf) \\ &= (ac - bd, ad + bc)(e, f) \\ &= [(a, b)(c, d)](e, f).\end{aligned}$$

The reason for each step is either the definition of multiplication of complex numbers or properties of real numbers, and should be supplied by the student.

The left-distributive law of multiplication over addition can be proved as follows, where (a, b), (c, d), and (e, f) are arbitrary complex numbers:

$$(a, b)[(c, d) + (e, f)] = (a, b)(c + e, d + f)$$
$$= (ac + ae - bd - bf, ad + af + bc + be)$$
$$= (ac - bd, ad + bc) + (ae - bf, af + be)$$
$$= (a, b)(c, d) + (a, b)(e, f).$$

Again, the reasons should be supplied by the student. The right-distributive law follows from the left and commutativity of multiplication. This completes the proof that $\mathbf{C}$ is a commutative ring.

The element $(1, 0)$ is the unity in $\mathbf{C}$, since $(1, 0)(a, b) = (a, b)$ for every (a, b) in $\mathbf{C}$.

Suppose that (a, b) is any nonzero element of $\mathbf{C}$. Since $(a, b) \neq (0, 0)$, either $a \neq 0$ or $b \neq 0$, and hence $a^2 + b^2 > 0$. The multiplicative inverse of (a, b) is

$$\left(\frac{a}{a^2 + b^2}, \frac{-b}{a^2 + b^2} \right),$$

since

$$(a, b)\left(\frac{a}{a^2 + b^2}, \frac{-b}{a^2 + b^2} \right) = \left(\frac{a^2 + b^2}{a^2 + b^2}, \frac{-ab + ab}{a^2 + b^2} \right) = (1, 0),$$

the unity of $\mathbf{C}$. This completes the proof that $\mathbf{C}$ is a field.

Next, we will show that the complex numbers contain a subset isomorphic to the set of real numbers. Let the set of real numbers be designated by $\mathbf{R}$, and let R' denote the set of all complex numbers of the form $(r, 0)$. The mapping φ from $\mathbf{R}$ into R', defined as $\varphi(r) = (r, 0)$, is clearly a one-to-one mapping of $\mathbf{R}$ onto R'. This follows from the fact that $(r, 0) = (s, 0)$ if and only if $r = s$ by definition of equality in $\mathbf{C}$. Further, φ preserves both addition and multiplication since

$$\varphi(rs) = (rs, 0) = (r, 0)(s, 0) = \varphi(r)\varphi(s)$$

and

$$\varphi(r + s) = (r + s, 0) = (r, 0) + (s, 0) = \varphi(r) + \varphi(s).$$

Hence $\mathbf{R}$ and R' are isomorphic. That is, except for notation, $\mathbf{R}$ and R' are the same set.

The element $(0, 1)$ is of special interest in the field of complex numbers. First, we note that $(0,1)^2 = (0, 1)(0, 1) = (-1, 0)$, the negative of the unity element in $\mathbf{C}$. Next, if (a, b) is any complex number,

$$(a, b) = (a, 0) + (b, 0)(0, 1).$$

Recall that $(a, 0)$ and $(b, 0)$ are numbers in R', the set isomorphic to the real numbers. If we designate $(0, 1)$ by the symbol i, and use the real numbers a and *b* instead of their counterparts $(a, 0)$ and $(b, 0)$, we obtain the notation $(a, b) = a + bi$. This is called the *normal form* for the complex number (a, b). In this notation, as before, we call *a* the real part and *b* the imaginary part of the complex number $a + bi$. From now on, we will use this notation exclusively. That is, any complex number will be expressed as $a + bi$, where *a* and *b* are real numbers and *i* is a special symbol identified by the property that $i^2 = -1$. The notation is reasonable in the light of the discussion above.

Associated with any complex number $z = a + bi$ is the number $\bar{z}$ called the *conjugate of z* and defined by $\bar{z} = a - bi$. The conjugate of a complex number is of interest in several conections, including the discussion of solutions of equations.

Example 3–6. As numerical examples of the rules and definitions of this section, consider the following:

$$(2 + 3i) - (5 + 4i) = 2 + 3i - 5 - 4i = -3 - i.$$

Also,

$$(2 + i)(3 - 2i) = 6 - 2i^2 + 3i - 4i = 8 - i.$$

In these cases *i* is treated as any letter in elementary algebra, except that i^2 is always replaced by -1. That this is true can be readily checked from the definition of operations in **C**.

As a final remark, division is defined for complex numbers in the same way that it is defined in an arbitrary field—as multiplication by the inverse. Thus $(a + bi) \div (c + di) = (a + bi)(c + di)^{-1}$, where the form of the inverse has been given above. We will also write such a quotient in the usual fractional form as $(a + bi)/(c + di)$. In practice, a specific procedure is available for computation as follows:

$$\frac{a + bi}{c + di} = \frac{a + bi}{c + di} \cdot \frac{c - di}{c - di}$$

$$= \frac{(ac + bd) + (bc - ad)i}{c^2 + d^2}$$

$$= \frac{ac + bd}{c^2 + d^2} + \frac{bc - ad}{c^2 + d^2} i.$$

The multiplication of numerator and denominator of the fraction by the conjugate of the denominator produces a fraction which can be readily placed in normal form.

Example 3–7.

$$(2 + 3i) \div (-3 - 5i) = \frac{2 + 3i}{-3 - 5i} \cdot \frac{-3 + 5i}{-3 + 5i}$$

$$= \frac{-21 + i}{9 + 25} = \frac{-21}{34} + \frac{1}{34} i.$$

EXERCISES

1. Find the negative, the inverse, and the conjugate of each of the following complex numbers.   Express all answers in normal form, that is, as $a + bi$ for real numbers a and b.

a) $(2, 3)$ b) $(4, 6)$ c) $(1, 0)$ d) $(0, 2)$ e) $1 + i$

f) $2 - i$ g) $3 + \sqrt{2}\, i$ h) $7 - \sqrt{3}\, i$ i) i j) 3

2. Perform the following operations and reduce all answers to normal form.

a) $(2 + i) + (3 - 7i)$ b) $(5 - 6i) - (4 + 8i)$ c) $(2 + 3i)(5 - 6i)$

d) $(2 - i)^3$ e) $(1 - i)^2(2 + 3i)^3$ f) $(3 + 4i) \div (1 - i)$

g) $(2 + 3i) \div (3 - i)$ h) $\dfrac{(3 + i)(4 - i)}{1 + 2i}$ i) $(2 + \sqrt{3}\, i)(3 - \sqrt{2}\, i)$

j) $\dfrac{\sqrt{2} + 3i}{2 - \sqrt{3}\, i}$

3. Prove that the commutative law of multiplication holds in **C**.   Give complete reasons for each step in the proof.

4. Without using the left-distributive law, prove that the right-distributive law of multiplication over addition holds in **C**.   Give complete reasons for each step in the proof.

5. Prove that $z \cdot \bar{z}$ is a nonnegative real number for any complex number z and its conjugate $\bar{z}$.   Show also that $z \cdot \bar{z} = 0$ if and only if $z = 0$.

6. Prove directly (without using the fact that a nonzero complex number has an inverse) that there are no zero divisors in the set of complex numbers.

7. Graph, in the complex plane, the complex numbers $u = 2 + 3i$ and $v = 3 - 5i$.   Also locate $-u, -v, \bar{u}, \bar{v}, u + v, u - v$, and uv on the same graph.

8. Prove that the "parallelogram law" for the addition of complex numbers holds.   That is, if $u = a + bi$ and $v = c + di$ are graphed in the complex plane, then $u + v$ is the fourth vertex of the parallelogram having the origin, u, and v as its first three vertices.

9. Show that the set R'' of all complex numbers of the form $(0, a)$ is not isomorphic to the set of real numbers under the mapping θ defined by $\theta(r) = (0, r)$ for every real number r.

10. Using the notation of pairs, justify explicitly the computational procedure (given in the last paragraph of this section) for reducing a quotient of complex numbers to normal form.

CHAPTER 4

GROUPS

4-1 PERMUTATIONS OF *n* SYMBOLS

The emphasis in earlier chapters has been on mathematical structures in which two operations, addition and multiplication, are basic. These systems, which arise naturally in connection with sets of numbers, were introduced first because they are closer to the experience of the average student than the systems to be discussed here.

We turn our attention to structures called groups, which have a single basic operation. We will look at some systems with more than one operation but will restrict our attention to a single operation, such as addition. Other systems to be considered possess only one natural operation. The structures with only a single operation are simpler, in that they usually require fewer axioms for their specification. We have delayed the treatment of groups until now because examples are less familiar to the student.

The set of all permutations of *n* symbols with which this section deals is an important example of a system with a single operation, written as multiplication. While it is possible to define a second operation, division, it is neither necessary nor customary to do so. The most significant property of permutations is the fact that every group is essentially the same as some set of permutations. For the moment, however, we will consider permutations as simply another example of a mathematical system.

A *permutation of n symbols* is a one-to-one mapping of the set of *n* symbols onto itself. For convenience we will use the integers $1, 2, 3, \ldots, n$ to represent the set of *n* symbols. Any other set could be used, but this choice is standard. One notation for such a mapping is to write the integers in natural order on one line and the image elements on the line below, so that the image of each integer appears directly beneath that integer. We will enclose this array in brackets to distinguish it from matrices. For any arrangement $i_1, i_2, \ldots, i_n$ of the integers $1, 2, \ldots, n$, the permutation which maps 1 into i_1, 2 into $i_2, \ldots, n$ into i_n is indicated below.

General form of a permutation: $\begin{bmatrix} 1 & 2 & 3 & \ldots & n \\ i_1 & i_2 & i_3 & \ldots & i_n \end{bmatrix}$.

As an example, let θ be the permutation in the set of permutations of the integers from 1 to 5 such that $\theta(1) = 2$, $\theta(2) = 1$, $\theta(3) = 4$, $\theta(4) = 5$, and $\theta(5) = 3$. The notation here is the standard functional notation introduced in Section 1–6. That is, $\theta(a)$ is the notation for the image of a under the mapping θ. We would write this permutation as

$$\theta = \begin{bmatrix} 1 & 2 & 3 & 4 & 5 \\ 2 & 1 & 4 & 5 & 3 \end{bmatrix}.$$

We will denote the set of all permutations on the integers $1, 2, \ldots, n$ by the symbol S_n. If α and β are two of these permutations, we define the *product* of α and β by $\alpha\beta(i) = \alpha(\beta(i))$ for each $i = 1, 2, \ldots, n$. That is, α times β means perform the mapping β first, then perform the mapping α on the result. Consider as an example the permutation θ defined above and the following permutation σ, in S_5:

$$\sigma = \begin{bmatrix} 1 & 2 & 3 & 4 & 5 \\ 5 & 4 & 3 & 2 & 1 \end{bmatrix}.$$

To determine $\theta\sigma$, we apply the definition separately to each integer 1 through 5. Thus, $\theta\sigma(1) = \theta(\sigma(1)) = \theta(5) = 3$ and $\theta\sigma(2) = \theta(\sigma(2)) = \theta(4) = 5$. Continuing in this way, we see that

$$\theta\sigma = \begin{bmatrix} 1 & 2 & 3 & 4 & 5 \\ 3 & 5 & 4 & 1 & 2 \end{bmatrix}.$$

We can compute $\sigma\theta$ in the same way and obtain

$$\sigma\theta = \begin{bmatrix} 1 & 2 & 3 & 4 & 5 \\ 4 & 5 & 2 & 1 & 3 \end{bmatrix}.$$

Next, we define *equality* for two permutations to mean that every element of the set has the same image element under each of the two permutations. It is now apparent that in the above example, $\theta\sigma \neq \sigma\theta$. The binary operation of multiplication for permutations is *not* commutative. The set S_n is closed, however, with respect to the operation, and the operation can be shown to be associative. The proof of associativity is not difficult, but will be postponed until later. The student should check associativity in several specific cases.

The identity permutation for S_n is denoted by ε and is given below:

$$\varepsilon = \begin{bmatrix} 1 & 2 & 3 & \ldots & n \\ 1 & 2 & 3 & \ldots & n \end{bmatrix}.$$

That this permutation has the property required of an identity element can be readily verified by inspection.

Each permutation in S_n has a multiplicative inverse, and this inverse can be found by reading the permutation from bottom to top instead of from top to bottom. In general, if a permutation φ in S_n maps the integer m onto i_m, then φ^{-1} will map i_m onto m. That is, if $\varphi(m) = i_m$, then $\varphi^{-1}(i_m) = m$ for each integer m. Therefore, $\varphi^{-1}\varphi(m) = \varphi^{-1}(\varphi(m)) = \varphi^{-1}(i_m) = m$. Thus $\varphi^{-1}\varphi = \varepsilon$, the identity element, since the image of each integer under the mapping $\varphi^{-1}\varphi$ is the same as under the mapping ε. Now since a permutation is a one-to-one mapping, the set of integers appearing as image elements is the entire set, and we may consider i_m as the general member of the set for the purpose of examining $\varphi\varphi^{-1}\colon \varphi\varphi^{-1}(i_m)$ $= \varphi(\varphi^{-1}(i_m)) = \varphi(m) = i_m$. Thus $\varphi\varphi^{-1}$ is also the identity mapping. This shows that φ^{-1} is the multiplicative inverse of φ. Using this result, the inverse of θ defined above is

$$\theta^{-1} = \begin{bmatrix} 1 & 2 & 3 & 4 & 5 \\ 2 & 1 & 5 & 3 & 4 \end{bmatrix}.$$

The student should check the products $\theta^{-1}\theta$ and $\theta\theta^{-1}$ to verify this statement. Note that since multiplication is not commutative, both products need to be checked. An element and its inverse commute even though the operation is not commutative in general.

Because inverses of permutations exist, S_n satisfies the cancellation law for multiplication. There is no zero element to form an exception, and consequently this law is stated for permutations as follows: If $\alpha\theta = \beta\theta$ for permutations α, β, and θ, then $\alpha = \beta$. This can be proved by multiplying both sides of the first equation by θ^{-1} and simplifying.

Equations of the form $\alpha x = \beta$, where α and β are in S_n, always have solutions in S_n. The form of this solution is $\alpha^{-1}\beta$, since $\alpha(\alpha^{-1}\beta) = (\alpha\alpha^{-1})\beta = \varepsilon\beta = \beta$. Note that $\beta\alpha^{-1}$ is ordinarily not a solution of the equation. Referring to the permutations θ and σ defined earlier, we can find the solution for $\theta x = \sigma$ as $x = \theta^{-1}\sigma$. That is,

$$x = \begin{bmatrix} 1 & 2 & 3 & 4 & 5 \\ 4 & 3 & 5 & 1 & 2 \end{bmatrix}$$

will satisfy the equation.

EXERCISES

1. Check the example in this section to verify that $\theta\theta^{-1} = \theta^{-1}\theta = \varepsilon$.

2. Check the solution of the equation given in the last paragraph of this section.

3. Given the permutations

$$\alpha = \begin{bmatrix} 1 & 2 & 3 & 4 & 5 & 6 \\ 3 & 2 & 1 & 4 & 6 & 5 \end{bmatrix},$$

$$\beta = \begin{bmatrix} 1 & 2 & 3 & 4 & 5 & 6 \\ 2 & 5 & 4 & 1 & 3 & 6 \end{bmatrix},$$

and

$$\gamma = \begin{bmatrix} 1 & 2 & 3 & 4 & 5 & 6 \\ 6 & 5 & 3 & 1 & 2 & 4 \end{bmatrix},$$

find (a) $\alpha\beta$, (b) $\beta\alpha$, (c) α^{-1}, (d) β^{-1}, (e) $\beta^{-1}\alpha$, (f) $\alpha(\beta\gamma)$, (g) $(\alpha\beta)\gamma$, (h) the solution of $\alpha x = \beta$, (i) the solution of $\beta x = \gamma$.

4. Write out all permutations in S_3, i.e., the permutations on the integers 1, 2, 3. Let ρ_1 be ε, the identity, and label the remaining five as $\rho_2, \rho_3, \rho_4, \rho_5$ ρ_6 in some order for use in later problems.

5. Find the inverse of each permutation ρ_i in Exercise 4.

6. Fill out a complete "multiplication table" for S_3, as we did for Z_7 and Z_6 in Section 2–3, where the general entry in the table is the product of the element listed on the left margin times the element listed at the top, in that order. In each position write the actual result rather than the indicated product. If $\rho_3\rho_2 = \rho_5$, for instance, write ρ_5 in place of $\rho_3\rho_2$ in the table.

7. Check the associative law in S_4 in three specific examples. Note that this does not constitute a proof.

8. Consider the subset A_3 of S_3 as follows:

$$A_3 = \left\{ \begin{bmatrix} 1 & 2 & 3 \\ 1 & 2 & 3 \end{bmatrix}, \quad \begin{bmatrix} 1 & 2 & 3 \\ 3 & 1 & 2 \end{bmatrix}, \quad \begin{bmatrix} 1 & 2 & 3 \\ 2 & 3 & 1 \end{bmatrix} \right\}.$$

Show that A_3 is closed for the operation of multiplication and that each element in A_3 has an inverse in A_3.

9. How many permutations are there in the set S_n for an arbitrary positive integer n?

10. An element other than the identity is an *involution* if its square is the identity. Find all involutions, if any, in the set S_3. (Here, σ^2 means $\sigma \cdot \sigma$, as one might expect.)

4-2   DEFINITION AND EXAMPLES OF GROUPS

There are several reasons why a chapter on groups should be included in an introductory text on algebra designed primarily for prospective teachers. The most practical reason is the light that the concept of a group sheds upon the subject of geometry. A brief discussion of geometry as it relates to group theory is contained in Chapter 5, Sections 5–1 and 5–2.

The reader can expect to profit from a study of groups in another way as well. The rather simple axiomatic structure of a group furnishes an excellent opportunity to develop an understanding of the axiomatic method, which is the heart of mathematics. In the study of number systems, it is difficult for the student to free himself of the large body of facts accumulated over a lifetime in order to appreciate the necessity for precise proofs based directly on axioms and definitions. Since groups are less familiar, one more readily sees the necessity for a rigorous formal treatment. The simplicity of the axiom set makes this formal treatment a reasonable and pleasant task.

Definition. A *group* is a set G of elements, together with a binary operation $\circ$, satisfying the following postulates.
1) The set G is closed with respect to the operation $\circ$.
2) The operation $\circ$ is associative in G.
3) There exists in G an identity element e for the operation $\circ$.
4) For each element a in G there exists an inverse a^{-1} in G, relative to the operation $\circ$.

A group is a *commutative* group if and only if the operation is commutative.

The student should recall the definitions of closure and associativity given in Chapter 1, Section 1–7. In particular, since it is not required that the operation in a group be commutative, recall that an identity element is an element e of G such that $e \circ x = x \circ e = x$ for every $x \in G$. Similarly, a^{-1} is an inverse of a in G if and only if $a \circ a^{-1} = a^{-1} \circ a = e$. In showing that a set is a group, justification should be given for each part of these equalities.

As an example of a group, the set of all permutations of n symbols is a group under the operation of multiplication of permutations. This group is referred to as the *symmetric group* on n symbols and is designated by S_n. Each of the sets of all integers, of all real numbers, and of all complex numbers forms a group under the operation of addition. In fact, a more general statement can be made. If R is any ring, then the set of all elements in R, together with the operation of addition, forms a group, often referred to as the *additive group* of the ring R.

There are two groups naturally associated with any field. Since a field is first of all a ring, one of these groups is the additive group of the field. Let F denote an arbitrary field, and let F' be the set of all nonzero elements of F. It is easy to verify, directly from the axioms for a field, that F' is a group under the operation of multiplication. This group is referred to as the *multiplicative group* of the field F.

Further specific examples of groups are the sets Z_6 and Z_7 that were introduced with the operations of addition modulo 6 and modulo 7, respectively, in Chapter 2. The nonzero elements of Z_7 also form a group under the operation of multiplication modulo 7. Why is this not also true for the nonzero elements of Z_6?

As a final example, the set of all 2×2 matrices with integers as elements forms a group under the operation of addition. Why do the nonzero 2×2 matrices not form a group under the operation of multiplication?

That each of the above sets is a group under the specified operations follows from the discussion of properties given when the sets were first introduced. There are many other groups, some of which are of considerable importance. We will introduce four more examples of somewhat different types to illustrate further the nature of a group and to indicate the steps necessary in proving that a set is a group. Further examples will appear in the exercises.

Example 4–1. Let S be the set $S = \{2, 4, 6, 8\}$ and define the operation to be multiplication modulo 10. Thus $2 \cdot 6 = 2$, and $4 \cdot 8 = 2$. Table 4–1 is a complete multiplication table for S. Each entry in the table corresponds to the product, modulo 10, of the element from the left margin opposite the given entry and the element from the top margin above the given entry, taken in that order. By inspection of the table, we verify that S is closed under the operation. It follows from the associativity of ordinary multiplication of integers that the operation is associative. The identity element is 6, as one can verify readily from the table.   We see that 2 and 8 are inverses of each other, while both 4 and 6 are their own inverses.   Thus we have verified that the set forms a group, and, in fact, that it is a commutative group.   Here we have used inspection of the group table as the primary method of proof.   This method can be used on groups with only a small number of elements, but it does not work for many other groups.

TABLE 4–1

	2	4	6	8
2	4	8	2	6
4	8	6	4	2
6	2	4	6	8
8	6	2	8	4

TABLE 4–2

	1	i	-1	$-i$
1	1	i	-1	$-i$
i	i	-1	$-i$	1
-1	-1	$-i$	1	i
$-i$	$-i$	1	i	-1

Example 4–2. Consider the set $M = \{1, -1, i, -i\}$ of the fourth roots of the complex number 1 and the operation of multiplication of complex numbers. Again, the multiplication table will be helpful.   From Table 4–2 it can be seen that the set is closed under multiplication and that multiplication is commutative.   Since multiplication is associative for the set of all complex numbers, it is associative for the set M.   The identity element is 1 and both 1 and -1 are their own inverses.   The inverse of i is $-i$, and that of $-i$ is i.   Hence, the set M forms a commutative group under multiplication.

Example 4–3. Symmetries of the square.   A plane figure is symmetric with respect to a line m if for every point P on the figure there is a second point Q such that the line m is the perpendicular bisector of the segment PQ.   A circle is symmetric with respect to every diameter, and an equilateral triangle is symmetric with respect to every median.   If a figure is symmetric with respect to a line, the line is termed a *line*, or *axis*, *of symmetry* for the figure.   If m is a line of symmetry for a figure F, then a revolution of F in space through an angle of 180°, using line m as an axis, leaves the figure unchanged.   Such a rotation is termed a *reflection* in the line m.

Consider a square located in the coordinate plane so that its center is at the origin and its sides are parallel to the coordinate axes, as in Fig. 4–1.   This figure has four lines of symmetry, the coordinate axes and the two diagonals.   For convenience, we will call the diagonal in quadrants I and III the first diagonal, and that in quadrants II and IV the second diagonal.   Because of the symmetric properties of the square, there is a set of motions which carry the square into itself.   We may think of the square as being cut from a piece of paper and placed on the coordinate plane so that it may be moved freely.   We will number the vertices of the square, as indicated in Fig. 4–1, so that we may identify each vertex in any position.   The motions which carry the square into itself are the reflection of the square in each of its four lines of symmetry and counterclockwise rotations

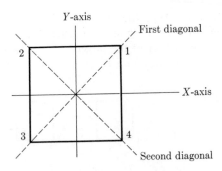

Fig. 4–1. Lines of symmetry for the square.

in the plane of multiples of 90°, using the origin as a center of rotation. We identify all rotations leaving the square in the same final position, and designate the rotation by an angle less than 360° which has this result. We now agree to identify these motions by the following symbols:

R_0—counterclockwise rotation in the plane of 0°
R_1—counterclockwise rotation in the plane of 90°
R_2—counterclockwise rotation in the plane of 180°
R_3—counterclockwise rotation in the plane of 270°
X—reflection in the x-axis
Y—reflection in the y-axis
D_1—reflection in the first diagonal
D_2—reflection in the second diagonal

If a motion is applied to the square, the motion may always be identified by the final position of the square, as indicated by the position of the numbered vertices. If two motions leave the square in the same final position, then they are said to be equal. Figure 4–2 illustrates the effect of two of these motions on the square.

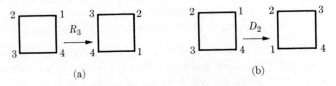

Fig. 4–2. Effect of motions R_3 and D_2.

Next, an operation referred to as multiplication is defined for the set

$$S = \{R_0, R_1, R_2, R_3, X, Y, D_1, D_2\}.$$

If a and b represent any two motions, then ab is defined to be the motion resulting from the performance of motion a followed by motion b. Thus $R_2 D_1$ means the

notion obtained by first rotating the square 180° counterclockwise and then
reflecting the result in the first diagonal. Figure 4–3 illustrates this product.
The end result is the same as that of the motion D_2. Consequently, we say that
$R_2 D_1 = D_2$. In this way we may construct a table for the operation of mul-

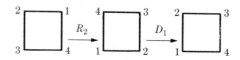

Fig. 4–3. The motion $R_2 D_1$.

tiplication. From Table 4–3 it can be seen that the set of motions is
closed under multiplication, that R_0 is the identity, and that each element has
an inverse. The associative law holds, but this is not self-evident. A general
argument might be given to show associativity, but it will be omitted. Another
possibility is to verify the law by consideration of all possible triples of elements

TABLE 4–3

	R_0	R_1	R_2	R_3	X	Y	D_1	D_2
R_0	R_0	R_1	R_2	R_3	X	Y	D_1	D_2
R_1	R_1	R_2	R_3	R_0	D_2	D_1	X	Y
R_2	R_2	R_3	R_0	R_1	Y	X	D_2	D_1
R_3	R_3	R_0	R_1	R_2	D_1	D_2	Y	X
X	X	D_1	Y	D_2	R_0	R_2	R_1	R_3
Y	Y	D_2	X	D_1	R_2	R_0	R_3	R_1
D_1	D_1	Y	D_2	X	R_3	R_1	R_0	R_2
D_2	D_2	X	D_1	Y	R_1	R_3	R_2	R_0

$X \circ D_1 = R_3$
$X \circ D_2 = R_1$

and their products as they appear in the statement of the law. This would involve
checking 216 cases. The student should verify the law in several specific cases, even
though this will not constitute a complete proof. The set is a group, commonly
called the group of symmetries of the square. It is not commutative. Why?

Example 4–4. The final example is not of special interest except to emphasize
the fact that not all groups are finite and that the group table cannot always be
used in proving that a given set is a group. Let P be the set of all real numbers
except the integer 1. Let the operation $*$ be defined by $a * b = a + b - ab$,
where $+$, $-$, and $\cdot$ are the usual arithmetic operations. Then P is a group with
respect to the operation $*$, as we now prove.

For any real numbers a and b in P (that is, any real numbers except 1), $a * b$
is a real number. In order to show that this number is in P, we only show that
it cannot be 1. Suppose that $a + b - ab = 1$. Then, since $a \neq 1$, we can solve
for b in terms of a and obtain $b = (1 - a)/(1 - a)$, or, in other words, we see that

$b = 1$.   But this cannot be the case since $b \in P$ and P does not contain the number 1. Hence it is impossible that $a * b = 1$.   This shows that the set P is closed under the operation $*$.

The operation $*$ is associative on the set P.   This fact was given in Section 1–7 and will not be repeated here.   The student should turn back and review the proof.

To find the identity element, we ask if there is a number x in P such that $a * x = a$ for every a in P.   This implies that $a + x - ax = a$, or that $x(1 - a) = 0$. Since 1 is not in P, $1 - a \neq 0$ and hence $x = 0$.   By direct evaluation we can check that $a * 0 = 0 * a = a$ for every a in P.   That is, 0 is the identity in P.

The inverse y of an element a in P must satisfy $a * y = 0$, or $a + y - ay = 0$, since 0 is the identity in P.   Solving for y, we find that $y = (-a)/(1 - a)$.   This solution is possible, since $a \neq 1$, and a is a real number.   Furthermore, this number is not 1, and hence is in P.   By direct evaluation we may check that for this value of y, $a * y = y * a = 0$, and hence every element a in P has an inverse in the set P. This completes the proof that P is a group under the operation $*$.   It is also easy to verify that $*$ is commutative, so that P is a commutative group.

It is a common convention in mathematics that when a group is commutative, we usually write the operation as addition, using the symbol $+$ and denoting the identity by the symbol 0.   In this case we use the term *abelian* rather than the term *commutative* to refer to the group.   The term abelian originated as a commemoration of the work of the famous mathematician Niels Henrik Abel (1802–1829).   For nonabelian groups, or for groups where the operation is not known to be commutative at the outset, the group operation is customarily written as ordinary multiplication, a convention that we will follow in the future.

EXERCISES

1. Determine whether or not each of the following sets forms a group with respect to the given operation.   If the set is a group, prove it, and if not, show why not.

    a) The set of real numbers of the form $a + b\sqrt{2}$ where a and b are integers and the operation is addition.

    b) The set of nonzero real numbers of the form $a + b\sqrt{2}$ where a and b are rational numbers and the operation is multiplication.

    c) The set $\{0, 1, 2, 3, 4, 5, 6\}$ with the operation of multiplication modulo 7.

    d) The set $\{1, 2, 3, 4\}$ with the operation of multiplication modulo 5.

    e) The set $\{1, 5, 7, 11\}$ with the operation of multiplication modulo 12.

    f) The set of all *integers* except the integer 1, with the operation $*$ defined in Example 4–4.

    g) The set $\{R_0, R_1, R_2, R_3\}$ defined as in Example 4–3, with the operation given in the example.

    h) The set $\{R_0, X, Y, D_1, D_2\}$ defined as in Example 4–3, with the operation given in the example.

    i) The set of permutations,
    $$S = \left\{ \begin{bmatrix} 1 & 2 & 3 \\ 1 & 2 & 3 \end{bmatrix}, \begin{bmatrix} 1 & 2 & 3 \\ 2 & 3 & 1 \end{bmatrix}, \begin{bmatrix} 1 & 2 & 3 \\ 3 & 1 & 2 \end{bmatrix} \right\},$$
    with the operation of multiplication of permutations.

j) The set of permutations,

$$T = \left\{ \begin{bmatrix} 1 & 2 & 3 \\ 1 & 2 & 3 \end{bmatrix}, \begin{bmatrix} 1 & 2 & 3 \\ 1 & 3 & 2 \end{bmatrix} \right\},$$

with the operation of multiplication of permutations.

k) The set $U = \{x, y\}$, with the operation given in the table below.

	x	y
x	x	y
y	y	x

l) The set of all 2×2 matrices

$$\begin{pmatrix} a & b \\ c & d \end{pmatrix}$$

such that a, b, c, and d are real numbers and $ad - bc \neq 0$, with the operation of multiplication of matrices.

2. Prove that neither of the following is a group.
   a) The nonzero elements of Z_6, with multiplication modulo 6.
   X b) The set of nonzero 2×2 matrices, with matrix multiplication.

3. Each of the motions of the square described in Example 4–3 may be represented as a permutation of the vertices.   Thus D_2 corresponds to the permutation.

$$\begin{bmatrix} 1 & 2 & 3 & 4 \\ 3 & 2 & 1 & 4 \end{bmatrix}.$$

List the permutations corresponding to each of the elements of the group of Example 4–3 and check, by multiplication of permutations, at least five entries in the group table.

4. Prove by a counterexample that the group of symmetries of the square is not commutative.

5. Prove that the set of all elements of an arbitrary ring form a group with respect to the operation of addition.

6. Prove that the nonzero elements of any field form a commutative group with respect to the operation of multiplication.

7. Explain the significance of postulates (1), (3), and (4) of the definition of a group in determining the nature and arrangement of elements in the table of a group with a finite number of elements.

8. Describe the group of symmetries for an equilateral triangle, in a manner similar to that in Example 4–3.

9. Describe the group of symmetries of a regular hexagon.

10. Describe the group of symmetries of a circle.

4-3   ELEMENTARY PROPERTIES OF GROUPS

The definition in Section 4–1 requires that each group must contain an identity element e, but does not specifically exclude the possibility that there may be two or more distinct identities.   In the proof of the next theorem, we will show that this cannot happen. Similarly, postulate (4) requires that for each element in the group, there is at least one inverse, but it does not specify that an element in a group never has more than one inverse. The following theorem clarifies the situation.

Theorem 4–1. (a) The identity element of a group G is unique. (b) Each element in a group G has a unique inverse.

Suppose, first, that a group contains identity elements e and e'. Then, since e is an identity element, $ee' = e'$. Similarly, e' is an identity element and hence $ee' = e$. Therefore, $e = ee' = e'$. That is, any two identity elements must be equal and hence the identity element of a group is unique.

Next, suppose that both a^{-1} and a' are inverses of the element a in a group G, so that $a^{-1}a = aa^{-1} = e$ and $a'a = aa' = e$. Then:

$$
\begin{aligned}
a' &= ea' && \text{by definition of the identity } e, \\
&= (a^{-1}a)a' && \text{by definition of the inverse } a^{-1}, \\
&= a^{-1}(aa') && \text{by the associative law,} \\
&= a^{-1}e && \text{by definition of the inverse } a', \\
&= a^{-1} && \text{by definition of the identity } e.
\end{aligned}
$$

Thus the assumption that two elements are both inverses of a leads to the conclusion that they are equal, that is, the same element. This is exactly what is needed to say that the inverse of an element is unique, and hence completes the proof of the theorem.

We have examined mathematical systems in which the cancellation law for one or more operations is valid, and in which equations of simple types have solutions within the system. The following theorem states these properties for groups.

Theorem 4–2. (a) (Cancellation law). If $a, b,$ and c are elements of a group G and $ac = bc$, then $a = b$. Similarly, if $ca = cb$, then $a = b$.

(b) If a and b are elements of a group G, then there exist unique elements x and y in G such that $ax = b$ and $ya = b$.

To prove the first part of (a), we assume that $ac = bc$ for elements $a, b,$ and c in G. Since G is a group, c^{-1} is also an element of G. Multiplying both members of the given equation on the right by c^{-1}, we obtain $(ac)c^{-1} = (bc)c^{-1}$. Using the associative law, we see that $a(cc^{-1}) = b(cc^{-1})$. This equation reduces to $a = b$ since cc^{-1} equals e, the identity element of G. The proof of the second cancellation law is similar and is left to the reader.

Now, to show that there exists an element x in G such that $ax = b$ for any a and b in G, we consider $x = a^{-1}b$. This element is a solution since $a(a^{-1}b) = (aa^{-1})b = eb = b$. Next, suppose that both the elements x and x' satisfy the equation. That is, $ax = b$ and $ax' = b$. Then $ax = ax'$, and by the cancellation law, $x = x'$. Thus the solution is seen to be unique. The solution for the equation $ya = b$ is $y = ba^{-1}$, and is also unique. This can be checked by direct substitution into the equation, as was done for the case shown. Note that in a noncommutative group the order of the factors is important.

These theorems and the next are not difficult, but they are extremely important. They form the basis for computations involving group elements. The counterparts of the theorems are valid for the real number system as well, but familiarity with real numbers is apt to cause one to take them for granted. One of the values to be gained from a study of group theory is the development of an appreciation for such concepts. The theorems of this section will form the basis for many proofs in later sections.

Theorem 4–3. (a) If a is an element of a group G, then $(a^{-1})^{-1} = a$. (b) If a and b are elements of a group G, then $(ab)^{-1} = b^{-1}a^{-1}$.

We will prove only part (b) of the theorem. The proof of part (a) is similar. Since a and b are in G, a^{-1} and b^{-1} are also elements of G. Then,

$$
\begin{aligned}
(b^{-1}a^{-1})(ab) &= ((b^{-1}a^{-1})a)b && \text{by the associative law,} \\
&= (b^{-1}(a^{-1}a))b && \text{by the associative law,} \\
&= (b^{-1}e)b && \text{by definition of the inverse } a^{-1}, \\
&= b^{-1}b && \text{by definition of the identity } e, \\
&= e && \text{by definition of the inverse } b^{-1}.
\end{aligned}
$$

By the same sequence of arguments, it can be shown that $(ab)(b^{-1}a^{-1})$ reduces to the element e. Hence $b^{-1}a^{-1}$ has the properties that are required of the inverse of the element ab. We have already proved that each element has a unique inverse. Hence $(ab)^{-1} = b^{-1}a^{-1}$, and the proof is complete.

The generalized associative law, Theorem 2–10, Section 2–6, holds in every group G. This law states that a product of elements is not changed by a change in location of parentheses within the product. The proof given in Appendix A requires only that the operation be associative. Hence the proof applies to any group and need not be repeated. From now on, unless the grouping is intended for emphasis, we will omit the parentheses in writing products. The reader should note how this convention would simplify the notation used in the proof of Theorem 4–3.

Integral exponents can be defined for group elements as they were for rings (see Section 2–7). Since every element in a group has an inverse, negative powers of group elements are always defined. The definition and the basic theorem on exponents are repeated for convenience, but the proofs are omitted. The proofs given for rings need no change to be valid for groups as well.

Definition of integral exponents. If a is an element of a group G, then

a) $a^0 = e$, where e is the identity of G.
b) $a^1 = a$, and $a^{n+1} = a^n a$ for every natural number n.
c) $a^{-n} = (a^{-1})^n$ for every natural number n.

Theorem 4-4. If a is an element of a group G, with identity e, and if m and n are integers (positive, negative, or zero), then

a) $e^n = e$,   b) $a^{m+n} = a^m a^n$,   c) $(a^m)^n = a^{mn}$.

If the group G is commutative, the law of exponents $(ab)^n = a^n b^n$ also holds. If the group is not commutative, there may be special cases for which the law holds, but it will not be true in general.

Groups may be classified in many ways. We have already mentioned the classification into commutative and noncommutative groups. Another classification comes from consideration of the number of elements in a group. A *finite group* is a group containing only a finite number of elements. The *order* of a finite group G is the number of elements in G. An *infinite group* is a group containing infinititely many elements. An infinite group is said to have *infinite order*.

EXERCISES

1. For the group of Example 4–1, Section 4–2, find a) the solution of the equation $8x = 2$; b) the solution of the equation $y \cdot 4 = 2$; c) 8^5; d) 4^0; e) 2^{-3}.

2. For the group of Example 4–2, Section 4–2, find a) X^4, X^{-3}, and X^0; b) $(R_3)^5$, and $(R_3)^0$; c) $(R_1 D_1)^{-1}$; d) $(R_1)^3 (D_1)^{-3}$; e) the solution for ω of the equation $D_1 \omega = R_3$; f) the solution for w of the equation $Yw = X$.

3. For the group of Example 4–4, Section 4–2, find a) 4^3, 4^{-3}, and 4^0; b) $2^2 * 3^{-1}$; c) $(3 * 5)^{-1}$; d) the solution of the equation $3 * x = 5$; e) the solution of the equation $5 * x = -2$.

4. Show why the existence of solutions of equations mentioned in Theorem 4–2(b) requires that the group table for a finite group must contain each element of the group once and only once in any row or column of the table.

5. Let G be the set $\{a, b, c\}$. Define a binary operation on the set G so that G becomes a group with respect to this operation. Define the operation by filling in the group table for the set (similar to Tables 4–1, 4–2, and 4–3 of Section 4–2).

6. Does the set of all integers form a group with respect to the operation of subtraction? If so, prove it. If not, show which postulates for a group are not satisfied.

7. Rewrite each theorem and definition in this section for a group with operation written as addition $(+)$, with identity 0, and with inverses written as negatives.

8. Rewrite the proof given in Theorem 4–3(b), using the additive notation described in Exercise 7.

9. The set S of all integers forms a group with respect to the operation $*$ defined by $a * b = a + b - 5$ for integers a and b. Find the identity element of this group and find a formula for the inverse of an arbitrary element of the group.

10. Complete the proofs of Theorems 4–2 and 4–3.

4-4   PERMUTATION GROUPS

Permutations were introduced in Section 4-1. The student is urged to review carefully the definitions, notation, and properties of permutations presented in this example before reading further.

We will continue the study of sets of permutations in this section. It is not necessary to limit our discussion to permutations of finite sets, as we did in the example of Section 4-1. More generally, a *permutation* is a one-to-one mapping of a set onto itself. When this is a finite set, we speak of a permutation of n symbols. The definition of equality of permutations of infinite sets is the same as for finite sets. That is, two permutations, α and β, of an arbitrary set A are equal if and only if $\alpha(a) = \beta(a)$ for every element a in the set A.

There are several notations for permutations in common use. Since a permutation is a mapping, the functional notation is always appropriate and will be used in the proof of Theorem 4-5. The bracket notation is often used when the set involved is finite. A third notation for a special purpose will be introduced later.

The product of two permutations of n symbols was defined previously. The same definition is suitable for the infinite case as well; namely, if α and β are permutations of a set A, then $\alpha\beta$ is that permutation of A defined by $\alpha\beta(a) = \alpha(\beta(a))$ for every element a in A. Since each of α and β are one-to-one mappings of A onto itself, so is the mapping $\alpha\beta$. That is, the set of all permutations of a set A is closed with respect to multiplication of permutations.

We are now ready for our theorem that refers to permutations of a set A that may be either finite or infinite.

Theorem 4-5. The set S of all permutations of an arbitrary nonempty set A forms a group with respect to the operation of multiplication of permutations.

By the remarks of the preceding paragraph, we first note that S is closed with respect to multiplication.

The associative law in S follows directly from the definition of multiplication. That is, for any permutations α, β, γ in S,

$$\alpha(\beta\gamma)(a) = \alpha(\beta\gamma(a)) = \alpha\,\beta(\gamma(a)))$$

for each element a in A. Similarly,

$$(\alpha\beta)\gamma(a) = \alpha\beta(\gamma(a)) = \alpha(\beta(\gamma(a)))$$

for each a in A. From the definition of equality, this implies that $\alpha(\beta\gamma) = (\alpha\beta)\gamma$, as was to be proved.

Let ε be the permutation of A defined by $\varepsilon(a) = a$ for each a in A. For any permutation α in S, we consider the products $\varepsilon\alpha$ and $\alpha\varepsilon$. Let a be any element of A. Then,

$$\varepsilon\alpha(a) = \varepsilon(\alpha(a)) = \alpha(a) \qquad \text{and} \qquad \alpha\varepsilon(a) = \alpha(\varepsilon(a)) = \alpha(a).$$

The justification for these steps is merely the definition of the product of two permutations. Since $\varepsilon\alpha$, $\alpha\varepsilon$, and α each maps the arbitrary element a of A onto $\alpha(a)$, the three permutations are equal. That is, $\varepsilon\alpha = \alpha\varepsilon = \alpha$, which shows that ε is the identity element of S.

Finally, for any permutation α in the set S, we define α^{-1} by $\alpha^{-1}(a) = b$ if and only if $\alpha(b) = a$, where a and b are elements of A. Thus, if α maps b onto a, then α^{-1} maps a onto b. Since α is one-to-one, so is α^{-1}. The permutation α^{-1} is the inverse of α in S, as was shown in Section 4-1. Even though we considered only finite sets A at that time, the proof is also valid for the infinite case and will not be repeated here.

This completes the proof that S is a group. If A is a set with n elements, the group of all permutations of A is called the *symmetric group* on n symbols and is denoted by S_n. We will ordinarily designate the elements of A by the integers $1, 2, \ldots, n$, as we did in Section 4-1. For the remainder of this section, we will limit our attention to permutations of finite sets.

A permutation α of a finite set A is a *cycle of length k* if and only if there exist distinct elements $a_1, a_2, \ldots, a_k$ such that

$$\alpha(a_1) = a_2, \alpha(a_2) = a_3, \ldots, \alpha(a_{k-1}) = a_k, \alpha(a_k) = a_1$$

and for every a in A other than $a_1, a_2, \ldots, a_k$, $\alpha(a) = a$. Such a permutation may be represented by the notation $(a_1 a_2 a_3 \cdots a_k)$.

The permutation

$$\begin{bmatrix} 1 & 2 & 3 & 4 & 5 & 6 \\ 1 & 4 & 2 & 6 & 5 & 3 \end{bmatrix}$$

is a cycle and can be denoted by the symbol (2 4 6 3). This permutation maps 2 onto 4, 4 onto 6, 6 onto 3, and 3 onto 2. We refer to this permutation by saying that it permutes 2, 4, 6, and 3 *cyclically*. The permutation could also be written (4 6 3 2), or (3 2 4 6), or (6 3 2 4).

In cyclic notation the identity permutation ε is usually denoted by (1). In all cases, an integer not appearing in the cycle is presumed to be mapped onto itself by the permutation.

Two cycles α and β in S_n are said to be *disjoint* if no integer appears in both α and β. Thus (1 3 5) and (2 4 6) are disjoint, but (1 3 5) and (2 3 4) are not disjoint. We will be interested in the fact that every permutation in S_n may be written as a product of disjoint cycles. Let us consider an example before we discuss the proof of this result.

Example 4–5. For the permutation

$$\alpha = \begin{bmatrix} 1 & 2 & 3 & 4 & 5 & 6 & 7 \\ 5 & 1 & 3 & 7 & 6 & 2 & 4 \end{bmatrix},$$

we begin with any integer, say 1: $\alpha(1) = 5$, so we next determine $\alpha(5)$, which is 6. Continuing, we see that $\alpha(6) = 2$ and $\alpha(2) = 1$. Since 1 is the integer we started with, we write down the cycle $\alpha_1 = (1\ 5\ 6\ 2)$, a factor of α. Next, select any integer not affected by α_1, say 3. Since $\alpha(3) = 3$, we ignore 3 and continue. The integer 4 has not yet been considered. We find that $\alpha(4) = 7$ and $\alpha(7) = 4$, indicating that α has as a second factor the cycle $\alpha_2 = (4\ 7)$. Since there are no further integers mapped by α, we conclude that $\alpha = \alpha_1\alpha_2$. A direct check will verify this equality.

Theorem 4–6. Every permutation of a finite set is a cycle or it can be expressed as a product of two or more disjoint cycles.

The method of proof was indicated in the above example. Let α be any permutation of the finite set A. First, we select any element a_1 in A and determine $\alpha(a_1)$, which we call a_2. If $a_1 = a_2$, then (a_1) is the first cycle in the factorization of α. If not, we determine $\alpha(a_2) = a_3$, etc. Having found a_i as the image of the preceding element at any given step, we then determine $\alpha(a_i)$. Since α is one-to-one, $\alpha(a_i)$ cannot equal $a_2, a_3, \ldots, a_{i-1}$. If $\alpha(a_i) = a_1$, we close the cycle and $(a_1 a_2 \cdots a_i)$ is the first factor of α. If $\alpha(a_i) \neq a_1$, we designate it by a_{i+1} and continue. Since A is a finite set, this process must terminate. After the first factor is found, we select any remaining element of A and proceed as before to determine a second factor. Continuing in this way, we eventually exhaust the set A and determine the factorization of α. A more formal proof might be given by mathematical induction.

A cycle of length two is called a *transposition*. We will show that every permutation can be expressed as a product of transpositions. In fact, this can always be done in more than one way. For instance,

$$(2\ 4\ 6\ 8) = (6\ 8)(4\ 8)(2\ 8) = (2\ 8)(2\ 6)(2\ 4) = (4\ 8)(2\ 4)(6\ 8)(4\ 8)(2\ 6).$$

Even though this factorization is not unique, a given permutation can never be expressed as both a product of an odd number of transpositions and as a product of an even number of transpositions. The following theorem states these facts.

Theorem 4–7. Every permutation of a finite set S containing two or more elements is a transposition or it can be expressed as a product of transpositions. Further, if a permutation can be expressed as a product of u transpositions and again as a product of v transpositions, then $u \equiv v \pmod 2$.

The identity element ε in the set of all permutations of S can be factored into $\varepsilon = (1\ 2)(1\ 2)$. Note that this requires that S must possess at least two elements. Here these elements are written as 1 and 2, in keeping with the convention of considering the elements of the set S as if they were positive integers.

We now need to show only that every cycle $(a_1 a_2 \cdots a_k)$ for $k > 1$ can be expressed as a product of transpositions, since we have already proved that every permutation equals a product of cycles. A direct check shows that

$$(a_1 a_2 \cdots a_k) = (a_1 a_k)(a_1 a_{k-1}) \cdots (a_1 a_3)(a_1 a_2).$$

Recall, when checking this factorization, that in a product of two permutations, the right-hand factor is applied first. Thus if α is used to denote the cycle above, $\alpha(a_1) = a_2$, since the right-hand factor maps a_1 onto a_2 and the remaining factors do not affect a_2. Similarly, $\alpha(a_2) = a_3$, since the right factor maps a_2 onto a_1 and the next factor maps a_1 onto a_3, while the remaining factors do not affect a_3.

The second part of the proof concerns an arbitrary permutation in S_n. We first form a special product of integers that will help in constructing a proof. Let P_n denote the product of all integers of the form $i - j$ satisfying $0 < i \le n, 0 < j \le n$, and $j < i$. For example, if n is 4,

$$P_4 = (2 - 1)(3 - 1)(4 - 1)(3 - 2)(4 - 2)(4 - 3).$$

For any permutation β, define βP_n to be the product obtained from P_n by performing the permutation β on the integers i, j appearing in the factors of P_n. Thus, if β is the cycle (132),

$$\beta P_4 = (1 - 3)(2 - 3)(4 - 3)(2 - 1)(4 - 1)(4 - 2).$$

The effect on P_n of the mapping β is to rearrange the factors of P_n and to change the sign of certain factors. In every case, $\beta P_n = \pm P_n$.

If δ is a transposition, then $\delta P_n = -P_n$. To see this, suppose that $\delta = (r\ s)$ for integers r and s. We may as well assume that $r < s$. Exactly one factor of P_n involves both r and s, the factor $s - r$. The transposition δ changes this factor to $r - s$, the negative of $s - r$. All other factors involving r or s can be grouped in pairs of the form $\pm(t - s)(t - r)$ for some integer t. But the transposition δ merely interchanges these factors and does not change the sign of the product. Any factors not involving r or s are unchanged by δ. Hence, the effect of δ on P_n is that one factor is changed in sign and $\delta P_n = -P_n$.

Now let γ be any permutation in S_n. Suppose that it can be expressed as the product of u transpositions. Then $\gamma P_n = (-1)^u P_n$, by the discussion in the preceding paragraph. If γ can also be written as the product of v transpositions, $\gamma P_n = (-1)^v P_n$. Hence $(-1)^u = (-1)^v$, and both u and v are either odd or even integers. Thus $u \equiv v \pmod 2$ and the proof is complete.

Definition 1. A permutation in S_n is *even* if it can be expressed as the product of an even number of transpositions and *odd* if it can be expressed as the product of an odd number of transpositions.

Note that the identity permutation of S_n is even for $n > 1$, since we have shown in the proof of Theorem 4–7 that $\varepsilon = (12)(12)$.

The definition of even and odd permutations would be meaningless if we had not proved Theorem 4–7. This definition is used in many places in other mathematics courses. One use of interest to the high school teacher is in the definition of a determinant. In order to understand why the usual definition gives a unique value to every determinant, it is necessary to understand the content of Theorem 4–7. We will state the definition of a third-order determinant here to indicate this connection. The notation employed makes use of our knowledge of permutations, and agrees, except perhaps for notation, with definitions given in high school or college texts. The definition of higher-order determinants is analogous to the one given here for third-order determinants.

Definition 2. The symbol

$$\begin{vmatrix} a_1 & a_2 & a_3 \\ b_1 & b_2 & b_3 \\ c_1 & c_2 & c_3 \end{vmatrix}$$

where a_i, b_i, and c_i are real numbers for $i = 1, 2, 3$, is called a determinant and represents a real number D. This number D is given by the formula,

$$D = \sum_{\alpha \varepsilon S_3} (\text{sign } \alpha) a_{\alpha(1)} b_{\alpha(2)} c_{\alpha(3)}.$$

The symbol $\sum_{\alpha \varepsilon S_3}$ means that the sum is to be taken over all permutations α belonging to S_3. The symbol $(\text{sign } \alpha)$ is defined to be 1 if α is an even permutation and -1 if α is an odd permutation.

Example 4–6. We will write out the terms of the determinant

$$D = \begin{vmatrix} a_1 & a_2 & a_3 \\ b_1 & b_2 & b_3 \\ c_1 & c_2 & c_3 \end{vmatrix}$$

to make sure that the above definition is understood. The definition calls for a sum of terms each containing the product of an element from each row. The subscripts are determined by the permutations of the set $\{1, 2, 3\}$, and a term is used for each of the permutations in S_3. The permutations in S_3 can be written in cyclic notation as $\varepsilon = (1)$, $\alpha = (12)$, $\beta = (13)$, $\gamma = (23)$, $\delta = (123)$ and $\eta = (132)$. The term corresponding to α is

$$(\text{sign } \alpha) a_{\alpha(1)} b_{\alpha(2)} c_{\alpha(3)} = -a_2 b_1 c_3.$$

The value of D can found as follows (the terms are written in the same order as the corresponding permutations given above):

$$D = a_1 b_2 c_3 - a_2 b_1 c_3 - a_3 b_2 c_1 - a_1 b_3 c_2 + a_2 b_3 c_1 + a_3 b_1 c_2.$$

With determinants of higher order it is easier to use double subscripts to represent the elements than to employ a separate letter for each row. But the use of permutations, and particularly the necessity for distinguishing between odd and even permutations is the same.

EXERCISES

1. Given that

$$\alpha = \begin{bmatrix} 1 & 2 & 3 & 4 & 5 \\ 2 & 1 & 4 & 3 & 5 \end{bmatrix} \quad \text{and} \quad \beta = \begin{bmatrix} 1 & 2 & 3 & 4 & 5 \\ 6 & 4 & 2 & 5 & 1 \end{bmatrix},$$

find each of the following products and leave your answer in the bracket notation.

a) α^2 b) β^2 c) $\alpha\beta$ d) $\beta\alpha$

2. Given that $\alpha = (1\ 3\ 5\ 2\ 4)$ and that $\beta = (1\ 3)(2\ 4\ 5)$, find each of the following products and leave the answer as a product of disjoint cycles.

   a) α^2 b) α^3 c) β^2 d) β^3 e) $\alpha\beta$ f) $\beta\alpha$

3. Show that every transposition $(r\ s)$ is its own inverse. That is, $(r\ s)^{-1} = (r\ s)$.

4. Find the inverse of each of the following. Leave the answer in the notation of the given permutation.

   a) $\begin{bmatrix} 1\ 2\ 3\ 4\ 5 \\ 3\ 2\ 1\ 5\ 4 \end{bmatrix}$ b) $\begin{bmatrix} 1\ 2\ 3\ 4\ 5 \\ 2\ 1\ 5\ 3\ 4 \end{bmatrix}$ c) $(1\ 3\ 5)(2\ 4\ 6)$

   d) $(1\ 2)(3\ 4)(5\ 6)$

5. Express each of the following permutations as a cycle or as a product of disjoint cycles.

   a) $\begin{bmatrix} 1\ 2\ 3\ 4\ 5\ 6 \\ 2\ 1\ 4\ 3\ 6\ 5 \end{bmatrix}$ b) $\begin{bmatrix} 1\ 2\ 3\ 4\ 5\ 6 \\ 5\ 4\ 6\ 3\ 1\ 2 \end{bmatrix}$

   c) $\begin{bmatrix} 1\ 2\ 3\ 4\ 5\ 6 \\ 4\ 5\ 1\ 3\ 6\ 2 \end{bmatrix}$ d) $\begin{bmatrix} 1\ 2\ 3\ 4\ 5\ 6 \\ 1\ 2\ 5\ 3\ 4\ 6 \end{bmatrix}$

   e) $\begin{bmatrix} 1\ 2\ 3\ 4\ 5\ 6 \\ 6\ 5\ 4\ 2\ 3\ 1 \end{bmatrix}$

6. Express each of the following permutations as a product of transpositions in two ways, one of which contains more factors than the other.

   a) $(1\ 3\ 5)$ b) $(2\ 5\ 4\ 6\ 7\ 3)$ c) $(1\ 2\ 3\ 4\ 5)$ d) (1)

7. Determine whether each of the following permutations is odd or even.

   a) $\begin{bmatrix} 1\ 2\ 3\ 4\ 5 \\ 3\ 2\ 4\ 1\ 5 \end{bmatrix}$ b) $\begin{bmatrix} 1\ 2\ 3\ 4\ 5 \\ 5\ 3\ 4\ 2\ 1 \end{bmatrix}$ c) $(123)(45)(678)$

   d) $(135)(246)$

8. Write out a group table for S_3. To simplify the notation, let $\varepsilon = (1)$, $\alpha = (123)$, $\beta = (132)$, $\gamma = (12)$, $\delta = (13)$, and $\lambda = (23)$.

9. Show that the set of permutations $\{(1), (123), (132)\}$ forms a group with respect to multiplication of permutations.

10. a) Show that the set of all even permutations in S_n is a group with respect to multiplication of permutations. This group is referred to as the alternating group and is denoted by A_n.

    b) Show that the order of A_n is $n!/2$.

11. Evaluate each of the determinants below, making use of the definition given in this section.

    a) $\begin{vmatrix} x_1 & x_2 & x_3 \\ y_1 & y_2 & y_3 \\ z_1 & z_2 & z_3 \end{vmatrix}$ b) $\begin{vmatrix} 2 & 5 & 1 \\ 7 & 3 & 4 \\ 0 & 5 & 6 \end{vmatrix}$ c) $\begin{vmatrix} 4 & 2 & 1 \\ 3 & 1 & 2 \\ 1 & 1 & -1 \end{vmatrix}$ d) $\begin{vmatrix} 2 & 0 & 0 \\ 0 & 3 & 0 \\ 0 & 0 & 4 \end{vmatrix}$

4-5   SUBGROUPS

It often happens that a set which forms an algebraic system of a certain kind, group, ring, or field contains a subset which forms the same type of system with respect to the operations of the larger set.   We refer to such systems as subsystems. In particular, we refer to subgroups, subrings, and subfields.

> **Definition.** A *subgroup* of a group G is a subset of G which forms a group with respect to the operation in G.

Recall that a group must contain an identity element, and hence a subgroup cannot be an empty set.   We should emphasize, also, that a subgroup must be a group with respect to the operation in the larger group.   Thus the additive group of Z_7 is *not* a subgroup of the additive group of the integers.   The operation in the set Z_7 is addition modulo 7, while that in $\mathbf{Z}$, the set of integers, is ordinary addition. However, the set of all even integers under addition forms a subgroup of the additive group of the integers.   Exercises 9 and 10 in the preceding section give other examples of subgroups.

The subset $\{4, 6\}$ of the set S in Example 4–1, Section 4–2, forms a subgroup of S.   The set $\{R_0, R_1, R_2, R_3\}$ from Example 4–3 forms a subgroup of the group of symmetries of the square.   Can you find two other subgroups of this group?

Every group has a unique identity element, and since a subgroup is a group, it must have an identity.   One might ask whether it is possible that a subgroup has for its identity an element which is different from the identity of the group. The following theorem guarantees that this cannot happen.

> **Theorem 4–8.** If H is any subgroup of a group G, then the identity element of G is in H and is the identity element of H.

For this proof, let e be the identity element of G, e' the identity of H.   There exists in G an element x such that $xe' = e$ by Theorem 4–2(b), Section 4–3.   Multiplying this equation on the right by e', we obtain $xe'e' = ee'$.   But e' is the identity of H so that $e'e' = e'$.   Further, e is the identity of G so that $ee' = e'$.   Hence $xe' = e'$.   Since $xe' = e$ and $xe' = e'$, we see that $e = e'$ and hence e is the identity element of H.

We have proved that the identity element of a group belongs to every subgroup.   It is possible that this is the only element in the subgroup.   The subset consisting of the identity element alone is always a subgroup of a given group. Similarly, the entire group is a subgroup of itself, since it satisfies all requirements of the definition.   Thus every group G has at least two subgroups—G itself and the subgroup consisting of the identity element alone.   These two subgroups are referred to as the *trivial* subgroups of G.   All other subgroups, if any exist, are called *proper* subgroups of G.

> **Theorem 4–9.** A subset H of a group G is a subgroup if and only if:
> a) H is not the empty set.
> b) For every pair of elements a and b in H, the product ab^{-1} is an element of H.

If we assume that H is a subgroup of G, H contains the identity element of G and so is not empty.   Further, if a and b are elements of H, b^{-1} is also in H by the fourth postulate for groups.   Then ab^{-1} is in H since H is closed under multiplication.   We have shown that every subgroup H satisfies properties (a) and (b) of Theorem 4–9.

Next, assume that H is a subset of the group G which satisfies (a) and (b).   We will show that H is a group.   Since H is not empty, H contains at least one element x. Then x and x are a pair of elements in H, and by property (b), xx^{-1} is an element of H.   But $xx^{-1} = e$, the identity of G, so H contains the identity element.

To show that every element in H has an inverse which is also in H, we let y be an arbitrary element of H.   Since e is also in H, we apply assumption (b) to the pair e, y of elements of H.   That is, $ey^{-1} = y^{-1}$ is an element of H.

Now, consider any two elements a and b of H.   By the preceding paragraph, $b^{-1} \in H$.   Applying assumption (b) to the pair a, b^{-1}, we find that $a(b^{-1})^{-1} = ab$ is an element of H.   That is, H is closed with respect to multiplication.

Finally, the associative law holds for all elements of G and therefore must hold for those elements of G which are in H.   This completes the proof that H is a group and establishes the theorem.

The preceding theorem can often be used to shorten the proof that a particular subset of a group is a subgroup.   At other times it is easier to verify each of the four group postulates directly.

Example 4–7. Suppose we consider the problem of finding a proper subgroup of the group of symmetries of the square which has three or more elements.   Let us call this subgroup we wish to construct H.   To begin with, R_0 must be in H by Theorem 4–8 if H is to be a subgroup.   Suppose now that we agree to put X in H. For the set H to be closed with respect to the operation of multiplication, we need to be sure that $X \cdot X = X^2$ is in H.   But $X^2 = R_0$, which is in H, so this is no restriction.   Similarly, $R_0 X$, R_0^2 X^3, etc., must be in H.   But all such products are either R_0 or X and are already in H.   This means that no further elements need to be included in H to obtain closure.   Then, $R_0^{-1} = R_0$ and $X^{-1} = X$, showing that each element of H has an inverse in H.   The group properties are all satisfied, but we have only two elements in H.   Let us select Y to include in H. Then to preserve closure, XY must be in H.   Since $XY = R_2$, we must include R_2 in H if we hope to make it into a subgroup.

A check of the possible products of R_0, X, Y, and R_2 shows that this set is now closed.   Further, $Y^{-1} = Y$ and $R_2^{-1} = R_2$ so that each element of H has an inverse in H.   Since the associative law holds in the entire group of symmetries, it also holds in H.   This completes the proof that the set

$$H = \{R_0, R_2, X, Y\},$$

with the operation of multiplication of elements, is a subgroup.   We will prove in Section 4–6 that subgroups of the group of symmetries of the square must have 1, 2, 4, or 8 elements.   There are no subgroups with 3, 5, 6, or 7 elements.

A special class of subgroups is of particular interest in the study of group theory. Such subgroups are sets of group elements such that each member of the set can be expressed as an integral power of a single element of the set. We first prove that the set of all integral powers of a group element always forms a subgroup.

Theorem 4–10. If a is an element of a group G, the set

$$H = \{a^k \mid k \text{ is any integer}\}$$

is a subgroup of G.

First, H is not empty since $a = a^1$ is an element of H. Suppose that a^m and a^n are any two elements of H. Then $a^m(a^n)^{-1} = a^m a^{-n} = a^{m-n}$. Since H contains all integral powers of a, a^{m-n} is an element of H. Thus we have proved that the product of any element of H times the inverse of any other element of H is also an element of H. By Theorem 4–9, H is a subgroup of G.

Definition 1. A group H (or a subgroup H of a group G) is *cyclic* if and only if there exists an element a in H such that $H = \{a^k \mid k \text{ is an integer}\}$. The element a is called the *generator* of the group H.

A cyclic group may be either finite or infinite. While there are infinitely many integers k, it frequently happens that only a finite number of the elements a^k are distinct. For instance, the group $\{1, -1, i, -i\}$ of Example 4–2 is a finite cyclic group with operation multiplication and either i or $-i$ as generators of the group; $i^1 = i, i^2 = -1, i^3 = -i,$ and $i^4 = 1$, the identity of the group. All other integral powers of i are equal to one or the other of these four elements. Similarly, $-i$ can be shown to be a generator of the group. Every finite cyclic group has properties similar to this. The next theorem generalizes these facts.

Theorem 4–11. If a cyclic group G with generator a has order n, then $a^n = e$ and the distinct elements of G are the set

$$\{a, a^2, \ldots, a^{n-1}, a^n = e\}.$$

Suppose that $a^m = e$ for $m < n$. Then if k is any integer, there exist integers q and r with $0 \le r < m$ such that $k = qm + r$, by the division algorithm. Then $a^k = a^{qm+r} = (a^m)^q a^r = e^q a^r = a^r$. Hence a^k is one of the elements $a^0, a, a^2, \ldots, a^{m-1}$. That is, G contains at most m elements, a contradiction. Therefore, our assumption that $a^m = e$ for $m < n$ is false.

Next, suppose that $a^i = a^j$ for $0 < i < j \le n$. Then, multiplying by a^{-i}, we have that $e = a^{j-i}$. Since $i < j$ and $j < n$, the integer $j - i$ satisfies $0 < j - i < n$. This is a contradiction of the results of the preceding paragraph. Hence, the elements $a, a^2, \ldots, a^n$ are distinct. But G contains exactly n elements, so this set must include all elements of G. Further, $e \in G$, so that e is one of the elements a^i for $1 \le i \le n$. We have already proved that $a^m \ne e$ for $m < n$. Therefore $a^n = e$, and the proof is complete.

Definition 2. If a is an element of a group G, the *order* of a is defined to be the order of the cyclic subgroup of G which has generator a.

Because of the preceding theorem, we may also say that the order of an element a in a group is the smallest positive integer n such that $a^n = e$. If no such n exists, the order of a is infinite.

As an example, consider the additive group of Z_6; that is, the set

$$\{0, 1, 2, 3, 4, 5\}$$

with operation of addition modulo 6. The group is cyclic with generator 1, or 5. In this group, 1 has order 6, 2 has order 3, 3 has order 2, 4 has order 3, 5 has order 6, and 0 has order 1.

In the group of symmetries of the square, R_0 has order 1, R_1 has order 4, R_2 has order 2, R_3 has order 4, and X, Y, D_1, and D_2 all have order 2.

EXERCISES

1. Prove that the set of even integers (including 0) is a subgroup of the additive group of the integers.

2. Find all subgroups of the symmetric group S_3.

3. Find all subgroups of the group of symmetries of the square.

4. Find all subgroups of a cyclic group of order 12 with generator a. The elements of this group are $\{a, a^2, a^3, \ldots, a^{12} = e\}$.

5. Find the order of each element of the group in Exercise 4.

6. Find the order of each element in the additive group of Z_7, the integers modulo 7.

7. Find the order of each element in the symmetric group S_3.

8. Show that the order of any nonzero integer is infinite in the additive group of the integers.

9. Show that the additive group of Z_7 is cyclic. What are the possible generators of this group?

10. Rewrite the definition of cyclic group and the statement and proof of Theorem 4–11, using $+$ as the notation for the group operation. As usual, where the operation is addition, denote the identity by 0, denote the inverse of a by $-a$, and use integral multiples instead of integral powers of elements.

11. If H and K are subgroups of a group G, prove that $H \cap K$ (the set of elements common to the sets H and K) also is a subgroup of G.

12. Suppose that n is the smallest positive integer such that $a^n = e$ for an element x in a group G. Show that $a^i = a^j$ if and only if $i \equiv j \pmod{n}$.

4-6   COSETS AND THE THEOREM OF LAGRANGE

The definitions of equivalence relation and equivalence sets were introduced in Section 1–8. Since then we have considered several special cases of equivalence relations, such as the equivalence relation on the set of ordered pairs of integers which we used to introduce rational numbers. The notion of an equivalence relation is one of the most important concepts of mathematics. The equivalence relation most often encountered in the study of groups is associated with the partition of a group into cosets of a subgroup, defined below.

Definition 1. If H is a subgroup of G and a is an arbitrary element of G, then the set of all elements of the form ha, for $h \in H$, is called a *right coset of H in G*. We denote this coset by Ha and refer to a as a *representative* of the coset.

Similarly, the set of elements of the form ah for $h \in H$ is a *left coset of H in G* with representative a, and is denoted by aH.

Example 4–8. Consider the group of permutations S_3, the set

$$\{(1), (123), (132), (12), (13), (23)\}.$$

Let $H = \{(1), (23)\}$. Each element of S_3 can be used as representative of a coset but these sets are not all distinct. There are three distinct right cosets of H in S_3. Each can be expressed in terms of two representatives. The following is a complete list.

$$H = H(1) = H(23) = \{(1), (23)\},$$
$$H(123) = H(13) = \{(123), (13)\},$$
$$H(132) = H(12) = \{(132), (12)\}.$$

The left cosets of H in S_3 are formed in a similar way. The list of left cosets follows.

$$H = (1)H = (23)H = \{(1), (23)\},$$
$$(123)H = (12)H = \{(123), (12)\},$$
$$(132)H = (13)\ H = \{(132), (13)\}.$$

Note that the right cosets form a partition of S_3 into subsets, each having two elements. Similarly, the left cosets partition S_3. Note also that except for the coset H itself, no left coset is the same as the right coset having the same representative. For instance, $(123)H \neq H(123)$.

The following theorem gives necessary and sufficient conditions for two right cosets to be equal. These conditions will be useful in checking whether or not two elements belong to the same coset. This theorem and the remaining ones in this section are stated for right cosets only. Similar results are valid for left cosets as well.

Theorem 4–12. If H is a subgroup of the group G and if a and b are elements of G, the following conditions are equivalent.

a) $a \in Hb$ b) $Ha = Hb$ c) $ab^{-1} \in H$

We begin the proof by assuming that condition (a) holds. That is, $a \in Hb$, which means that $a = hb$ for some $h \in H$. For any element x in Ha, $x = h'a$

for some $h' \in H$. Substituting, we have that $x = h'(hb) = (h'h)b$. Since H is a subgroup, $h'h \in H$ and hence $x \in Hb$. But x was an arbitrary element in Ha, so $Ha \subseteq Hb$. Since $a = hb$, $b = h^{-1}a$. Again, from the properties of subgroups, $h^{-1} \in H$, so we may say that $b \in Ha$. Repeating the above argument, with a and b interchanged, we can show that $Hb \subseteq Ha$. Since we also proved $Ha \subseteq Hb$, the two sets must be equal. That is, $Ha = Hb$. We have shown that if condition (a) holds, then condition (b) must also hold.

Next, assume that condition (b) holds. The element a is in Ha since $e \in H$ and $a = ea$. Since by (b) $Ha = Hb$, the element a is in Hb. That is, $a = hb$ for some $h \in H$. Then $ab^{-1} = h \in H$. We have shown that if condition (b) holds, then condition (c) holds.

Finally, assume that condition (c) is satisfied, and $ab^{-1} = h$ for some $h \in H$. Then multiplying both sides on the right by b, we have that $a = hb$. By definition of Hb, this shows that $a \in Hb$, which is condition (a). Hence if condition (c) is satisfied, then condition (a) must also be satisfied. This completes the proof of the theorem.

Theorem 4–13. If H is a subgroup of G, the right cosets of H in G form a partition of G.

Every element g in G is in at least one right coset of H, namely Hg. Suppose that $x \in Ha \cap Hb$. Then by Theorem 4–12, $Ha = Hx = Hb$. Thus no element is in two distinct right cosets of H. These are the conditions required for the right cosets to form a partition of G.

Definition 2. If H is a subgroup of G, and if a and b are elements of G, a is *congruent to b modulo H* (written $a \equiv b \pmod{H}$) if and only if a and b belong to the same right coset of H in G.

Theorem 4–13 provides the proof that this relation is an equivalence relation if we recall from Chapter 1 that each partition of a set is associated with an equivalence relation. For the example at the beginning of this section, we see that $(123) \equiv (12) \pmod{H}$ and that $(13) \not\equiv (12) \pmod{H}$.

Theorem 4–12 provides three conditions, any one of which is necessary and sufficient in order that $a \equiv b \pmod{H}$. That is, $a \equiv b \pmod{H}$ if and only if one of the conditions $b \in Ha$, $Ha = Hb$, or $ab^{-1} \in H$ is satisfied.

Theorem 4–14 (Lagrange). If H is a subgroup of a finite group G, then the order of H is a divisor of the order of G.

The proof of this theorem follows from Theorem 4–13 if we can show that every coset of the subgroup H in G contains the same number of elements. Let g be an element of G which is not in H, so that $Hg \neq H$. Consider the mapping η of H into Hg defined by $\eta(h) = hg$ for each element h in H. Since every element of Hg is the product of an element h in H with g, the mapping is onto. Suppose, next, that $\eta(h_1) = \eta(h_2)$ for h_1 and h_2 in H. That is, $h_1g = h_2g$. By the cancellation law, $h_1 = h_2$. This shows that the mapping η is one-to-one. Hence the coset Hg contains the same number of elements as H.   This is true for any coset of H and, consequently, the order of the group G equals the product of the order of H times the number of distinct cosets of H in G.   The order of H must therefore be a divisor of the order of G.

Corollary 1. If the order of a group G is a prime number p, then G is cyclic and every element of G other than the identity is a generator of G.

If $a \neq e$ and $a \in G$, then a generates a cyclic subgroup $H = \{a^k \mid k \in I\}$.   The order of H divides p, a prime, and hence must equal p.   That is, $G = H$ and a is a generator of G.

Corollary 2. If the order of a group G is the integer n, then for every element a in G, $a^n = e$, where e is the identity of G.

Let a be an element of G.   Then the set $H = \{a^k \mid k \in I\}$ is a subgroup of G. Since G is finite, the order of H is also finite.   Denote the order of H by m.   By Theorem 4–11, $a^m = e$.   By Lagrange's theorem, m is a divisor of n.   That is, $n = md$ for an integer d.   Hence

$$a^n = a^{md} = (a^m)^d = e^d = e.$$

This completes the proof of Corollary 2.

Corollary 3. The order of every element of a finite group is a divisor of the group order.

In cases where the operation of a group is written as addition, we denote a right coset by $H + a$ instead of Ha.   The definition of coset is modified only by changing the notation for the operation.   Thus, if H is a subgroup of a group G, the coset $H + g$ is the set of all elements of the form $h + g$ for $h \in H$.

EXERCISES

1. Let G be the group of symmetries of the square (Example 4–3, Section 4–2) and let H be the subgroup consisting of the elements R_0, R_1, R_2, and R_3.   Find all right cosets of H in G.   Show that the left cosets of H in G are identical to the right cosets.   That is, $aH = Ha$ for every $a \in G$.

2. Let G be the group of symmetries of the square, and let H be the subgroup consisting of the elements R_0 and X.   Show that the left cosets of H in G are not the same sets as the right cosets.

3. Let G and H be as in Exercise 2.   Find a left coset $g_1 H$ and a right coset Hg_2 such that $g_1 H \neq Hg_2$ and yet such that $g_1 H$ and Hg_2 have an element in common.

4. Let H be a subgroup of a group G.   Show that each element in a given coset of H in G may be used as a representative of that coset.

5. Given the additive group T of integers, show that the set of all multiples of 7 (including zero) forms a subgroup H of T.

6. Find all right cosets of H in T for H and T of Exercise 5. Show that the left cosets of H in T are the same as the right cosets by verifying that for any integer n, $n + H = H + n$.

7. Let G be the cyclic group of order 24 with elements $\{a^0 = e, a, a^2, \ldots, a^{23}\}$. Let H be the subgroup $H = \{a^0, a^6, a^{12}, a^{18}\}$. Determine whether each of the following statements is true or false.

   a) $a^7 \equiv a^{11} \pmod{H}$ b) $a^{10} \equiv a^5 \pmod{H}$
   c) $a^{13} \equiv a^{19} \pmod{H}$ d) $a^5 \equiv a^{23} \pmod{H}$
   e) $a^{16} \equiv e \pmod{H}$ f) $a^3 \equiv a^{15} \pmod{H}$

8. Let G and H be the groups of Exercise 7. For each of the following congruences, find three distinct values of x for which the congruence is true.

   a) $a^7 \equiv x \pmod{H}$ b) $x \equiv a^{17} \pmod{H}$
   c) $x \equiv a^{12} \pmod{H}$ d) $a^{10} \equiv x \pmod{H}$

9. Find the order of each of the following elements of the group G of Exercise 7.

   a) e b) a^{10} c) a^{13} d) a^9
   e) a^{16} f) a^{20} g) a^{18} h) a^{12}

10. Find all subgroups of the group G of Exercise 7, using Lagrange's theorem. Note that each of these subgroups is a cyclic group.

11. Prove that if a group is not cyclic, it must have a proper subgroup.

12. Prove that every subgroup of a cyclic group is cyclic.

4-7   *Z_n* AND CONGRUENCE MODULO *n*

Congruence modulo a subgroup was defined in the preceding section. An important special case of this definition leads to a definition which is important in number theory. This section deals with that special case. It is important in its own right, but also illustrates the way in which the cosets of a subgroup can be made the elements of a new group called a quotient group. We will find that our discussion also leads to a new description of the rings Z_n which have been used repeatedly in this text.

Consider a fixed integer n and let N denote the set of all multiples of n,

$$N = \{kn \mid k \in \mathbf{Z}\}.$$

It is easy to show that the set N with the operation of addition forms a subgroup of the additive group of the integers. The right cosets of N in $\mathbf{Z}$ are the sets $N + a$ for $a \in \mathbf{Z}$. The change in notation from Na to $N + a$ is necessary because the group operation is addition rather than multiplication as indicated in Section 4–6. However, let us adopt a more familiar notation. Each coset is an equivalence set modulo N so let us denote $H + a$ by $[a]$. Now from Theorem 4–12 we know that two integers a and b are in the same coset, or equivalently that $[a] = [b]$, if and only if $a - b \in N$. Since N is the set of multiples of n, we are led to a new definition of congruence modulo N, which is the definition customarily used in number theory.

Definition 1. If n is a fixed integer, then for any integers a and b, $a \equiv b(\bmod n)$, read "a is congruent to b modulo n," if and only if $a - b$ is divisible by n.

For example, $7 \equiv 2(\bmod 5)$ since $7 - 2 = 1 \cdot 5$, and $-4 \equiv 30(\bmod 17)$ since $-4 - 30 = (-2)(17)$. Remember, this definition is merely a reformulation of congruence modulo a subgroup, and hence all previous results carry over immediately. In particular, we have the following theorem.

Theorem 4–15. For any fixed $n \in Z$, congruence modulo n is an equivalence relation in Z and the equivalence sets are exactly the right cosets of $N = \{kn \mid k \in Z\}$ in the additive group of Z.

Example 4–9. Suppose we consider congruence modulo 5. The equivalence sets are:

$$[0] = \{0, \pm 5, \pm 10, \pm 15, \ldots\},$$
$$[1] = \{1, -4, 6, -9, 11, \ldots\},$$
$$[2] = \{2, -3, 7, -8, 12, \ldots\},$$
$$[3] = \{3, -2, 8, -7, 13, \ldots\},$$
$$[4] = \{4, -1, 9, -6, 14, \ldots\}.$$

Of course, although there are only five equivalence sets, each may be expressed in many ways by changing the representative. For instance,

$$[3] = [-2] = [8] = [-7] = [138] = \ldots.$$

The sets involved here may be written in other ways as well. A useful and more precise way of representing the members of this partition is the following:

$$[0] = \{5n \mid n \text{ is an integer}\},$$
$$[1] = \{5n + 1 \mid n \text{ is an integer}\},$$
$$[2] = \{5n + 2 \mid n \text{ is an integer}\},$$
$$[3] = \{5n + 3 \mid n \text{ is an integer}\},$$
$$[4] = \{5n + 4 \mid n \text{ is an integer}\}.$$

Remember that in this form of set notation we include all integers for which the sentence defining the set is a true sentence. Thus $\{5n + 2 \mid n \text{ is an integer}\}$ is the set of all integers obtained by replacing n by any integer whatsoever in the expression $5n + 2$. Replacing n by 0, we get 2; replacing n by -1 we get -3; replacing n by 10 we get 52; etc.

Definition 2. Let C_n be the set of all equivalence sets in Z with respect to congruence modulo n. Let the operations of addition and multiplication in C_n be defined by

$$[a] + [b] = [a + b],$$
$$[a][b] = [ab].$$

This definition states that to add (or multiply) two equivalence sets, we merely add (or multiply) the representatives, using ordinary addition (or multiplication) of integers. The answer is the equivalence set containing this sum (or product).

Example 4–10. Consider, as in Example 4–9, equivalence modulo 5. The following are examples of sums and products in the class C_5:

$$[2] + [4] = [6],$$
$$[-3] + [17] = [14],$$
$$[2][4] = [8],$$
$$[-3][17] = [-51].$$

We could, of course, write these answers as [1], [4], [3], and [4], respectively, since these sets are equal to the given ones.

Before considering properties of these operations, we need to establish the fact that they are well defined. Let us consider another example which illustrates, but does not prove, the property involved.

Example 4–11. Again considering congruence modulo 5 as in Example 4–9, note that $[3] = [-2]$ and $[4] = [14]$ in C_5. We can form the sum of these sets using either representation: $[3] + [4] = [7]$, by definition, and $[-2] + [14] = [12]$. Note now that $[7] = [12] = [2]$, so that the same sum is given in either case, although the representation is not the same. We can also form the product of these two sets using either representation: $[3][4] = [2]$ and $[-2][14] = [-28]$. Now we note that $[2] = [-28]$ because $2 \equiv -28 \pmod 5$. This is true because $2 - (-28) = 30$ and 30 is a multiple of 5.

Theorem 4–16. The operations of addition and multiplication in C_n are well defined.

Proof. Suppose that $[a] = [a']$ and that $[b] = [b']$. Then $a - a' = pn$ and $b - b' = qn$ for some integers p and q. Then $(a - a') + (b - b') = pn + qn$, or $(a + b) - (a' + b') = (p + q)n$ so that $a + b \equiv a' + b' \pmod n$. This means that $[a + b] = [a' + b']$ and hence addition is well defined.

Further, from the above equations $a = a' + pn$ and $b = b' + qn$ so that $ab = (a' + pn)(b' + qn) = a'b' + (a'q + pb' + pqn)n$. Hence $ab - a'b'$ is a multiple of n and $ab \equiv a'b' \pmod n$. This means that $[ab] = [a'b']$ and multiplication is also well defined.

When we consider the set C_n with the operation of addition only, the set forms a group. Its elements are cosets of N in $\mathbf{Z}$ and it is referred to as the *quotient group* of N in $\mathbf{Z}$. However, it is even more interesting to consider C_n with both operations. It can be proven, directly from the definitions we have given, that this system is a commutative ring with unity element. Instead, we will show that C_n is isomorphic to Z_n, and since isomorphic systems have the same algebraic properties, this will establish the fact that C_n is a ring.

Theorem 4–17. The sets Z_n and C_n, with their respective operations, are isomorphic for every natural number n.

Consider then the set $Z_n = \{0, 1, \ldots, n - 1\}$ of integers modulo n with operations of addition and multiplication modulo n and the set

$$C_n = \{[0], [1], \ldots, [n - 1]\}$$

of equivalence sets of integers congruent modulo n with the operations defined above. To show that Z_n is isomorphic to C_n, we need to find a one-to-one mapping of Z_n onto C_n which preserves operations. Let the mapping $\varphi: Z_n \to C_n$ be defined by $\varphi(m) = [m]$ for $m = 0, 1, \ldots, n - 1$. This is, quite obviously, a one-to-one mapping of Z_n onto C_n.

Recall that in Z_n, addition is defined modulo n. Since we will need to consider ordinary addition as well, it will be necessary to distinguish between these operations. For the purpose of this proof only, let us designate addition modulo n by $+_n$ and ordinary addition by $+$. Similarly, we will use $\cdot_n$ for multiplication modulo n and the usual notation for ordinary multiplication. Now we are ready to prove that the mapping φ preserves operations.

Let p and q be any two elements of Z_n. Then $\varphi(p +_n q) = [p +_n q]$ by definition of φ. We need to show that this set is the same as $\varphi(p) + \varphi(q)$. Since $\varphi(p) = [p]$ and $\varphi(q) = [q]$ and $[p] + [q] = [p + q]$, our problem reduces to showing that $[p +_n q] = [p + q]$. Recall that the operation $+_n$ is performed by discarding multiples of n from $p + q$. Hence $p + q = p +_n q + kn$ for some integer k. But this means that $(p + q) - (p +_n q) = kn$, or that $p + q \equiv p +_n q \pmod{n}$. Hence $[p +_n q] = [p + q]$, as was to be proved. This shows that φ preserves the operation of addition.

We prove in a similar way that φ preserves the operation of multiplication. Again let p and q be arbitrary elements of Z_n. Then $\varphi(p \cdot_n q) = [p \cdot_n q]$ by definition of φ. Further, $\varphi(p)\varphi(q) = [p][q] = [p \cdot q]$ by definition of φ and of multiplication in C_n. To show that $[p \cdot_n q] = [p \cdot q]$, we recall that $p \cdot_n q$ is found by discarding multiples of n from the product $p \cdot q$. Hence $p \cdot q = p \cdot_n q + k'n$ for some integer k'. That is, $p \cdot q - p \cdot_n q = k'n$, or $p \cdot q \equiv p \cdot_n q \pmod{n}$. Hence $[p \cdot_n q] = [p \cdot q]$, showing that multiplication is preserved. This completes the proof that the two systems are isomorphic.

Whenever two algebraic systems are isomorphic, they are identical except for notational differences. All algebraic properties, such as existence of inverses or zero divisors, are the same for both systems. Thus all theorems proved for the various systems Z_n hold in the sets C_n described in this section. The properties depend on the integer n, particularly on whether or not n is a prime, as was the case for Z_n. This discussion reveals the fact that we could have described C_n rather than Z_n in the beginning, and used the rings C_n for our principal examples of finite rings. At the time, however, the concepts which led to the definition of C_n had not been developed and we adopted the more expedient procedure.

The concept of congruence modulo n is an important one in number theory.

The reader is referred to Appendix *B* for a further discussion of the topic which indicates the way congruences are treated in this subject. The properties of congruence developed there have no direct relation to this text but are included in the appendix as a matter of interest.

Example 4–12. Let us illustrate the properties of equivalence sets in C_5 by performing some computations involving subtraction and division; $[0]$ is the zero and $[1]$ the unity of the ring C_n. The operations of subtraction and division are defined in the standard way.

$$[1] - [4] = [1] + (-[4]) = [1] + [1] = [2].$$

Note that $-[4] = [1]$, since $[4] + [1] = [5]$ and $[5] = [0]$.

$$[4] \div [3] = [4][3]^{-1} = [4][2] = [8] = [3].$$

Note that $[3]^{-1} = [2]$, since $[3][2] = [6]$ and $[6] = [1]$.

Example 4–13. Consider the solving of simple equations in the set C_5. This is carried out as in any ring. The reader should check the answers obtained by substitution into the given equations.

The equation $[3] + X = [2]$ has solution $X = [2] - [3] = [4]$.

The equation $[3]X = [2]$ has solution $X = [3]^{-1}[2] = [4]$.

Example 4–14. The operation of subtraction is defined in C_6 as usual, but division is not defined, since not all elements have inverses. (Compare Section 2–4.) Thus

$$[2] - [5] = [2] + (-[5]) = [3],$$

but $[5] \div [2]$ is not defined, since $[2]^{-1}$ does not exist. Similarly, the equation $[2]X = [5]$ has no solution in C_6, although the equation $[2]X = [4]$ has the solution $X = [2]$, as can be readily verified.

EXERCISES

1. List all equivalence sets for the equivalence relation on the integers of congruence modulo 7. Express each of these sets in both of the notations used in Example 4–9.

2. Express each equivalence set in Exercise 1 in terms of three different representatives, including as a representative at least one negative and at least one positive integer. (For example, $[3] = [10] = [-4]$.)

3. Consider the set C_7 of equivalence sets modulo 7. Perform the following operations, expressing each answer in terms of a representative less than 7.

a) $[4] + [6]$ b) $[3] + [4]$
c) $[2] - [4]$ d) $[3] - [5]$
e) $[3][6]$ f) $[5][4]$
g) $[3] \div [5]$ h) $[5] \div [3]$
i) $[1] \div [2]$ j) $[4] \div [6]$

4. Illustrate that addition and multiplication of equivalence sets of integers congruent modulo 7 are well defined by giving several examples similar to those in Example 4–11.

5. Use the definitions of the set C_n of equivalence sets modulo n, and of operations of addition and multiplication, to prove that C_n is a ring. If you have difficulty doing this for an arbitrary integer n, consider C_5 first and then return to the general proof.

6. In the proof of Theorem 4–11, it was necessary to prove that $[p + q] = [p +_n q]$. Illustrate this equality with several examples for the case $n = 5$.

7. In the proof of Theorem 4-17, it was necessary to prove that $[p \cdot q] = [p_n \cdot q]$. Illustrate this equality with several examples for the case $n = 5$.

8. Solve each of the following equations in C_7.

a) $[5] + X = [3]$　　　　　　　b) $X + [6] = [1]$
c) $[5]X = [2]$　　　　　　　　d) $[2]X = [5]$
e) $[6]X = [3]$　　　　　　　　f) $[4]X = [5]$

9. Determine which of the following equations can be solved in C_6. Find all solutions that exist.

a) $[5] + X = [1]$　　　　　　　b) $X + [4] = [3]$
c) $[2]X = [0]$　　　　　　　　d) $[3]X = [5]$
e) $[4]X = [1]$　　　　　　　　f) $[5]X = [1]$

CHAPTER 5

THE GROUP OF RIGID MOTIONS OF THE PLANE

5-1 THE GROUP OF RIGID MOTIONS

Until the nineteenth century there was a great deal of confusion among mathematicians concerning the nature of geometry and concerning the subject matter which should be included under this label. By that time geometries other than Euclidean geometry had been introduced, although not all mathematicians recognized the value of these. In 1872, Felix Klein gave a definition of geometry which is referred to as the Erlanger program. This definition served to dispel the confusion and led to a new understanding of the subject. Klein described geometry as the study of those properties of sets of points and lines which are unchanged by prescribed sets of transformations (mappings).

In Euclidean geometry, the set involved is the set of rigid motions. In all cases, the sets of mappings have properties which classify them as groups. The purpose of this chapter is to examine the meaning of this definition of geometry, now accepted as one of the most important aspects of the subject.

Let us designate the set of all points in the plane by the symbol $\mathbf{P}$. Each point Q in $\mathbf{P}$ will be identified by a pair (x, y) of real numbers, called the *cartesian* (or rectangular) *coordinates* of the point. The treatment of points and lines will be the standard one used in high school algebra or analytic geometry courses.

Mappings of geometric spaces (for example, of $\mathbf{P}$) are usually referred to in geometry as *transformations*. We visualize a transformation of $\mathbf{P}$ as causing a displacement or motion of the points from an initial to a terminal position. For this reason the set of transformations discussed here is often referred to as the set of *rigid motions* of the plane. The adjective "rigid" refers to the fact that, among other things, the distance between two points is not affected by the motion. That is, if α is a rigid motion and Q and R are points of $\mathbf{P}$, then the distance QR equals the distance $\alpha(Q)\alpha(R)$. The functional notation $\alpha(Q)$ refers as usual to the image of Q under the mapping α.

A transformation may be written in more than one way. We may express it in terms of a set of pairs or by writing equations for the coordinates of the image point in terms of the coordinates of the pre-image. We will use the second method here, partly because the points of $\mathbf{P}$ are already written as pairs of real numbers, which makes the set notation cumbersome. If the transformation $\alpha : \mathbf{P} \rightarrow \mathbf{P}$

maps Q into Q' so that $\alpha(Q) = Q'$, we will designate Q by (x, y) and Q' by (x', y'). The equations of α will be equations which express x' and y' in terms of x and y.

Definition. The set E of *rigid motions* (also called *Euclidean transformations*) is the set of all transformations of **P** into **P** whose equations can be expressed in the form

$$\begin{cases} x' = x \cos A - y \sin A + c \\ y' = ex \sin A + ey \cos A + d, \end{cases}$$

where A represents an arbitrary angle, where c and d represent arbitrary real numbers, and where the symbol e is either 1 or -1.

Example 5–1. Consider the rigid motion σ given by the equations

$$x' = -\frac{x\sqrt{3}}{2} - \frac{y}{2} + 2$$

$$y' = \frac{x}{2} - \frac{y\sqrt{3}}{2} - 1.$$

This corresponds to the angle $A = 150°$, $c = 2$, $d = -1$, and $e = 1$ in the form prescribed by the definition. Let $R = (0, 0)$, $S = (0, 1)$, and $T = (-1, 2)$. Then by substituting into the equations for σ, we obtain

$$\sigma(R) = (2 \ -1), \qquad \sigma(S) = \left(\frac{3}{2}, -\frac{\sqrt{3}}{2} - 1\right),$$

and

$$\sigma(T) = \left(\frac{\sqrt{3}}{2} + 1, -\frac{1}{2} - \sqrt{3}\right).$$

The operation of multiplication of rigid motions is defined for E just as the product of any two mappings has been defined. Thus, if α and β are rigid motions and $Q \in \mathbf{P}$, then $\beta\alpha(Q) = \beta(\alpha(Q))$. Note that this definition means that the transformation $\beta\alpha$ is the result of first performing the transformation α and then applying β to the result.

When we are considering the product of two transformations, it is convenient to alter the notation slightly. If α maps Q into Q', then we denote the image of Q' under β as Q''. That is, $\alpha(Q) = Q'$ and $\beta(Q') = Q''$. This is reflected in the equations of the transformation β by using x'', y'', x', and y' in place of x', y', x, and y, respectively. This notation helps to keep things straight in the process of applying the successive transformations.

The following theorem justifies the inclusion of the set of rigid motions in a chapter on group theory.

Theorem 5–1. The set E of rigid motions, together with the operation of multiplication of transformations, forms a group.

The first step in the proof is to establish the fact that E is closed with respect to multiplication.   That is, we need to prove that the product of any two rigid motions is another rigid motion.   For this purpose, suppose that α and β are any two rigid motions.   Then their equations can be written in the form required by the definition, as follows.

1) Equations for α: $\begin{cases} x' = x \cos A - y \sin A + c, \\ y' = ex \sin A + ey \cos A + d. \end{cases}$

2) Equations for β: $\begin{cases} x'' = x' \cos B - y' \sin B + g, \\ y'' = fx' \sin B + fy' \cos B + h \end{cases}$

Here A and B are arbitrary angles; c, d, g, and h are real numbers; e and f are each either 1 or -1.   To determine the equations for the transformation $\beta\alpha$, we may substitute the values of x' and y' from (1) directly into equations (2).   We obtain equations (3) after suitable collecting of terms.

(3) Equations of $\beta\alpha$: $\begin{cases} x'' = x(\cos A \cos B - e \sin A \sin B) \\ \quad - y (\sin A \cos B + e \cos A \sin B) + s, \\ y'' = fx(e \sin A \cos B + \cos A \sin B) \\ \quad + fy(e \cos A \cos B - \sin A \sin B) + t, \end{cases}$

where s is the real number $c \cos B - d \sin B + g$ and t is the real number $fc \sin B + fd \cos B + h$.   Now if $e = 1$, equations (3) reduce to

$$\begin{cases} x'' = x \cos (A + B) - y \sin (A + B) + s, \\ y'' = fx \sin (A + B) + fy \cos (A + B) + t. \end{cases}$$

These equations clearly represent a rigid motion.   If $e = -1$, equations (3) reduce to

$$\begin{cases} x'' = x \cos (A - B) - y \sin (A - B) + s, \\ y'' = (-f)y \sin (A - B) + (-f)y \cos (A - B) + t. \end{cases}$$

Since f is 1 or -1, $-f$ also satisfies the condition of being either 1 or -1.   Hence in the case $e = -1$, equations (3) again represent a rigid motion.   This completes the proof that E is closed with respect to multiplication.

The associative law of multiplication is implied by the definition of the operation.   The proof has already been given in Section 4–4 in the proof of Theorem 4–5 for permutations.   The proof here is identical and will not be repeated.   In fact, one could show that the set E of rigid motions is a subset of the set of all permutations of $\mathbf{P}$ and that therefore the former proof includes this as a special case.

The identity in the set E is the mapping ε given by equations (4).

4) Equations for ε: $\begin{cases} x' = x, \\ y' = y. \end{cases}$

These equations are of the form required by the definition.   The angle A is $0°$.
e is 1, and both c and d are zero.   We can see that this is the identity of E by noting
that for every point Q in P. $\varepsilon(Q) = Q$.   Hence if α is any element of E, $\varepsilon\alpha(Q) = \varepsilon(\alpha(Q)) = \alpha(Q)$, by the definition of product and by the above remark.   Similarly,
$\alpha\varepsilon(Q) = \alpha(\varepsilon(Q)) = \alpha(Q)$.   By the definition of equality of mappings, $\varepsilon\alpha = \alpha\varepsilon = \alpha$.   Hence ε is the identity element in E.

The inverse of α, designated α^{-1}, is given by equations (5).

5) Equations for α^{-1}:

$$
\begin{cases}
x' = x \cos(-A) - \dfrac{y}{e} \sin(-A) + \left(-c \cos A - \dfrac{d}{e} \sin A\right), \\[2mm]
y' = x \sin(-A) + \dfrac{y}{e} \cos(-A) + \left(c \sin A - \dfrac{d}{e} \cos A\right).
\end{cases}
$$

These equations are derived by first solving equations (1) for x and y in terms
of x' and y'.   Then the replacement of x by x', y by y', x' by x, and y' by y is made
to conform to our usage of the prime with the coordinate of the image point.
Direct computation of the product according to the method given earlier in this
proof shows that $\alpha\alpha^{-1} = \alpha^{-1}\alpha = \varepsilon$, the identity transformation.   The computation is not particularly interesting and will be left for the reader.   To show
that α^{-1} is in the set E, we recall that e is either 1 or -1.   If e is 1, then equations
(5) are in the form required by the definition.   If $e = -1$, then $1/e = -1$, and
we rewrite equations (5) in the form

$$
\begin{cases}
x' = x \cos A - y \sin A + (d \sin A - c \cos A), \\
y' = (-1)x \sin A + (-1)y \cos A + (c \sin A + d \cos A),
\end{cases}
$$

which also satisfies the requirements of the definition of E.   This completes the
proof of the theorem.

Example 5–2.   We let the rigid motion α be given by

$$
\begin{cases}
x' = -y + 3, \\
y' = x - 2.
\end{cases}
$$

This is a transformation of the general form, with $A = 90°$, $e = 1, c = 3$, and
$d = -2$.   Then let β be given by the equations,

$$
\begin{cases}
x'' = -\dfrac{\sqrt{2}}{2} x' + \dfrac{\sqrt{2}}{2} y', \\[3mm]
y'' = \dfrac{\sqrt{2}}{2} x' + \dfrac{\sqrt{2}}{2} y' + 5.
\end{cases}
$$

For the transformation β, we used $A = 225°$, $e = -1$, $c = 0$, and $d = 5$. Then $\beta\alpha$ is given by the equations

$$\begin{cases} x'' = \dfrac{\sqrt{2}}{2} x + \dfrac{\sqrt{2}}{2} y - \dfrac{5\sqrt{2}}{2}, \\[3mm] y'' = \dfrac{\sqrt{2}}{2} x - \dfrac{\sqrt{2}}{2} y + 5 + \dfrac{\sqrt{2}}{2}. \end{cases}$$

The angle in $\beta\alpha$ is $135°$ and the value of e is -1.

Example 5-3. The inverse of the rigid motion α of Example 5-2 is given by

$$\begin{cases} x' = y + 2, \\ y' = -x + 3. \end{cases}$$

These equations can be found by using equations (5) from the proof of the theorem or, more easily, by solving the equations of α for x and y and then changing notation. This method was also indicated in the proof of the theorem. As a special case to illustrate the fact that every point is mapped onto itself by the product of a rigid motion and its inverse, consider the image of the point $(2, 1)$ under $\alpha\alpha^{-1}$ and $\alpha^{-1}\alpha$. Using the given equations, we have $\alpha\alpha^{-1}(2, 1) = \alpha(3, 1) = (2, 1)$. Similarly, $\alpha^{-1}\alpha(2, 1) = \alpha^{-1}(2, 0) = (2, 1)$. The equations for $\alpha\alpha^{-1}$ or $\alpha^{-1}\alpha$ are, of course, equations (4) of the identity.

Example 5-4. In order to illustrate a special case of the associative law, consider the rigid motion γ with equations

$$\begin{cases} x''' = \dfrac{\sqrt{3}}{2} x'' - \dfrac{y''}{2} + 1, \\[3mm] y''' = -\dfrac{x''}{2} - \dfrac{\sqrt{3}}{2} y'' - 2, \end{cases}$$

corresponding to the angle $30°$, with $e = -1$, $c = 1$, and $d = -2$. To compute $\gamma(\beta\alpha)$, we find the product of γ with $\beta\alpha$ (given in Example 5-2). Substitution shows the equations of $\gamma(\beta\alpha)$ to be

6)
$$\begin{cases} x''' = \dfrac{\sqrt{6} - \sqrt{2}}{4} x + \dfrac{\sqrt{6} + \sqrt{2}}{4} y - \dfrac{5\sqrt{6} + \sqrt{2} + 6}{4}, \\[3mm] y''' = -\dfrac{\sqrt{2} + \sqrt{6}}{4} x + \dfrac{\sqrt{6} - \sqrt{2}}{4} y + \dfrac{5\sqrt{2} - 10\sqrt{3} - \sqrt{6} - 8}{4}. \end{cases}$$

To compute $(\gamma\beta)\alpha$, we first find the equations for the product $\gamma\beta$. These are

$$\begin{cases} x''' = \dfrac{-\sqrt{6} - \sqrt{2}}{4} x' + \dfrac{\sqrt{6} - \sqrt{2}}{4} y' - \dfrac{3}{2}, \\[3mm] y''' = \dfrac{\sqrt{2} - \sqrt{6}}{4} x' - \dfrac{\sqrt{2} + \sqrt{6}}{4} y' - \dfrac{5\sqrt{3} + 4}{2}. \end{cases}$$

Next we find the product of $\gamma\beta$ with α, which gives exactly equations (6), showing that in this special case, $\gamma(\beta\alpha) = (\gamma\beta)\alpha$.

Example 5–5. Although the rigid motions are mappings of **P**, the set of points in the plane, we can also consider the effect of the mappings on lines. Let m be the line $x - 2y + 1 = 0$, and consider the rigid motion α of Example 5–2. The easiest way to obtain $\alpha(m)$ is to substitute for the values of x and y in the equation of m. Solving the equations of α for x and y, we obtain $x = y' + 2$ and $y = -x' + 3$. Upon substitution into the equation of m, we find that $\alpha(m)$ has the equation $2x' + y' - 3 = 0$. Now consider the points $Q = (1, 1)$ and $R = (-5, -2)$, which are on line m. Then $Q' = \alpha(Q) = (2, -1)$ and $R' = \alpha(R) = (5, -7)$. Now we note that the points Q' and R' lie on the line $\alpha(m)$, as one would expect. That is, if a point lies on a given line, then its image must lie on the image of the given line.

We need to introduce another term in order to point out the significance of the group of rigid motions to the study of geometry.

> **Definition.** a) A property which applies to a set of points is *invariant under a transformation* if and only if the points of every set for which the property is true are mapped by the transformation onto a set of points for which the property is also true.
>
> b) A property of a set of points is *invariant under a group of transformations* if and only if it is invariant under each transformation in the group.

For example, the property that a set of points is collinear (lie on one line) is invariant under the group of rigid motions. We illustrated this fact in a special case in Example 5–5.

The importance of the group of rigid motions to the study of Euclidean geometry is that the properties of points and figures which we study in this geometry are exactly those properties which are invariant under the group E of rigid motions. The following theorem states that the distance between two points (a property that applies to sets of two points) is invariant under the group of rigid motions. Other properties, such as the angle between lines and the area of geometric figures, are also invariant under the group E. Some of these are mentioned in the exercises.

> **Theorem 5–2.** If α is any rigid motion and if S and T are any two points in **P**, then the distance between S and T is equal to the distance between $\alpha(S)$ and $\alpha(T)$.

We will not give the proof of this theorem, since the proof involves a rather messy computation. However, we will illustrate the meaning of the theorem by proving it for a single specific rigid motion in the following example.

Example 5–6. Let τ be the rigid motion with equations

$$\begin{cases} x' = \dfrac{x}{2} + \dfrac{\sqrt{3}}{2}\,y, \\[2mm] y' = -\dfrac{\sqrt{3}}{2}\,x + \dfrac{y}{2} + 1. \end{cases}$$

Now if $S = (x, y)$ and $T = (u, v)$ are any two points of **P**, the distance between them is

$$\sqrt{(x - u)^2 + (y - v)^2}$$

by a familiar formula from analytic geometry. Applying τ to S and T, we obtain the images

$$S' = \left(\frac{x}{2} + \frac{y\sqrt{3}}{2},\ -\frac{x\sqrt{3}}{2} + \frac{y}{2} + 1 \right)$$

and

$$T' = \left(\frac{u}{2} + \frac{v\sqrt{3}}{2},\ -\frac{u\sqrt{3}}{2} + \frac{v}{2} + 1 \right).$$

Again applying the distance formula, we find that the square of the distance from S' to T' is

$$\left(\frac{x}{2} + \frac{y\sqrt{3}}{2} - \frac{u}{2} - \frac{v\sqrt{3}}{2} \right)^2 + \left(-\frac{x\sqrt{3}}{2} + \frac{y}{2} + \frac{u\sqrt{3}}{2} - \frac{v}{2} \right)^2$$

$$= \frac{x^2}{4} + \frac{3y^2}{4} + \frac{u^2}{4} + \frac{3v^2}{4} + \frac{xy\sqrt{3}}{2} - \frac{xu}{2} - \frac{xv\sqrt{3}}{2} - \frac{uy\sqrt{3}}{2} - \frac{3yv}{2}$$

$$+ \frac{uv\sqrt{3}}{2} + \frac{3x^2}{4} + \frac{y^2}{4} + \frac{3u^2}{4} + \frac{v^2}{4} - \frac{xy\sqrt{3}}{2} - \frac{3ux}{2}$$

$$+ \frac{xv\sqrt{3}}{2} + \frac{uy\sqrt{3}}{2} - \frac{yv}{2} - \frac{uv\sqrt{3}}{2}$$

$$= x^2 - 2ux + u^2 + y^2 - 2yv + v^2 = (x - u)^2 + (y - v)^2.$$

Thus the distance from S' to T' is

$$\sqrt{(x - u)^2 + (y - v)^2},$$

as was to be proved.

EXERCISES

1. Find the rigid motion corresponding to $A = 240°, e = -1, c = 2$, and $d = -5$, where $A, e, c,$ and d are the constants in the general equations of a rigid motion given in the definition.

2. For each of the rigid motions below, find the values of A, e, c, and d as given in the general equations of a rigid motion.

a) $\begin{cases} x' = -x + 5 \\ y' = y + 2 \end{cases}$

b) $\begin{cases} x' = \dfrac{x\sqrt{2}}{2} + \dfrac{y\sqrt{2}}{2} - 1 \\[2mm] y' = -\dfrac{x\sqrt{2}}{2} + \dfrac{y\sqrt{2}}{2} \end{cases}$

3. Find the image of $(2, -4)$ and of $(-1, 7)$ under each of the rigid motions given in Exercise 2.

4. Find the image of each of the following lines under the rigid motion given in Exercise 2(a).

   a) $3x - 2y + 5 = 0$ b) $5x + y - 6 = 0$

5. a) Given the rigid motion δ with equations

$$\begin{cases} x' = \dfrac{x\sqrt{3}}{2} - \dfrac{y}{2} + 3, \\[3mm] y' = -\dfrac{x}{2} - \dfrac{y\sqrt{3}}{2} - 5, \end{cases}$$

   find $\delta(R)$ and $\delta(S)$ if $R = (2, -3)$ and $S = (-2, 0)$. Also compute the distance RS and the distance $\delta(R)\,\delta(S)$.

   b) Repeat part (a) if $R = (13, -2)$ and $S = (1, 3)$

6. a) Let $R = (2, 1)$, $S = (5, 1)$, and $T = (5, 5)$. Find $\delta(R)$, $\delta(S)$, and $\delta(T)$ for the transformation δ of Exercise 5.

   b) Compute the cosine of the angle TRS.

   c) Compute the cosine of the angle $\delta(T)\,\delta(R)\,\delta(S)$ and compare with the answer in (b). [*Note:* This is a special case of the general theorem that the angle between two lines is invariant under the group of rigid motions.]

7. For the points R, S, T, and $\delta(R)$, $\delta(S)$, and $\delta(T)$ in Exercise 6, compute the area of triangles RST and $\delta(R)\,\delta(S)\,\delta(T)$ and show that they are the same. [*Note:* This is a special case of the general theorem that the area of a triangle is invariant under the group of rigid motions.]

8. a) List three properties, other than those mentioned in the text, of figures which you would expect to be invariant under the group of rigid motions.

   b) Test one of the invariants in (a) in a special case.

5-2   SUBGROUPS OF THE GROUP OF RIGID MOTIONS

The purpose of this section is to investigate the nature of rigid motions by considering three important subgroups of the group E. We will determine what happens to points and sets of points when they are mapped by a rigid motion. So far, we have had formulas which allow us to compute the images of points under specific rigid motions, but we have given no clear picture of what happens to points and figures under an arbitrary rigid motion. In answering questions about the general effect of such transformations, we will be studying elementary geometry. For instance, we will learn that the effect of a rigid motion is to move a figure in the plane in exactly the way plane geometry books describe for testing whether or not two figures are congruent. In this discussion, the properties of groups will play a central role.

The rigid motion ρ with equations (1), below, is of special interest. It is obtained from the general form by setting $A = 0°$, $e = -1$, and $c = d = 0$.

1) Equations of the reflection in the x-axis: $\begin{cases} x' = x, \\ y' = -y. \end{cases}$

This rigid motion is called the *reflection in the x-axis*. The effect of the reflection ρ is to map each point in the plane into the point symmetrical to it with respect to the x-axis. Every point on the x-axis is mapped into itself. The effect of this mapping could be visualized as a rotation of the plane through $180°$ with the x-axis as the axis of the rotation. Figure 5–1 illustrates this mapping for several points.

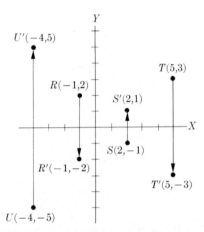

Fig. 5–1.   The reflection in the x-axis.

Theorem 5–3. The set $H = \{\varepsilon, \rho\}$, where ε is the identity transformation and ρ is the reflection in the x-axis, forms a subgroup of the group of rigid motions.

To prove this theorem, we need only note that $\rho^2 = \varepsilon$ to show that the set $\{\varepsilon, \rho\}$ is the cyclic subgroup of E generated by the element ρ. This implies that $\rho^{-1} = \rho$. Throughout the remainder of this section, the symbol H will be used only to designate this subgroup.

The equations for the two elements of H can be combined as in (2) to give a general form,

2) $\begin{cases} x' = x, \\ y' = ey, \end{cases}$

where e is either 1 or -1.   Equations (2) represent ε if $e = 1$ and represent ρ if $e = -1$.

It is interesting to note the effect of the reflection ρ on the vertices of a triangle. We will illustrate this with a single example, but the result noted is true for an arbitrary triangle.   Consider the triangle with vertices $X = (1, 1)$, $Y = (3, 2)$, and $Z = (2, 5)$.   The images of the vertices are $X' = (1, -1)$, $Y' = (3, -2)$, and $Z' = (2, -5)$.   The important fact to note about the image triangle can best be described by imagining that one "walks" around the triangles, proceeding from X to Y to Z in the first case and from X' to Y' to Z' in the second.   (See Fig. 5–2).   In the first case, the interior of the triangle is on the left of the path, and in the second case it is on the right.   We refer to this by saying that the triangle XYZ is changed from *positive orientation* to *negative orientation* by the transformation ρ.

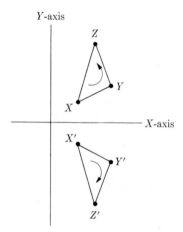

Fig. 5–2.   The effect of reflection on the orientation of a triangle.

The concept of orientation is of special importance in topology, but it is also of interest in analytic geometry.   It appears in the formula for determining the area of a triangle in terms of the coordinates of its vertices.   If $(x_1, y_1), (x_2, y_2)$, and (x_3, y_3) are the coordinates of three points in the plane, the area of the triangle formed is one-half the absolute value of the determinant

$$\begin{vmatrix} x_1 & y_1 & 1 \\ x_2 & y_2 & 1 \\ x_3 & y_3 & 1 \end{vmatrix}$$

This determinant will be positive if the points are listed with positive orientation and negative if the points are listed with negative orientation.

The student of plane geometry has worked with the problem of proving two triangles congruent in cases where they have the same orientation and in other cases where their orientation is opposite.   It is always easier to visually recognize congruent triangles (or similar triangles) when the orientation is the same for both.

We next consider the set of rigid motions whose equations can be expresed in the form of equations (3).   These transformations are called *translations*.

3) Equations of a translation: $\begin{cases} x' = x + a, \\ y' = y + b. \end{cases}$

In equations (3), a and b represent arbitrary real numbers.   These equations are in the form prescribed by the definition of a rigid motion with angle $0°$ and $e = 1$. The effect of a translation on points of the plane is to map each point onto an image point which is located a units to the right and b units above the original point if a and b are positive.   If a is a negative number, then the image point is $|a|$ units to the left of the original point.   Similarly, if b is negative, the image point is $|b|$ units below the original point.   Figure 5–3 shows the effect on four points of the mapping given by the equations $x' = x - 3$ and $y' = y + 1$.

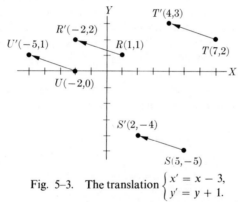

Fig. 5–3.   The translation $\begin{cases} x' = x - 3, \\ y' = y + 1. \end{cases}$

Theorem 5–4.   The set J of all translations forms a subgroup of the group of rigid motions.

Let α and β be any two translations in J, and suppose that they are given by the equations

$$\alpha: \begin{cases} x' = x + c, \\ y' = y + d. \end{cases} \qquad \beta: \begin{cases} x'' = x' + g, \\ y'' = y' + h. \end{cases}$$

Then the transformation $\beta\alpha$ has the equations

$$\beta\alpha: \begin{cases} x'' = x + (c + g), \\ y'' = y + (d + h). \end{cases}$$

Clearly $\beta\alpha$ is an element of J, showing that J is closed with respect to multiplication of transformations.

Associativity holds in all of E, hence in J.   Further, the identity ε is in J since setting both a and b equal to zero in the general equation of a translation gives the equations of ε.

Finally, the inverse of any element in J is in J.   Consider the arbitrary element α of J, with equations given above.   Then α^{-1} has the equations

$$\alpha^{-1}: \quad \begin{cases} x' = x - c, \\ y' = y - d. \end{cases}$$

Since $-c$ and $-d$ are real numbers, α^{-1} is in J.   This completes the proof that J is a subgroup of E.

The final subgroup of E to be discussed is the group of rotations about the origin.   We define a *rotation about the origin* to be a rigid motion whose equations can be written in the form (4).

4)   Equations of a rotation: $\begin{cases} x' = c \cos A - y \sin A, \\ y' = x \sin A + y \cos A. \end{cases}$

Rotations are rigid motions which correspond to the general form given in Section 5–1, with $e = 1$ and with $c = d = 0$.   The effect of a rotation on points in the plane is to shift each point along an arc of a circle with center at the origin, where the distance from a point to its image depends upon the radius of this circle. For each point Q and its image Q', the angle QOQ' is equal to the angle A used to specify the rotation.   Here O is used to represent the origin.   The proof of the preceding statement on the effect of a rotation is commonly given in analytic geometry and will not be repeated here.   Figure 5–4 illustrates the situation for the general point $R = (x, y)$.

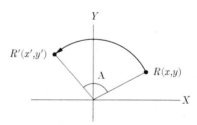

Fig. 5–4.   The rotation $\begin{cases} x' = x \cos A - y \sin A, \\ y' = x \sin A + y \cos A. \end{cases}$

Theorem 5–5.   The set K of all rotations forms a subgroup of the group of rigid motions.

To establish the closure of K, we consider the arbitrary rotations α and β with the equations below.

$$\alpha: \begin{cases} x' = x \cos A - y \sin A, \\ y' = x \sin A + y \cos A. \end{cases} \qquad \beta: \begin{cases} x'' = x' \cos B - y' \sin B, \\ y'' = x' \sin B + y' \cos B. \end{cases}$$

Then the tranformation $\beta\alpha$ has the following equations.

$$\beta\alpha: \begin{cases} x'' = x \cos (A + B) - y \sin (A + B), \\ y'' = x \sin (A + B) + y \cos (A + B). \end{cases}$$

The form of the equations for $\beta\alpha$ shows clearly that $\beta\alpha$ is in K, and hence K is closed with respect to the multiplication of transformations.

Associativity in K follows from associativity in E.   The identity element ε is in K, as we see by specializing the angle A.   If A is taken to be $0°$, the resulting equations are those of ε.

Finally, the inverse of an arbitrary element, say α, of K is given by the following equations.

$$\alpha^{-1}: \begin{cases} x' = x \cos (- A) - y \sin (- A), \\ y' = x \sin (- A) + y \cos (- A). \end{cases}$$

That these equations represent α^{-1} can be checked by direct computation of the products $\alpha\alpha^{-1}$ and $\alpha^{-1}\alpha$, or can be seen intuitively by considering the effect of these products on points in the plane.   This completes the proof that K is a subgroup of E.

One indication of the importance of the subgroups H, J, and K is contained in Theorem 5–6.   The set J of translations is also of interest in analytic geometry in connection with curve sketching.   For instance, the standard method of sketching a conic section whose equation contains no xy-terms is to first reduce the equation to type form by completing the square.   Suppose that the equation of a conic section reduces to

$$\frac{(x - 2)^2}{9} + \frac{(y + 3)^2}{4} = 1.$$

This equation is compared to the standard equation

$$\frac{x'^2}{9} + \frac{y'^2}{4} = 1,$$

an ellipse with center at the origin (in terms of x' and y').   The original curve is located by noting that x, y, x', and y' are related by the equations

$$\begin{cases} x' = x - 2, \\ y' = y + 3. \end{cases}$$

That is, under a translation, one curve can be considered as the image of the other. This information and a knowledge of translations allow the curve to be readily sketched.

Theorem 5–6. If δ is an arbitrary rigid motion, then $\delta = \gamma\beta\alpha$ where α is an element of K, β is an element of H, and γ is an element of J.

The proof of this theorem consists of exhibiting the required factors of an arbitrary rigid motion.   Suppose, then, that δ is any rigid motion.   By definition, the equations for δ can be written as equations (5).

5)
$$\begin{cases} x' = x \cos A - y \sin A + c, \\ y' = ex \sin A + ey \cos A + d. \end{cases}$$

Consider the rigid motions α, β, and γ given below and note that α is in K, β is in H, and γ is in J.

$$\alpha: \begin{cases} x' = x \cos A - y \sin A, \\ y' = x \sin A + y \cos A. \end{cases}$$

$$\beta: \begin{cases} x'' = x', \\ y'' = ey'. \end{cases}$$

$$\gamma: \begin{cases} x''' = x'' + c, \\ y''' = y'' + d. \end{cases}$$

In these equations for α, β, and γ, the constants A, e, c, and d are taken as those in the equations of δ.   Now, direct computation of the equations for $\gamma\beta\alpha$ verifies that $\gamma\beta\alpha = \delta$.   Since this computation is straightforward, it is omitted.   This completes the proof of the theorem.

Theorem 5–6 gives us a means for determining the effect on the points in **P** of a general rigid motion.   Every such motion can be considered as a succession of a rotation about the origin, followed by either a reflection or the identity transformation, followed in turn by a translation.   This provides the simplest intuitive description of rigid motions, and is one which is completely general.

We have used the subgroups of the group of rigid motions primarily to analyze the effect of a rigid motion upon the points of the plane.   It has been suggested that the subgroup of translations has practical uses in the study of analytical geometry.   The same can be said of the subgroup of rotations.   We include a brief discussion of this application for the benefit of future teachers.   More details can be found in books such as Thomas [53] or Wexler [54].

It is proved in texts on analytic geometry that equations of the form

6)
$$Ax^2 + Bxy + Cy^2 + Dx + Ey + F = 0$$

represent conic sections.   It is frequently necessary to identify and sketch the graph of such an equation.   Direct inspection of the equation does not usually suffice, but the application of a suitable rotation to points in the plane simplifies the problem so that the graph can be readily drawn.   The main difficulty in identifying the curve (6) is the presence of the term Bxy.   A rotation can always be chosen so that the new equation of the curve contains no xy-term.

Consider, then, the effect of a rotation α of the plane upon equation (6).   The easiest approach is to substitute into equation (6) the values of x and y given by the equations of the rotation.   Suppose that the equations for α are

$$\alpha: \begin{cases} x' = x \cos M - y \sin M, \\ y' = x \sin M + y \cos M. \end{cases}$$

From the proof of the preceding theorem, we know that solving for x and y in these equations leads to the equations

$$x = x' \cos N - y' \sin N,$$

$$y = x' \sin N + y' \cos N,$$

where the angle N is the negative of the angle M.   If these values for x and y are substituted into equation (6), we obtain the new equation

7) $A'x^2 + B'xy + C'y^2 + D'x + E'y + F' = 0,$

where A', B', C', D', E', and F' are constants involving functions of the angle N. The formulas for these new coefficients are given by (8) below.   The reader may verify these by direct computation.

$$\begin{cases} A' = A \cos^2 N + B \cos N \sin N + C \sin^2 N \\ B' = B(\cos^2 N - \sin^2 N) + 2(C - A) \sin N \cos N \\ C' = A \sin^2 N - B \sin N \cos N + C \cos^2 N \\ D' = D \cos N + E \sin N \\ E' = -D \sin N + E \cos N \\ F' = F \end{cases}$$

These equations are valid for an arbitrary angle N.   Now we wish to choose angle N so that $B' = 0$.   This will enable us to determine by inspection the nature of the graph.   Therefore, we set B' equal to zero and attempt to solve for the angle N.   If we note that

$$\cos^2 N - \sin^2 N = \cos 2N$$

and that

$$2 \sin N \cos N = \sin 2N,$$

we obtain

9) $$\cos 2N = \frac{A - C}{B}.$$

Since we are only interested in this rotation for cases where $B \neq 0$, equation (9) allows us to compute $\cos 2N$, and from it N in all cases of interest.   When N is chosen in this manner, the resulting equation, (7), will contain no xy-term, and its graph can be readily drawn.

   Let us now consider equations (6) and (7) and the relations between the respective coefficients given by equations (8).   We will show that the sum of the coefficients of the two squared terms in the general quadratic equation (6) is an invariant of the group of rotations.   To see this, consider the sum $A' + C'$.   From (8) we have that

$$A' + C' = A(\cos^2 N + \sin^2 N) + B(\cos N \sin N - \cos N \sin N)$$
$$+ C(\sin^2 N + \cos^2 N) = A + C.$$

That is, the sum of coefficients of x^2 and y^2 is unchanged by a rotation.   Hence, this sum is an invariant of the group of rotations.

Finally, we define the quantity $B^2 - 4AC$ to be the *discriminant* of equation (6). That is, the discriminant of such a quadratic equation is the square of the coefficient of the xy-term minus four times the product of the coefficients of the x^2 and the y^2 terms. A lengthy but straightforward computation, using equations (8), shows that $B'^2 - 4A'C' = B^2 - 4AC$. Thus, the discriminant of a quadratic equation in x and y is an invariant of the group of rotations of the plane.

The fact that the discriminant is an invariant of the group of rotations can be put to practical use. Suppose that an equation of the form (6) is given in which $B \neq 0$. We know a rotation can be performed to yield a new equation in which B', the coefficient of the new xy-term, is zero. In this case $B^2 - 4AC = -4A'C'$. Now, if either A' or C' is zero, the curve is clearly a parabola. If A' and C' have the same sign, so that $-4A'C' < 0$, the curve is an ellipse. If A' and C' have opposite signs, so that $-4A'C' > 0$, the curve is an hyperbola. Now, since $-4A'C' = B^2 - 4AC$, this quantity can be computed from the original equation *without* actually performing the rotation. That is, the following test can be used to identify a conic as an ellipse, parabola, or hyperbola.

$$\text{Equation (6) represents} \begin{cases} \text{an hyperbola if } B^2 - 4AC > 0, \\ \text{a parabola if } \quad B^2 - 4AC = 0, \\ \text{an ellipse if } \quad B^2 - 4AC < 0. \end{cases}$$

For example, the discriminant of $3x^2 - 4xy + 2y^2 = 6$ is -8, and hence the curve is an ellipse. The discriminant of $x^2 - 4xy + 2y^2 = 6$ is 8, and hence the curve is an hyperbola. The discriminant of $2x^2 - 4xy + 2y^2 + 1 = 0$ is 0, and hence the curve is a parabola.

The test given above appears to fail in three special cases that should be mentioned. The equation $x^2 - y^2 = 0$ can be written as $(x + y)(x - y) = 0$. In this and all other cases where the left member of equation (6) can be factored, the equation has two lines as its graph. The discriminant test will indicate either an hyperbola (if the lines intersect) or a parabola (if the lines are parallel). These are considered as *degenerate*, or limiting cases of the conic section in question. The equation $x + y + 1 = 0$, or any other linear equation, obviously represents a single straight line. However, if considered as an example of equation (6), with $A = B = C = 0$, the discriminant is zero, indicating a parabola. Again, the graph is referred to as a degenerate parabola. Finally, the equation $x^2 + y^2 + 1 = 0$, or any equation of the form (6) whose left member can be expressed as a sum of squares, one of which is a positive real number, has no real locus. The graph consists of two imaginary lines which cannot be plotted on the real cartesian plane. This is referred to as a degenerate case of the ellipse, and the discriminant test in such a case will indicate an ellipse.

We have seen in the last two sections that the theory of groups is not a sterile subject but is highly significant to the study of geometry. The illustrations given have been restricted to geometry because of the familiarity of the reader with the subject. Group theory plays an equally important role in many other areas of mathematics. Much of the research done in topology during the past few years depends so heavily upon group theory that it is difficult to decide whether the work should be classified as algebra or as topology.

Because of the significance of group theory in all branches of mathematics, it is quite common to find material on groups included in texts designed as enrichment material for high school students. No high school teacher can consider himself well trained if he lacks understanding of at least the definition and simple properties of groups.

EXERCISES

1. Prove directly, without using Theorem 5–2, that the distance between two points is an invariant of the group of translations.

2. Prove that the area of a triangle is invariant under the group of translations. (Use the definition of area in terms of a determinant that was given in this section.)

3. Express each of the following rigid motions as a product $\gamma\beta\alpha$ with α in K, β in H, and γ in J. [*Note:* The identity transformation is an element of all three subgroups and may be used as a factor whenever this is appropriate.]

a) $\begin{cases} x' = -x + 3 \\ y' = -y - 2 \end{cases}$

b) $\begin{cases} x' = -y \\ y' = -x \end{cases}$

c) $\begin{cases} x' = \dfrac{\sqrt{3}}{2}x - \dfrac{1}{2}y + 5 \\ y' = -\dfrac{1}{2}x - \dfrac{\sqrt{3}}{2}y + 2 \end{cases}$

d) $\begin{cases} x' = -\dfrac{\sqrt{2}}{2}x + \dfrac{\sqrt{2}}{2}y - 3 \\ y' = \dfrac{\sqrt{2}}{2}x + \dfrac{\sqrt{2}}{2}y - 5 \end{cases}$

e) $\begin{cases} x' = x + 3 \\ y' = -y - 5 \end{cases}$

f) $\begin{cases} x' = -\dfrac{\sqrt{3}}{2}x - \dfrac{1}{2}y \\ y' = -\dfrac{1}{2}x + \dfrac{\sqrt{3}}{2}y \end{cases}$

4. Describe, in words, the effect on the points in the plane of each of the rigid motions in Exercise 3.

5. Use the discriminant to classify the graph of each of the following equations as an ellipse, parabola, or hyperbola. [*Note:* In the expression $B^2 - 4AC$, A is the coefficient of x^2, B is the coefficient of xy, and C is the coefficient of y^2. Some or all of these constants can be zero.]

a) $x^2 + 2xy + 3y^2 - 6 = 0$
c) $x^2 + 2xy + y^2 - 6 = 0$
e) $x^2 - xy + 5y^2 - 3 = 0$
g) $9x^2 + 12xy + 4y^2 - 1 = 0$

b) $x^2 + 2xy - 6 = 0$
d) $3xy - y^2 + 5x - 2y = 0$
f) $x^2 + xy - 2y^2 + x + 2y = 0$
h) $4x^2 + 9y^2 + 1 = 0$

6. In each of the following cases, determine the rotation necessary to remove the xy-term. In each case find the transformed equation.

a) $x^2 - 2xy + y^2 - 5 = 0$
b) $2x^2 - \sqrt{3}xy + y^2 - 1 = 0$
c) $2x^2 + \sqrt{3}\,xy + y^2 - 1 = 0$
d) $16x^2 + 24xy - 9y^2 + 1 = 0$

7. Prove that the discriminant of a quadratic equation in x and y is an invariant of the group of rotations. [*Hint*: Use equations (8) to evaluate $B'^2 - 4A'C'$ in terms of A, B, and C, and reduce this to $B^2 - 4AC$.]

CHAPTER 6

RINGS AND FIELDS

6-1 FURTHER EXAMPLES OF RINGS

Rings were introduced briefly in Chapter 2 in connection with the study of certain properties of the ring of integers. This was done to avoid the necessity of proving theorems for integers and then repeating the proofs for general rings. In this section, we intend to continue the investigation of rings as abstract mathematical systems.

We will not give an extensive treatment of rings, but some additional material will be of value to a prospective teacher or to a beginning mathematician. (The reader may consult McCoy [39] or Birkhoff and Maclane [25] for further details.) Since all of the number systems that we have studied are rings, with the exception of the set of natural numbers, any results obtained for general rings will apply to these number systems as well. Perhaps the most important benefit from this short section on rings will be what is learned by contrast with the familiar number systems. One begins to appreciate the significance of the properties of numbers only when he studies other systems in which these properties do not hold. A student is apt to take the formulas of the elementary algebra of numbers for granted and to believe that they are universally valid. As a matter of fact, many of these formulas are more the exception than the rule, and hold only in very special cases, such as our number systems.

The reader should begin by reviewing carefully the definition of a ring (Section 2–4) and the elementary theorems concerning rings proved in Sections 2–6 and 2–7. A comparison of the definition of a ring with that of a group suggests that we might rephrase the definition of a ring as follows.

A *ring* is a set R of elements which is closed under two binary operations, addition and multiplication, such that

a) R is an abelian group with respect to the operation of addition,

b) multiplication is associative in R,

c) the right- and left-distributive laws of multiplication over addition hold in R.

Several examples of rings were given in Section 2–4, but it might be of value to consider two additional examples.

Example 6–1. Let R be the set $\{m, n, p, q\}$, with addition and multiplication defined by the following tables.

+	m	n	p	q
m	m	n	p	q
n	n	m	q	p
p	p	q	m	n
q	q	p	n	m

$\cdot$	m	n	p	q
m	m	m	m	m
n	m	n	m	n
p	m	p	m	p
q	m	q	m	q

This set is a ring, but we will not attempt to give a complete proof, since checking associative and distributive laws involves trying all combinations of elements, and this would be quite tedious. The reader is encouraged to check several instances of each law. For example, $n(p + n) = nq = n$, while $np + nn = m + n = n$. This does not prove the distributive law, but illustrates one case in which it holds.

The ring has m as its zero, and has no unity element. (Why?) The ring is not commutative since, for instance, $np = m$ while $pn = p$. The ring has zero divisors, since $np = m$, where m is the zero of the ring.

Example 6–2. Let U be an arbitrary, nonempty set and denote by S the set of all subsets of U. Note that both the set U and the empty set $\varnothing$ are elements of the set S, since each is a subset of U. Let multiplication of sets in S be set intersection, so that $XY = X \cap Y$ for any X and Y in S. We define the sum of two sets X and Y in S as the set of all elements of U which are in X or in Y, *but not in both X and Y.* In set notation

$$X + Y = \{x \mid x \in X \text{ or } x \in Y, \text{ but } x \notin X \cap Y\}.$$

Note that the sum of two sets in S is not the same as the union of these sets unless it happens that they are disjoint sets. In terms of set operations defined earlier, $X + Y = (X \cap Y') \cup (X' \cap Y)$. The Venn diagrams in Fig. 6–1 illustrate the operations of sum and product in S.

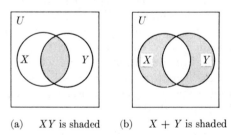

(a) XY is shaded   (b) $X + Y$ is shaded

Fig. 6–1.   Operations in the ring of subsets of the set U.

The set S, whose elements are subsets of U, with the operations defined above, is a commutative ring with unity. The zero of the ring is $\varnothing$, the empty set. The associative law of addition holds and is illustrated by the Venn diagrams in Fig. 6–2. A proof could be constructed by appealing directly to the definition of addition.

For any set X in S, the negative of X is X, since $X + X = \varnothing$, and $\varnothing$ is the zero of the ring. Addition is clearly commutative so that S is an abelian group for addition. The associative law of multiplication and the distributive laws are left to the reader to verify. The unity of S is U, and the operation of multiplication is clearly commutative.

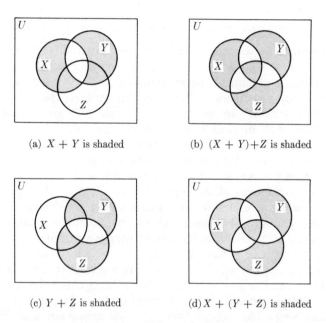

(a) $X + Y$ is shaded

(b) $(X + Y) + Z$ is shaded

(c) $Y + Z$ is shaded

(d) $X + (Y + Z)$ is shaded

Fig. 6–2. Associative law of addition in the set of subsets of U.

The ring S of Example 6–2 is an illustration of a Boolean ring. In general, a *Boolean ring* is a ring in which $x^2 = x$ for every element x of the ring. A Boolean ring is always commutative. These rings are important in the study of symbolic logic.

We defined coefficients and exponents for arbitrary rings in Section 2–7. Many of the computations involved in addition, multiplication, factoring, expanding, solving equations, and other familiar exercises can be carried out in the same way for arbitrary rings as for rings of numbers. However, there are some striking exceptions, and the reader should be careful to perform only those computations which have been shown valid for the ring under consideration.

For example, the factoring of integers is unique (see Section 2–10), but factoring in many rings is not unique. In the ring of Example 6–1, $p = pn$, but also $p = pq$. The property of unique factorization is closely related to the cancellation law, as we may see by carrying the above example a little farther. In the ring R,

$pn = pq$, since each product equals p; p is not the zero of the ring, and yet it is not true that $n = q$.

There are other ways in which some rings differ from rings of numbers that a student familiar only with properties of numbers might consider strange. The well-known formula, $(a + b)^2 = a^2 + 2ab + b^2$, for example, is not valid in every ring. For the ring R of Examples 6–1, consider $(p + q)^2$, which may be evaluated directly from the tables as n. Note that $p + q = n$ and $n^2 = n$. On the other hand,

$$p^2 + 2pq + q^2 = m + 2p + m = 2p = p + p = m.$$

using the definition of exponent and the right-distributive law. Continuing, $(a + b)^2 = a^2 + ab + ba + b^2$, by use of the left-distributive law to simplify the result previously obtained. Since ab does not always equal ba in a ring, we cannot justify writing the sum as $2ab$, and this explains the difficulty with the formula given originally. In the ring of Example 6–2, a still simpler formula holds that is true in all Boolean rings but is not true in general. For such rings $(a + b)^2 = a + b$, since $a + b$ is an element of the ring and by definition of Boolean ring, the square of an element equals the element itself.

As a final example, consider the solution of the equation $(x - n)(x - m) = m$, where m and n are elements of the ring R in Example 6–1. As one might expect, $x = n$ and $x = m$ are solutions of this equation, since m is the zero of R. However, p is also a solution. We can check this by direct computation. We have already shown that each element of R is its own negative, so that $p - n = p + n = q$, and $p - m = p + m = p$. Thus on substitution of p for x in the equation, the left member reduces to qp, which equals m. This verifies that $x = p$ is a solution of the equation. As this example illustrates, solving equations with coefficients chosen from arbitrary rings is quite a different problem from that where the coefficients are numbers. The difficulty here arose because p and q are zero divisors. This situation cannot occur with real numbers, since no real number is a zero divisor.

The rings of Examples 6–1 and 6–2 have a property in common which deserves special attention. For any element x in either ring, the sum $x + x = 2x$ is equal to the zero of the ring.

Definition. The smallest positive integer m, if one exists, such that $ma = 0$ for every element a in a ring is called the *characteristic* of the ring. If no such integer exists, the characteristic is defined to be zero.

The rings of Examples 6–1 and 6–2 have characteristic two. The ring of integers has characteristic zero, since if n is any nonzero integer, $mn \neq 0$ for any integer m. The ring of integers modulo 6 has characteristic six, since $6x = 0$ for every x in the ring. The reader should check that no integer smaller than 6 satisfies this property. For instance, 5 cannot be the characteristic, since $5(2) = 4$ in Z_6 and $4 \neq 0$.

The characteristic of a ring is important because it reflects a property of the additive group of the ring which affects many calculations with ring elements. For instance, in a commutative ring with characteristic two, $(a + b)^2 = a^2 + b^2$ for all a and b in the ring. Many students would appear to believe from answers submitted on test questions that the ring of integers has characteristic two.

It has been pointed out that the cancellation law for multiplication does not hold in all rings. However, if the ring is an integral domain, that is, a commutative ring with unity and with no zero divisors, then the cancellation law holds.

Theorem 6–1 (cancellation law) If a, x, and y are elements of an integral domain such that $ax = ay$ and $a \neq 0$, then $x = y$.

To prove this, suppose that $a \neq 0$ and $ax = ay$ for elements a, x, and y of an integral domain D. Then $ax - ay = 0$, and by the left-distributive law of multiplication over subtraction (see Exercise 6 of Section 3–6) we have that $a(x - y) = 0$. Now D has no zero divisors and $a \neq 0$, so that $x - y = 0$. From this we obtain $x = y$, as was to be proved.

EXERCISES

1. Refer to Example 6–2 and take U to be the set $\{1, 2, 3, 4, 5\}$. Let $X = \{1, 3, 5\}$, $Y = \{1, 2, 3\}$, and $Z = \{3, 4, 5\}$. Find

   a) XY b) $X + Y$ c) $X + Y + Z$
   d) $X^2 + 2Y$ e) $2XY + 3X^2Y$ f) $X(Y + Z)$

2. For the ring of the preceding exercise, show that the set $\{4\}$ is a value of W which satisfies the equation $XW + YW = \emptyset$, but that the set $\{2, 3, 4\}$ is not such a value.

3. Let F be the function given in set notation by

$$F = \{(x, y) \mid y = x^2 - 3x + p\}$$

   considered as a function from R into R, where R is the ring of Example 6–1. Evaluate as a single element of R each of the following. [*Note:* The symbol 3 is an integral coefficient, as defined in Section 2–7.]

   a) $F(m)$ b) $F(n)$ c) $F(p)$ d) $F(q)$
   e) $F(pq)$ f) $F(pn)$ g) $F(p^2 + q)$ h) $F(pq + n^2)$

4. By trial and error, find all solutions in the ring R of Example 6–1 for x in each of the following equations.

   a) $x^2 + px + q = m$ b) $3x + n + qx = m$
   c) $x^3 - 2x^2 = q$ d) $2x^2 + 3x - 2q = m$

5. Find two examples, other than the one in the text, to show that factorization is not unique in the ring R of Example 6–1.

6. Find two examples to show that factorization is not unique in the ring of subsets of the set $U = \{a, b, c, d\}$, using the definitions of addition and multiplication given in Example 6–2. For your answer specify each set mentioned by listing its elements in set notation.

7. For the ring of Exercise 6, find two examples of sets which are zero divisors.

8. For the ring of Example 6–2, using U as an arbitrary set, draw Venn diagrams to illustrate that the following laws hold in S.

   a) The associative law of multiplication.
   b) The left-distributive law for multiplication over addition.
   c) The right-distributive law for multiplication over addition.

9. Show that the set S of Example 6–2 is *not* a ring if multiplication is defined as set intersection ($\cap$) and addition is defined as set union ($\cup$).

10. Find the characteristic of each of the following rings.

    a) The ring of integers modulo 7, with addition and multiplication modulo 7.
    b) The ring of all real numbers, with ordinary addition and multiplication of numbers.
    c) The ring of even integers, with ordinary addition and multiplication of numbers.
    d) The ring of all 2×2 matrices with addition and multiplication of matrices.

6-2   IDEALS IN A RING

In the last chapter, we gave considerable attention to subgroups of a group.   We turn our attention now to subsets of rings that are equally interesting.   A subset of a ring R is called a *subring* of R provided that the subset is a ring with respect to the operations of R.   Not all subrings are of equal importance.   Before examining special types of subrings, we include the following theorem, which gives a simple test to determine whether or not a subset of a ring is a subring.

> **Theorem 6–2.**   A nonempty subset S of a ring R is a subring of R if and only if the following two conditions hold.
>
> a) S is closed under the operations of addition and multiplication defined on R.
>
> b) If $a \in S$, then $-a \in S$.

To prove this theorem, we first assume that a set S is a subring of R.   Since S is a subring, it must contain the zero of the ring and hence is not an empty set. Further, conditions (a) and (b) are required of all rings and hence must be satisfied by S.

Next, assume that S is a nonempty subset of the ring R satisfying (a) and (b). We will show that S is a subring.   Referring to the definition in Section 2–4, properties (1) and (6) are guaranteed by condition (a).   Since S is a subset of the ring R, properties (2), (5), (7), and (8), which hold in R, must also hold in S. Condition (b) is identical to property (4), and we need only prove that property (3) holds.   Since S is not empty, S contains at least one element, say x.   By condition (b), $-x$ is also in S.   Since by (a), S is closed under addition, $x + (-x)$ is an element of S.   But $x + (-x) = \mathbf{0}$, so that S contains the zero of the ring R. This completes the proof that S is a ring with respect to the operations of R, and is therefore a subring of R.

The most important subrings of a ring are known as *ideals*.   Three kinds of ideals are described in the following definition.

Definition. (a) A subset N of a ring R is a *left ideal* in R if and only if it is a subring of R such that $rx \in N$ for every $r \in R$ and every $x \in N$.

b) A subset M of a ring R is a *right ideal* in R if and only if it is a subring of R such that $xr \in M$ for every $r \in R$ and every $x \in M$.

c) A subset P of a ring R is an *ideal* (also a *two-sided ideal*) in R if and only if it is both a left ideal and a right ideal.

Note that the condition for a subset to be a left ideal (similarly, a right ideal, or an ideal) differs from the condition for it to be a subring only by a stronger closure property.   To be a subring, a subset S must satisfy the condition that $xy \in S$ for every $x \in S$ and $y \in S$.   For S to be a left ideal it is required that $rx \in S$ for *every* $r \in R$ and every $x \in S$.   This replaces the closure property with a stronger one which includes the other as a special case.   A proof that a subset S is a left ideal in a ring R would contain the proof that (a) $S \ne \varnothing$ (b) S is closed under addition; (c) for each $x \in S$, $-x \in S$; and (d) $rx \in S$ for every $r \in R$, $x \in S$.

Example 6–3. The subset $S = \{m, p\}$ of the ring $R = \{m, n, p, q\}$ given in Example 6–1 of Section 6–1 is an ideal in R.

To prove this, we note that $S \ne \varnothing$.   Then to show closure for addition, we examine the four possible sums, $m + m = m$, $p + p = m$, $m + p = p$, and $p + m = p$.   We note that each sum is an element of S.   Next, since $-m = m$ and $-p = p$, the negative of each element of S is in S.   Finally, we check that each of the products rx, for $r \in R$ and $x \in S$, is an element of S.   These products are mm, nm, pm, qm, mp, nq, pp, and qp.   Each product equals m, an element of S.   This proves that S is a left ideal.   To show that S is also a right ideal, we check the products xr for $x \in S$ and $r \in R$.   Since $mm = m$, $mn = m$, $mp = m$, $mq = m$, $pm = m$, $pn = p$, $pp = m$, and $pq = p$, each such product is either m or p, both of which are elements of S.   This shows that S is also a right ideal and hence S is an ideal.

Of course, if a ring is commutative, then every left ideal is also a right ideal. Why?

Example 6–4. The set N of all 2×2 matrices of the form

$$\begin{pmatrix} a & 0 \\ b & 0 \end{pmatrix}$$

for a, b integers is a left ideal but not a right ideal in the ring R of all 2×2 matrices with integers as elements.   That is, N is the subset of R consisting of those elements whose second column contains only zeros.

To show that N is a left ideal, we note that

$$\begin{pmatrix} 1 & 0 \\ 1 & 0 \end{pmatrix}$$

is a matrix in N, so that N is not empty.   Then if

$$A = \begin{pmatrix} a & 0 \\ b & 0 \end{pmatrix} \quad \text{and} \quad B = \begin{pmatrix} c & 0 \\ d & 0 \end{pmatrix}$$

are matrices in N, the sum,

$$A + B = \begin{pmatrix} a + c & 0 \\ b + d & 0 \end{pmatrix},$$

is also a matrix in N so that the set is closed under addition.   The negative of an arbitrary element A, as written above, is the matrix

$$\begin{pmatrix} -a & 0 \\ -b & 0 \end{pmatrix},$$

another element of N.   Finally, if

$$U = \begin{pmatrix} w & x \\ y & z \end{pmatrix}$$

is any element of R, and

$$A = \begin{pmatrix} a & 0 \\ b & 0 \end{pmatrix}$$

is any element of N, then the product $U A$ is

$$\begin{pmatrix} w & x \\ y & z \end{pmatrix}\begin{pmatrix} a & 0 \\ b & 0 \end{pmatrix} = \begin{pmatrix} wa + xb & 0 \\ ya + zb & 0 \end{pmatrix},$$

which is an element in N.   This proves that N is a left ideal.   It is *not* a right ideal, since

$$\begin{pmatrix} 1 & 0 \\ 1 & 0 \end{pmatrix} \text{ is in } N, \quad \begin{pmatrix} 1 & 2 \\ 0 & 1 \end{pmatrix} \text{ is in } R,$$

and yet the product

$$\begin{pmatrix} 1 & 2 \\ 1 & 2 \end{pmatrix} \text{ is not in } N.$$

Example 6–5. If n is a fixed integer, the set P of integers given by

$$P = \{mn \mid m \text{ is an integer}\}$$

is an ideal in the ring of all integers.

We note that P contains the elements $0 = 0 \cdot n$, $n = 1 \cdot n$, $-n = (-1)n$, and, in fact, is the set $\{0, \pm n, \pm 2n, \pm 3n, \ldots\}$.   We speak of P as the set of all integral multiples of n.   The set P is clearly not empty.   It is closed for addition, since if s and t are integers, so that $sn \in P$ and $tn \in P$, then

$$sn + tn = (s + t)n \in P.$$

The negative of each element of P is in P, since $-(mn) = (-m)n$ for each integer m. The set P is a left ideal, since for any $mn \in P$ and integer s, $s(mn) = (sm)n$. But sm is an integer so that $(sm)n \in P$. By the commutative law, P is also a right ideal and hence is an ideal in the ring of integers.

The theory of left ideals (or equally, the theory of right ideals) is of considerable interest in advanced mathematics and a wealth of material appears in the literature on the subject. However, most of the ideals which are of interest in elementary mathematics and which are related to topics covered in high school subjects are two-sided ideals. Consequently, we will confine our attention in sections that follow to two-sided ideals, which we will refer to simply as ideals.

In three-dimensional analytic geometry, a line, or any other curve in space, is specified by two equations. Each such equation represents a surface in space, and the points which lie on both surfaces have coordinates satisfying both equations simultaneously. The curve represented by the equations is the curve of intersection of the two surfaces. Where the curve is a straight line, one customarily uses two planes to determine the line. There is, of course, nothing unique about the surfaces used to represent a given curve. There are, in general, an infinite number of surfaces which pass through a given curve, and many different pairs of these surfaces could be selected to represent the curve. If one desires uniqueness in the expression for curves in space, one is naturally led to consideration of ideal theory.

We will prove in Chapter 7 that the set of all polynomials whose coefficients are real numbers forms a ring. Now consider a specific curve C in space. We say that C lies on a surface provided that every point of C is a point on the surface. It can be shown that the set $S = \{f(x) \mid f(x)$ is a polynomial and that C lies on the surface $f(x) = 0\}$ is an ideal in the ring of all polynomials. One could therefore use the ideal S to represent the curve, rather than use two particular elements of S, as is customarily done. The advantage would lie in the fact that S is uniquely determined by the curve C, and conversely. These comments will not be verified, but are included to illustrate a relatively simple situation in geometry where ideal theory is of interest.

EXERCISES

1. Prove that the set S of all 2×2 matrices of the form

$$\begin{pmatrix} a & 0 \\ 0 & b \end{pmatrix},$$

   with a and b integers, forms a subring of the ring R of all 2×2 matrices having integers as elements.

2. Prove that the set S of the preceding problem is neither a right ideal nor a left ideal in R.

3. Prove that the set P of all integers which are multiples of 7, including 0, is an ideal in the ring of all integers.

4. Find two right ideals, neither of which is a left ideal, in the ring R of Example 6–1.

5. Prove that the zero element of any ring R, considered as a set with one element, is an ideal in R.

6. Prove that the subset of all matrices of the form

$$\begin{pmatrix} a & b \\ 0 & 0 \end{pmatrix}$$

is a right ideal, but not a left ideal, in the ring R of all 2×2 matrices with integers as elements.

6-3   PRINCIPAL IDEALS IN COMMUTATIVE RINGS WITH UNITY

In discussing subgroups of a group, we discovered that the simplest, or smallest, subgroup containing a given element of the group was the subgroup of all powers of this element. Each power of the element had to belong to the subgroup in order that it be closed, and the set of all powers formed a subgroup, which was therefore the smallest subgroup containing the given element. We called this the subgroup generated by the element.

We can make a similar study for rings. That is, we can inquire as to the nature of the smallest ideal which contains a given element of the ring. This question might be asked about arbitrary rings, but we will restrict the discussion to commutative rings with unity. In these rings the ideals have a particularly simple form, and they are the rings which occur most frequently in elementary mathematics.

Theorem 6–3. If a is an element in a commutative ring R with unity, then the set $N = \{ra \,|\, r \in R\}$ is an ideal in R. Further, if M is an ideal in R and $a \in M$, Then $N \subseteq M$.

To prove this theorem, we first show that N is nonempty. Since R is a ring with unity, R contains at least one element, the unity of the ring. Then $1a = a$ is an element in N and $N \neq \varnothing$.

Next we show that N is closed under addition. Suppose that ra and sa are any two elements of N. Then $ra + sa = (r + s)a$ by the right-distributive law in R. But $r + s$ is an element of R so that $(r + s)a \in N$ by the definition of N. Hence $ra + sa \in N$ and N is closed under addition.

To show that the negative of each element of N is in N, consider an arbitrary element ra in N. The negative of ra is $-ra$, and by theorems in Section 3–6, $-ra = (-r)a$. Since $-r \in R$, $(-r)a$ is an element in N, as we wished to prove.

We show next that N is a left ideal in R. Let ra be any element of N and let s be any element of R. Then $s(ra) = (sr)a$ by the associative law in R. Thus $sr \in R$, since R is closed under multiplication, so that $(sr)a$ is an element in N. This shows that N is a left ideal in R. From the fact that R is commutative, N is also a right ideal in R. This completes the proof that N is an ideal.

Now suppose that M is any ideal such that $a \in M$. By the definition of a right ideal, $ra \in M$ for every $r \in R$. But $N = \{ra \mid r \in R\}$, so that $N \subseteq M$. This means that N is the smallest ideal in R which contains the element a.

Definition. The ideal N of Theorem 6–3 is called the *principal ideal* generated by the element a. A ring in which every ideal is a principal ideal is called a *principal ideal ring*.

Example 6–5 involved the principal right ideal in the ring of integers consisting of all multiples of a fixed integer m. It has not yet been shown that every ideal in the ring of integers is of this form. That is, the ring of integers is a principal ideal ring, as shown in the following theorem.

Theorem 6–4. The ring of integers is a principal ideal ring.

Let M be any ideal in the ring of integers. We will show that M is a principal ideal. If M contains only the zero element, then $M = \{m \cdot 0 \mid m$ is an integer$\}$ and is therefore a principal ideal consisting of all multiples of zero. Hence the theorem is true in this case.

In any other case, M contains at least one nonzero integer, say a. Since $a \neq 0$, by the law of trichotomy (see Section 2–2), either $a < 0$ or $0 < a$. If $0 < a$, then M contains a positive integer, namely a. If $a < 0$, then $-a > 0$. Since M is an ideal, $-a \in M$, and M contains the positive integer $-a$. In either case the set of positive integers in M is not empty. Denote this set by M'. By the well-ordering principle (Section 2–1), M' contains a smallest positive integer, which we will call s. We intend to show that M is the principal ideal generated by s. Denote this principal ideal by N.

Suppose that n is any integer in M. Then by the division algorithm (see Section 2–8) there exist integers q and r such that $n = qs + r$ with $0 < r < s$. Assume, in order to lead to a contradiction, that $r \neq 0$. Then $r = n - qs$. But $n \in M$ and $s \in M$. By the closure property of multiplication for ideals, $qs \in M$, and by the property (b) of Theorem 6–2, $-qs \in M$. Since r is the sum of n and $-qs$, the closure property for addition requires that $r \in M$. Now $r < s$ and r is positive, and yet s was the smallest positive element of M, an absurdity. Hence our assumption that $r \neq 0$ leads to a contradiction, which means that $r = 0$. But $r = 0$ implies that $n = qs$. That is, n is an element of the principal ideal N generated by s. Since n was an arbitrary integer in M, $M \subseteq N$. By the second part of Theorem 6–3, $N \subseteq M$, and these two statements imply that $N = M$. That it, M is a principal ideal, as we were to prove.

Since M was an arbitrary ideal in the ring of integers, we have shown that the ring of integers is a principal ideal ring.

Note that the proof of this theorem was based on the application of the well-ordering principle and the division algorithm. This proof illustrates the value of such properties of the integers in proving further theorems. It is unfortunate that not all rings share these two properties with the ring of integers. It is not reasonable, then, to expect that every ring is a principal ideal ring. Although we will not prove it, the ring of 2×2 matrices is not a principal ideal ring.

EXERCISES

1. Find a principal ideal in the ring of all integers.

2. Find a principal ideal in the ring R of subsets of the set $U = \{1, 2, 3, 4, 5\}$ (with operations of multiplication and addition as in Example 6–2, Section 6–1) which contains more than one element and is not the entire ring R.

3. Find a principal ideal in the ring Z_{12} of integers modulo 12 (with addition and multiplication modulo 12) which contains more than one element and is not all of Z_{12}.

4. Show that the only ideals in Z_5 are the ideals consisting of the zero element alone and the entire ring Z_5.

5. Find a principal ideal in the ring of all 2×2 matrices with integers as elements which contains more than one element and is not the entire ring of matrices.

6. If a is an element of a ring R which is not commutative, then the set $\{ra \mid r \in R\}$ is not necessarily an ideal.   Explain what requirement for an ideal may not be satisfied.

7. Find an example, in the ring R of all 2×2 matrices having integers as elements, of a matrix A such that $\{XA \mid X \in R\}$ is a left ideal but not a right ideal.   [*Hint:* Review Example 6–4].   Give proof that your example satisfies the required conditions.

8. Prove that the set S of 2×2 matrices of the form

$$\begin{pmatrix} r & 0 \\ 0 & 0 \end{pmatrix},$$

where r may be any real number, forms a subring of the ring R of all 2×2 matrices with real numbers as elements.

9. Prove that the subring S of Exercise 8 is neither a left ideal nor a right ideal in R.

6-4   FIELDS

A field has been previously defined as a commutative ring with unity in which every nonzero element has an inverse.   The fields of most interest in elementary mathematics are fields of numbers.   However, there are many other fields, some of which contain only a finite number of elements.   The following theorem describes some of these finite fields.

Theorem 6–5.   If p is a positive prime integer, then Z_p, the ring of integers modulo p, is a field.

We have already shown that Z_n is a ring for any $n \in Z^+$.   We will assume, then, that Z_p is a ring.   Multiplication is clearly commutative in Z_p and 1 is the unity of the ring.   We will prove next that any element, $m \neq 0$ in Z_p has an inverse.   Since p is a prime, m and p have 1 as their greatest common divisor.   By Theorem 2–15, there exist integers s and t such that $1 = sm + tp$.   Now s is not necessarily an integer in Z_p.   In fact, s might even be negative.   However, $s = qp + r$ for integers q and r, where $0 < r < p$.   That is, $r \in Z_p$.   Replacing s in the equation $1 = sm + tp$ by $s = qp + r$, we have that $1 = (pq + r)m + tp$, or that $rm = 1 - (qm + t)p$.   Consider the product rm in Z_p, where this represents multiplication modulo p.   By the preceding equation, we see that as a product in Z_p, $rm = 1$, since we disregard multiples of p in performing this operation. Hence r is the inverse of m. This shows that every nonzero element of Z_p has an inverse and hence that Z_p is a field.

It can be noted also that if n is not a prime, then Z_n is not a field. We will not prove this result, but recall that in Z_6 the elements 2, 3, and 4 had no inverses. It can be shown that in Z_n an integer has an inverse if and only if it is relatively prime to n. If $n = st$ for integers s and t, then at least s and t will fail to have inverses in Z_n.

The definition of a field prescribes properties of two binary operations, addition and multiplication. The familiar operations of subtraction and division may be introduced in either of two ways. We mention them both, but hereafter will use the second definition only. First, one might say that for elements a and b in a field F, $a - b = c$ if and only if $b + c = a$. While this is correct, it has the disadvantage of being a nonconstructive definition. That is, it does not give a method for computation, but depends upon a thorough knowledge of the addition tables in a field. Suppose, for instance, that F is a field with infinitely many elements. In attempting to compute $a - b$, it is necessary to check each sum of the form $b + x$ for $x \in F$ until an element x is found for which $b + x = a$. Similarly, one could say that $a \div b = d$, where $b \neq 0$, if and only if $bd = a$. The same comment applies. Consequently, we adopt an alternative definition which provides a formula for computation.

Definition. The binary operations of subtraction $(-)$ and division $(\div)$ are defined in a field F by

$$a - b = a + (-b) \quad \text{for every } a \text{ and } b \text{ in } F.$$

$$a \div b = ab^{-1} \quad \text{for every } a \text{ in } F \text{ and every } b \neq 0 \text{ in } F.$$

Since every element b in F has a unique negative, $-b$, and every nonzero element b has a unique inverse, b^{-1}, these operations are uniquely defined. The symbol a/b will be used interchangeably with $a \div b$.

Integral multiples of field elements and of integral powers of field elements have already been defined, since a field is a ring. (See Section 2–7.) Negative exponents have meaning for nonzero field elements, since inverses of such elements exist.

Example 6–6. Consider the field Z_5, with addition and multiplication modulo 5. We will evaluate $2 - 4$, $\frac{3}{4}$, and 3^{-2}.

$$2 - 4 = 2 + (-4) = 2 + 1 = 3,$$
$$\tfrac{3}{4} = 3 \div 4 = 3 \cdot 4^{-1} = 3 \cdot 4 = 2,$$
$$3^{-2} = (3^{-1})^2 = 2^2 = 4.$$

The reader should carefully check these numerical calculations to be sure that he understands the reason for each step.

Example 6–7. The set F of real numbers of the form $a + b\sqrt{2}$, where a and b are rational numbers, is a field.

Since the set F is a subset of the ring of real numbers, it can be shown to be a ring by using Theorem 6–2. Thus $S \neq \varnothing$, since $1 + 1\sqrt{2}$ is an element of S. If $x = a + b\sqrt{2}$ and $y = c + d\sqrt{2}$ are any two elements of S, $x + y = (a + c) + (b + d)\sqrt{2}$. This is an element of F since $a + c$ and $b + d$ are rational numbers. Why? Further,

$$xy = (ac + 2bd) + (bc + ad)\sqrt{2}$$

is in F, since $ac + 2bd$ and $bc + ad$ are rational numbers. Hence F is closed for addition and multiplication. For any element $a + b\sqrt{2}$ of F, the negative is $-a + (-b)\sqrt{2}$, and this is an element of F. Hence S is a ring.

Multiplication is commutative in F and 1 is the unity element of F, since 1 can be written as $1 + 0\sqrt{2}$. The inverse of an element $a + b\sqrt{2}$ is $1/(a + b\sqrt{2})$ if $a + b\sqrt{2} \neq 0$. We need to show that this is an element of F. Multiplying numerator and denominator of the fraction by $a - b\sqrt{2}$, we have that

$$(a + b\sqrt{2})^{-1} = \frac{a - b\sqrt{2}}{a^2 - 2b^2} = \frac{a}{a^2 - 2b^2} + \frac{-b}{a^2 - 2b^2}\sqrt{2}.$$

This is the correct form for elements of F provided that

$$\frac{a}{a^2 - 2b^2} \quad \text{and} \quad \frac{-b}{a^2 - 2b^2}$$

are rational numbers. The fractions are clearly rational numbers unless $a^2 - 2b^2$ is zero. But we have shown in Section 3–4 that $\sqrt{2}$ is not a rational number, hence it is impossible that $a^2 - 2b^2 = 0$. Otherwise, $2 = a^2/b^2$ and $\sqrt{2} = a/b$, a contradiction. This completes the proof that every nonzero element of F has an inverse in F and hence F is a field.

Example 6–8. In the field F of Example 6–7, let $x = 3 + 2\sqrt{2}$ and $y = 4 - 3\sqrt{2}$. Find $x \div y$ and y^{-3}.

First,

$$y^{-1} = \frac{1}{4 - 3\sqrt{2}} = \frac{4 + 3\sqrt{2}}{16 - 18} = -2 - \frac{3}{2}\sqrt{2}.$$

Then $x \div y = xy^{-1} = -12 - \frac{17}{2}\sqrt{2}$. Further,

$$y^{-3} = (y^{-1})^3 = -35 - \frac{99}{4}\sqrt{2}.$$

Example 6–9. Solve the equation $3x + 4 = 3$, considered as an equation with coefficients in Z_5, with all operations modulo 5.

First, we subtract 4 from both members of the equation. Since $-4 = 1$, we do this by adding 1 to each member, giving $3x = 4$. Next, we divide both sides by 3. Since division is defined as multiplication by the inverse and $3^{-1} = 2$ in Z_5, we multiply both members by 2. This leaves the solution $x = 3$. Of course, in this simple case the solution could be found by trial and error, since there are only five elements in Z_5 as possible solutions. The method shown here is more instructive, since the same steps would work in any field.

EXERCISES

1. Compute the following in the field Z_{11}.

a) $3 - 10$ b) $2 - 7$ c) $3 \div 5$

d) $\frac{5}{7}$ e) $-\frac{1}{2}$ f) $-\frac{2}{3}$

g) $(3^2)(9^{-3})$ h) 6^{-5} i) $(5 - 7)/(3 - 9)$

j) $\frac{1}{2} + \frac{2}{3} - \frac{1}{5}$ k)
$$\cfrac{1}{1 + \cfrac{1}{1 + \cfrac{1}{1 + 3}}}$$

2. Consider the field F of Example 6–7. Reduce each of the following to the form $a + b\sqrt{2}$ for a and b rational numbers and thus show that each is an element of F.

a) $(2 - 7\sqrt{2}) - (3 + 2\sqrt{2})$ b) $(2 + 5\sqrt{2})(3 - 2\sqrt{2})$

c) $(1 - 3\sqrt{2})^{-1}$ d) $(8 + 5\sqrt{2})^{-2}$

e) $(3 - 7\sqrt{2}) \div (6 + 3\sqrt{2})$ f) $(2 + 3\sqrt{2})^{-1} \div (5 - 4\sqrt{2})^{-1}$

3. Solve the following equations in Z_{11}. Interpret all operations as operations modulo 11. Carry out solutions, using properties of fields. Do not solve merely by trial and error.

a) $8 + x = 2$ b) $7x = 5$

c) $3x - 4 = 9x + 3$ d) $3x - (2 - 7x) = 5$

4. Solve the following equations in the field F of Example 6–7.

a) $(13 - 5\sqrt{2}) + x = 6\sqrt{2}$ b) $(-2 + \sqrt{2})x = 7 - 5\sqrt{2}$

c) $(11 - \sqrt{2})x = (9 + 3\sqrt{2})x - (5 + 4\sqrt{2})$

5. List all integers in Z_{15} which are relatively prime to 15. Find the inverse (relative to multiplication modulo 15) of each of these elements.

6. List all elements in Z_{15} which do not have inverses relative to multiplication modulo 15. Compare this set with the list in Exercise 5.

7. Prove that the set, $S = \{a + b\sqrt[3]{2} \mid a \text{ and } b \text{ are rational numbers}\}$, is not a field under addition and multiplication of numbers.

8. Prove that the set, $T = \{a + b\sqrt{5} \mid a \text{ and } b \text{ are rational numbers}\}$, is a field under addition and multiplication of numbers.

9. Let R be the set of all real numbers, and define the operations $\oplus$ (addition) and $\odot$ (multiplication) on R by $a \oplus b = a + b - 1$, and $a \odot b = a + b - ab$ for real numbers a and b. Prove that the set R is a field with respect to these operations.

6-5   SUBFIELDS AND EXTENSIONS

After the discussion of subgroups and subrings in earlier sections, it should not come as a surprise to the reader that we mention subfields.   As would be expected, a subset of a field K is a *subfield of* K if and only if the subset forms a field with respect to the operations of multiplication and addition defined in K.   In Example 6–7 we proved that the set F of all real numbers of the form $a + b\sqrt{2}$, for a and b rational numbers, is a field, and F is a subfield of the field of real numbers.   The field of all rational numbers is, in turn, a subfield of F.   It is not true, however, that the field Z_5 of integers modulo 5 is a subfield of the real numbers.   It is not a subfield because the operations in it are different from those in the set of real numbers.   For example, the sum of 3 and 2 is 0 in Z_5, while in the field of real numbers, the sum of 3 and 2 is 5.

When two fields F and K are related so that F is a subfield of K, we say that K is an *extension field* of F.   Thus the field,

$$F = \{a + b\sqrt{2} \,|\, a \text{ and } b \text{ are rational numbers}\},$$

is an extension field of the field of rational numbers.   The field of all real numbers is an extension field of F and also an extension field of the rational numbers.

An interesting problem in the study of fields is that of determining the structure of certain types of extensions of a given field.   We do not propose to consider the general case, which is beyond the scope of this course.   However, we will consider a special case that will give some insight into the problem.

Definition.   Let F be a subfield of a field K, and let c be an element of K.   The smallest subfield of K which contains c and contains F as a subfield is called the *extension of* F *formed by adjunction of* c.   We write this field $F(c)$.

Example 6–10.   The field F of Example 6–7 is the extension of the field of rational numbers formed by the adjunction of $\sqrt{2}$.   If the rational field is designated by $\mathbf{Q}$, then $F = \mathbf{Q}(\sqrt{2})$.   To prove that F is the smallest field containing both $\sqrt{2}$ and the set $\mathbf{Q}$, suppose that H is any field which contains $\mathbf{Q}$ and $\sqrt{2}$.   Every number of the form $a + b\sqrt{2}$, for a and b rational numbers, must be an element of H.   To see this, we note first that if b is any rational number, then b and $\sqrt{2}$ are in H, by definition of H.   The fact that H is closed under multiplication implies that $b\sqrt{2}$ must be an element of H.   For any $a \in \mathbf{Q}$, we have required that $a \in H$, since $\mathbf{Q}$ is a subset of H.   Then $a + b\sqrt{2}$ must be an element of H, since H is closed under addition.   Thus every element of F is an element of H, which means that $F \subseteq H$.   Since H was an arbitrary field satisfying the given conditions, this shows that F is the smallest such field.   That is, $F = \mathbf{Q}(\sqrt{2})$, as we wished to prove.

The element $\sqrt{2}$ in Example 6–10 is a root of the equation $x^2 - 2 = 0$, an equation whose coefficients are all elements of $\mathbf{Q}$.   It is not a coincidence that all elements of $\mathbf{Q}(\sqrt{2})$ can be expressed in the form $a + b\sqrt{2}$, with a and b in $\mathbf{Q}$.   It can be shown that if we adjoin to $\mathbf{Q}$ a root of *any* quadratic equation having coefficients in **Q**, then the elements of **Q**(r), where r is the root adjoined, may be expressed as $a + br$ for a and b in **Q**.

Now consider the next example in which we adjoin the root of a cubic equation whose coefficients are in **Q**. The equation is $x^3 - 2 = 0$, and the root adjoined is $\sqrt[3]{2}$.

Example 6–11. The field **Q**($\sqrt[3]{2}$) consists of all elements of the form $a + b\sqrt[3]{2} + c\sqrt[3]{4}$, where a, b, and c are numbers in **Q**.

Let us designate by J the set of all elements of the form $a + b\sqrt[3]{3} + c\sqrt[3]{4}$ for a, b, and c in **Q**. The set J is not empty since $1 + 2\sqrt[3]{2} + 3\sqrt[3]{4}$ is an element in J. The sum of two elements in J is easily seen to be an element of J. Let

$$a + b\sqrt[3]{2} + c\sqrt[3]{4} \quad \text{and} \quad x + y\sqrt[3]{2} + z\sqrt[3]{4}$$

be any two elements of J, which means that a, b, c, x, y, and z are any rational numbers. Then the product of these elements is

$$(ax + 2cy + 2bz) + (bx + ay + 2cz)\sqrt[3]{2} + (xc + by + az)\sqrt[3]{4},$$

which is another element of J. This shows that J is closed under multiplication. The negative of an element in J is clearly in J, so that J is a subring of the real numbers. Further, J is a commutative ring, since multiplication is commutative for all real numbers. The unity 1 is in J, since 1 may be written as

$$1 = 1 + 0 \cdot \sqrt[3]{2} + 0 \cdot \sqrt[3]{4}.$$

Further, if

$$w = a + b\sqrt[3]{2} + c\sqrt[3]{4}$$

is a nonzero number in J, then

$$w^{-1} = \frac{(a^2 - 2bc)}{D} + \frac{(2c^2 - ab)}{D}\sqrt[3]{2} + \frac{(b^2 - ac)}{D}\sqrt[3]{4},$$

where $D = a^3 + 2b^3 + 4c^3 - 6abc$. Note that w^{-1} is an element of J, although proving that $D \neq 0$ to show that the fractions are defined is nontrivial. The reader is encouraged to show that the product ww^{-1} equals 1, to verify that w^{-1} is the inverse of w. We will omit the steps of this computation. It would also be a good idea to compute D in several numerical examples to show that at least in these cases, $D \neq 0$. The element w^{-1} would not exist for any number for which the quantity D is zero, since one cannot divide by zero. The general proof that D is never zero is too difficult for inclusion here.

This discussion has shown that J is a field (except for the step in the proof we omitted). If we accept this fact, then it is easy to see that J must be the smallest field containing **Q** as a subfield and containing $\sqrt[3]{2}$. By closure properties of a field any field must at least contain all elements of J. Hence $J = R(\sqrt[3]{2})$.

Note that when we adjoined to $\mathbf{Q}$ the root $\sqrt[3]{2}$ of the cubic equation $x^3 - 2 = 0$, the elements of the new field were of the form $a + b\sqrt[3]{2} + c(\sqrt[3]{2})^2$, since $\sqrt[3]{4} = (\sqrt[3]{2})^2$. This expression involves both first and second powers of the root adjoined.   It can be shown that if r is a root of an equation of nth degree whose coefficients are in $\mathbf{Q}$, then

$$\mathbf{Q}(r) = \{a_0 + a_1 r + a_2 r^2 + \cdots + a_{n-1} r^{n-1} \mid a_0, a_1, \ldots a_{n-1} \in \mathbf{Q}\}.$$

We will not prove this theorem, although the preceding examples make the statement seem plausible.

Before concluding this chapter, we should consider still one further type of extension.   In Section 3–1 we extended the set of integers to the field of rational numbers.   This same extension can be made for a wide class of structures, as indicated in the following theorem.

Theorem 6–6. If D is an integral domain, then there exists a field F which contains a subset D' isomorphic to D.

We call the smallest field which contains a subset isomorphic to D the *field of quotients of D*.

The proof of this theorem is identical to the proof for the case of integers given in Section 3–1.   The only properties of the integers which were used in the proof were those that hold in every integral domain.   Hence a proof here could be written by copying the former proof and simply replacing the word "integer" by the phrase "element of the integral domain D" whenever the word appeared. Thus we would begin by forming pairs (a, b) of elements of D, with $b \neq 0$.   Next we would define an equivalence relation $\sim$ for pairs by $(a, b) \sim (c, d)$ if and only if $ad = bc$.   The equivalence sets $[a, b]$ would be the elements of the field F, as before.   Addition and multiplication would be defined in F by

$$[a, b] + [c, d] = [ad + bc, bd] \qquad \text{and} \qquad [a, b][c, d] = [ac, bd].$$

The proof that F is a field and contains a subset D' isomorphic to D would proceed exactly as in the case of the integers.   We omit here the details of the proof, but the reader is encouraged to study the former proof to justify the statements above.

EXERCISES

1. Find an extension field of the field of rational numbers (other than the examples in the text) which is a subfield of the field of real numbers.

2. Let i be the imaginary unit, that is, $i^2 = -1$, as defined in Section 3–7.   Prove that the set, $S = \{a + bi \mid a \text{ and } b \text{ are rational numbers}\}$, is a subfield of the field of complex numbers and is an extension field of the field of rational numbers.

7. Prove that the field S of Exercise 2 is neither a subfield nor an extension field of the field of all real numbers.

9. Is the field Z_5 a subfield of the field Z_7?   Justify your answer.

5. a) In Example 6–11, a formula for the inverse of an element in the field J was given. Use this formula to find the inverse of the number $x = 2 - \sqrt[3]{2} + 3\sqrt[3]{4}$. Check your answer by computing xx^{-1}. The product should be 1, of course.

   b) Compute the quantity D, which appears in the formula, for several numbers in J and note that in each case $D \neq 0$.

6. In Example 6–11, the statement is made that any field containing all rational numbers and also containing $\sqrt[3]{2}$ must contain every number of the form $a + b\sqrt[3]{2} + c\sqrt[3]{4}$, where a, b, and c are rational numbers. Prove this statement.

7. Let D be an integral domain, and let S be the set,

$$S = \{(a, b) \mid a \text{ and } b \text{ are elements of } D \text{ and } b \neq 0\}.$$

In the construction of the field of quotients for D, the relation $\sim$ is defined on S by $(a, b) \sim (c, d)$ if and only if $ad = bc$. Prove that this is an equivalence relation. [*Hint:* Refer to the proof in Section 3–1 for the case where D is the set of integers.]

8. Referring to Exercise 7, denote the equivalence set containing (a, b) by $[a, b]$. Let $Q = \{[a, b] \mid (a \ b) \in S\}$. Prove that Q is a field with respect to the operations of addition and multiplication defined by

$$[a, b] + [c, d] = [ad + bc, bd] \quad \text{and} \quad [a, b][c, d] = [ac, bd].$$

CHAPTER 7

POLYNOMIALS

7-1 DEFINITIONS RELATING TO POLYNOMIALS

Probably no subject regularly taught in high schools is less well understood by the average teacher and student alike than the subject of polynomials. High school texts are not always a help and often serve to perpetuate the misunderstandings and inconsistencies that abound in this area. Students are given equations involving a letter x where in one case the letter is a variable, in another an indeterminate, and in still a third an unknown. No attempt is made, in most cases, to explain the differences, and the student can learn only by trial and error what is expected of him in solving a problem. Again, the student may be told that $x^2 - 2$ cannot be factored, and yet in the next assignment, he solves the equation $x^2 = 2$, which depends on the fact that $x^2 - 2$ factors as

$$x^2 - 2 = (x + \sqrt{2})(x - \sqrt{2}).$$

It is little wonder that students find mathematics difficult, when even the language used is kept a mystery, to be understood only by professional mathematicians.

The purpose of this chapter is to present polynomials in a manner which will bring to light the nature of systems of polynomials and clarify the terminology and usages which relate to elementary problems involving polynomials. Not all the material presented here is suitable, as written, for presentation to high school students, but it is the belief of the author that mastery of the material in this chapter is an essential part of the training of every prospective teacher of mathematics. Intelligent judgments about what material and what approaches should be used with students cannot be made without a clear understanding of the subject involved.

There are many ways in which the subject of polynomials may be introduced. One approach often used is to introduce the standard symbols, such as $1 + 2x^2 + x^3$, and then attempt to describe the precise meaning of the notation. However, this approach causes the same difficulty that is encountered when a/b is used at the outset to designate a rational number. The symbol is so familiar that it is difficult to convince the reader that he has anything to learn. It is easy to completely miss the essential points of the discussion. The approach we will adopt is one which presents the main features of polynomials, without suggesting other properties which are not intended, and many of which are incorrect.

The polynomials which appear in elementary texts always involve numbers from some suitable set.   The set may be the set of integers, the set of real numbers, or some other set.   Each of the sets mentioned here is at least an integeral domain, and in some cases a field.   We will begin, then, by assuming that an integral domain D has been specified, and from it we will construct a set of polynomials.   The set of polynomials will represent an extension of D to a new integral domain called the *domain of polynomials over D*.   (This is also referred to as the domain of polynomials with coefficients in D.)   This extension is similar to the extension of integers to rational numbers, in that the larger domain contains a subset isomorphic to D.   Definition 2 below specifies this extension precisely

In order to give this definition, we need to first define an infinite sequence.

Definition 1.   An *infinite sequence* of elements of a set S is a function whose domain is the set of nonnegative integers and whose range is a subset of S. Such a sequence is represented by the symbol $(a_0, a_1, a_2, \ldots)$, where each $a_i \in S$ for every nonnegative integer i.

This definition requires that an infinite sequence assign to each nonnegative integer a unique element of S, called a *term* of the sequence.   There must be a zeroth term, a first term, a second term, etc., each of which is an element of S.   The notation $(a_0, a_1, a_2, \ldots)$ is one way in which such a function may be specified. For example, $(0, \frac{1}{2}, \frac{2}{3}, \frac{3}{4}, \ldots)$ is a sequence of rational numbers.   The notation merely lists, in order, the images of $0, 1, 2, \ldots$ under the function which is the sequence.   In functional notation, it easy to verify that this sequence is the function $f(n) = n/(n + 1)$, since $f(0) = 0$, $f(1) = \frac{1}{2}$, $f(2) = \frac{2}{3}$, $f(3) = \frac{3}{4}$, etc.   The language in common usage for sequences would say that 0 is the zeroth term, $\frac{1}{2}$ the first term, and $n/(n + 1)$ the nth (or general) term of the sequence.   It may seem strange that we count the initial term as the zeroth term, rather than the first term, but the reason is that we will use the sequences in describing polynomials, and with our method of counting terms, it will turn out that the nth term is the term of nth degree in the polynomial.   Had we counted in another manner, this would not be the case, and the resulting confusion would make the discussion seem more difficult than is necessary.

Definition 2.   If D is an integral domain, a *polynomial over D* is an infinite sequence of elements in D such that only a finite number of terms are different from zero.   The set of all polynomials over D is referred to as the *domain of polynomials over D* and is denoted by $D[x]$.

In the foregoing definition, the symbol $D[x]$ has no apparent motivation.   We will show later how the symbol x is related to a polynomial.   In the meantime, the notation $D[x]$ should be thought of merely as a symbol for this set of polynomials.   Any other symbol would do as well, but this is the standard notation. Another comment about this definition is that it should be clear that whatever else a polynomial may be, it is *not* an element of the integral domain D.

We are going to show in Section 7–3 that the set of all polynomials over an integral domain is itself an integral domain. Before we can do this, we need to define equality and the operations of addition and multiplication for the set.

Definition 3. If D is an integral domain and if $x = (a_0, a_1, a_2, \ldots)$ and $y = (b_0, b_1, b_2, \ldots)$ are any two elements of $D[x]$, then

a) $x = y$ if and only if $a_i = b_i$ for every nonnegative integer i.

b) $x + y = (c_0, c_1, c_2, \ldots)$ where $c_i = a_i + b_i$ for every nonnegative integer i.

c) $xy = (d_0, d_1, d_2, \ldots)$ where $d_i = a_0 b_i + a_1 b_{i-1} + \ldots + a_i b_0$ for every nonnegative integer i.

To explain this definition, it should be pointed out that the operations of multiplication and addition for x and y are new operations defined for elements of $D[x]$. In defining these, we use sums and products of elements in D. These sums and products are formed in terms of operations in D, since elements of D are being combined. For instance, $a_i + b_i$ appears in the definition as the formula for the ith term of $x + y$. This sum $a_i + b_i$ is the operation of addition already known to exist in D.

The above definition of equality merely states that to be equal, two sequences must be identical, term by term. Addition and multiplication are illustrated in the following examples.

Example 7–1. Let $x = (0, 2, 3, 0, 0, \ldots)$ and $y = (1, 0, 3, -2, 0, 0, \ldots)$, where all terms not shown are zero. These are polynomials in $Z[x]$. The sum $x + y$ is found by adding corresponding terms and is given by

$$x + y = (1, 2, 6, -2, 0, 0, \ldots).$$

The product xy is computed as follows:

$$
\begin{aligned}
xy = {} & (0, 2, 3, 0, 0, \ldots)(1, 0, 3, -2, 0, 0, \ldots) \\
= {} & (0 \cdot 1, \ 0 \cdot 0 + 2 \cdot 1, \ 3 \cdot 1 + 2 \cdot 0 + 0 \cdot 3, \ 0 \cdot 1 + 3 \cdot 0 + 2 \cdot 3 + (-2) \cdot 0, \ 0 \cdot 1 \\
& + 0 \cdot 0 + 3 \cdot 3 + 2 \cdot (-2) + 0 \cdot 0, \ 0 \cdot 1 + 0 \cdot 0 + 0 \cdot 3 + 3 \cdot (-2) + 2 \cdot 0 + 0 \cdot 0, \\
& 0 \cdot 1 + 0 \cdot 0 + 0 \cdot 3 + 0 \cdot (-2) + 3 \cdot 0 + 2 \cdot 0 + 0 \cdot 0, 0, 0, \ldots) = (0, 2, 3, \\
& 6, 5, -6, 0, 0, \ldots).
\end{aligned}
$$

After the fifth, all terms in the product are zero. Note that the terms are referred to as zeroth, first, second, etc., so that -6 is the fifth term.

Since a polynomial is a sequence, it is proper to speak of one of the elements which appears as a term. However, it is more common to refer to them as coefficients.

Definition 4. If $w = (a_0, a_1, a_2, 0, 0, \ldots)$ is a polynomial over an integral domain, a_i is referred to as the ith *coefficient* of w for each positive integer i. The element a_0 is called either the *constant term* of w or the *zeroth coefficient* of w.

An important definition in connection with polynomials is that of degree, given next.   Note that since a polynomial may have only a finite number of nonzero coefficients, the definition of degree can always be applied to give a unique positive integer or zero.

Definition 5. If $w = (a_0, a_1, a_2, \ldots)$ is a polynomial over an integral domain, the *degree of* w is n if and only if $a_n \neq 0$, but $a_m = 0$ for all $m > n$.   If all the coefficients of w are zero, then w has no degree.

In using Definition 5, we note, for example, that $(0, 0, 0, \ldots)$ has no degree. The degree of $(2, 0, 0, \ldots)$ is zero, the degree of $(0, 2, 0, 3, 0, 0, \ldots)$ is three, and the degree of $(1, 2, 3, 4, 5, 0, 0, \ldots)$ is four.

Theorem 7-1. If f and g are two nonzero polynomials over an integral domain D, then the degree of the product fg is the sum of the degrees of f and g.

Let $f = (a_0, a_1, \ldots, a_n, 0, \ldots)$ be a polynomial of degree n, and let $g = (b_0, b_1, \ldots, b_m, 0, \ldots)$ be a polynomial of degree m, both over an integral domain D. By definition of degree, $a_n \neq 0$ and $b_m \neq 0$, but all terms beyond the nth in f and beyond the mth in g are zero.   Now let the product fg be the polynomial $(c_0, c_1, c_2, \ldots)$.   By definition of product, the $(n + m)$-coefficient in fg, namely c_{n+m}, contains the product $a_n b_m$.   Since D is an integral domain, $a_n b_m \neq 0$.   All other terms in the sum which gives c_{n+m} are zero.   These terms are of the form $a_i b_j$, with $i + j = n + m$, and with the exception of the term $a_n b_m$, either $i > n$ or $j > m$, and hence either $a_i = 0$ or $b_j = 0$.   Further, if $k > n + m$, then $c_k = 0$, since each term in the sum which gives c_k is of the form $a_i b_j$, with $i + j = k$.   Since $k > n + m$, either $i > n$ or $j > m$, and hence these terms are all zero.   The degree of fg is $n + m$, since $c_{n+m} \neq 0$ and $c_k = 0$ for all $k > n + m$.   This completes the proof of the theorem.

EXERCISES

In the following problems, all nonzero coefficients are given for each polynomial mentioned. Answers should be written in the same way.

1. Let $u = (-1, 0, 2, 0, \ldots)$ and $v = (0, 2, -3, 0, \ldots)$ be polynomials over the integers. Find (a) $u + v$ (b) uv (c) u^2 (d) v^3

2. Let $u = (1, 2, 0, \ldots)$ and $v = (3, 4, 0, \ldots)$ be polynomials over the field Z_5.   Find (a) $u + v$ (b) uv (c) u^2 (d) v^2 (e) $u^2 v^2$ (f) v^3

3. Let $u = (0, 0, \frac{1}{2}, 0, \ldots)$ and $v = (-\frac{1}{3}, 0, \frac{2}{5}, 0, \ldots)$ be polynomials over the rational numbers.   Find (a) $u + v$ (b) uv (c) u^2 (d) u^3 (e) u^4 (f) v^2

4. Let $u = (2, \frac{1}{2}, 0, \ldots)$ and $v = (-2, 0, 0, \sqrt{3}, 0, \ldots)$ be polynomials over the real numbers.   Find (a) $u + v$ (b) uv (c) u^3 (d) v^2

5. Let $u = (1 + 2i, \frac{1}{2}, 0, \ldots)$ and $v = (0, 2 - i, \sqrt{2}i, 0, \ldots)$ be polynomials over the complex numbers.   Find (a) $u + v$ (b) uv (c) u^2 (d) v^2

6. Prove that the polynomial having all coefficients equal to zero is the zero element of the domain of polynomials over any given integral domain D.

7. Prove that if $w = (a_0, a_1, a_2, \ldots)$ is any polynomial in $D[x]$ for an integral domain D, then $(-a_0, -a_1, -a_2, \ldots)$ is the negative of w.

8. Prove that the set S of all polynomials of $D[x]$ which have zero constant term is closed under the operations of addition and multiplication, for any integral domain D. That is,

$$S = \{(0, a_1, a_2, \ldots) \mid a_i \in D \text{ and only finitely many } a_i \neq 0\}.$$

9. Prove that the set T of all polynomials in $Z[x]$ which have zero for all coefficients other than the constant term forms a ring. Note that the constant term may be zero or non-zero. That is,

$$T = \{(a, 0, 0, \ldots) \mid a \text{ is an integer}\}.$$

10. Prove the following theorems on factoring, where each polynomial is an element of $D[x]$ for an arbitrary integral domain D.

a) $(ab, ac, ad, 0, \ldots) = (a, 0, 0, \ldots)(b, c, d, 0, \ldots)$
b) $(-a^2, 0, b^2, 0, \ldots) = (a, b, 0, 0, \ldots)(-a, b, 0, 0, \ldots)$
c) $(a^2, 2ab, b^2, 0, \ldots) = (a, b, 0, \ldots)^2$
d) $(-a^3, 3a^2b, -3ab^2, b^3, 0, \ldots) = (-a, b, 0, \ldots)^3$

7-2   THE SUMMATION NOTATION

The formula for multiplication of polynomials given in Section 7–1 is somewhat awkward to use, and it is particularly cumbersome for use in proving theorems, such as the associative law for multiplication of polynomials, where a product of three polynomials is involved. In order to shorten the work of writing such proofs, it is advisable to introduce the summation notation. There are many other subjects, such as statistics and integral calculus, where this notation is used heavily. We believe it is of sufficient general interest to be included as a regular section in this text. Since no specific background is required for this text, we include this material for those who may not be familiar with the notation. If the reader has already learned to use the notation with facility, he may safely skip this section.

Definition 1. If m and n are integers with $m < n$, the symbol $\sum_{i=m}^{n} f(i)$ is defined to be

$$f(m) + f(m + 1) + f(m + 2) + \cdots + f(n).$$

We read the symbol as the sum from $i = m$ to $i = n$ of $f(i)$; m and n are referred to as the lower and upper limits of summation, respectively.

Although the definition above is really self-explanatory, a few examples may be helpful.

Example 7–2. $\sum_{i=1}^{5} i = 1 + 2 + 3 + 4 + 5$. That is, we replace i successively by the integers from 1 through 5, and add the results.

Example 7–3. $\sum_{i=6}^{10} x^i = x^6 + x^7 + x^8 + x^9 + x^{10}$. Here, the function $f(i)$ is x^i. In summing, we begin with $i = 6$ and write x^i for each integer i from 6 through 10, and add the results.

Example 7–4. $\Sigma_{i=2}^{7} a_i = a_2 + a_3 + a_4 + a_5 + a_6 + a_7$. In this summation, the i appears as a subscript, but the rule is the same. As before, we merely copy the expression, replacing i first by 2, then by 3, etc., and add the results.

In this notation, there is nothing sacred about the symbol i. We could use any other letter as well.

Example 7–5. $\Sigma_{n=-1}^{3} (n)^{n+1} = (-1)^{-1+1} + (0)^{0+1} + (1)^{1+1} + (2)^{2+1} + (3)^{3+1} = 1 + 0 + 1 + 8 + 81 = 91$.

A special case of interest is that in which the function referred to in the definition as $f(i)$ is a constant function. For instance, if $f(i) = 2$, the notation is

$$\sum_{i=1}^{4} 2 = 2 + 2 + 2 + 2 = 8.$$

This may seem strange, but a direct application of the definition yields the following result: $f(1) = 2$, $f(2) = 2$, $f(3) = 2$, and $f(4) = 2$. Then,

$$\sum_{i=1}^{4} f(i) = f(1) + f(2) + f(3) + f(4) = 2 + 2 + 2 + 2 = 8.$$

The reader may wonder why one would use this notation in a case such as this. The reason is that in stating general theorems using the summation notation, there are often special cases of this type. They must either be excluded from the cases to which the theorem applies or be treated as we have indicated above. The latter is preferred. The discussion above should point out why the following theorem is an immediate consequence of the definition.

Theorem 7–2. $\Sigma_{i=m}^{n} c = (n - m + 1)c$, where c is an element of any system in which addition is defined.

The only proof needed, in addition to the remarks preceding the theorem, is to point out that $n - m + 1$ is the number of terms indicated by the limits of summation. Thus, $\Sigma_{i=1}^{10} f(i)$ represents the sum of 10 terms and $\Sigma_{i=2}^{7} f(i)$ represents the sum of 6 terms.

Another elementary theorem on summation (Theorem 7–3 below) is merely a statement of the generalized distributive law. This holds in any system in which the distributive laws for multiplication over addition are valid. No further proof is needed, since we have already proved these laws, but the reader should be sure that he understands why this is the case.

Theorem 7–3. If S is any system in which multiplication is left- and right-distributive over addition, and if $a \in S$ and $f(i) \in S$ for each $i = m, m + 1, \ldots, n$, then

$$\sum_{i=m}^{n} af(i) = a \sum_{i=m}^{n} f(i) \qquad \text{and} \qquad \sum_{i=m}^{n} f(i)a = \left(\sum_{i=m}^{n} f(i) \right) a.$$

Example 7-6. In the field of real numbers,

$$\sum_{k=3}^{6} 2\sqrt{k} = 2\sqrt{3} + 2\sqrt{4} + 2\sqrt{5} + 2\sqrt{6}$$

$$= 2(\sqrt{3} + \sqrt{4} + \sqrt{5} + \sqrt{6}) = 2\sum_{k=3}^{6} \sqrt{k}.$$

These steps are self-explanatory.

Theorem 7-4. $\displaystyle\sum_{i=m}^{n} (f(i) + g(i)) = \sum_{i=m}^{n} f(i) + \sum_{i=m}^{n} g(i).$

This theorem is merely a statement in summation notation of the fact that a sum of terms may be rearranged before adding. It follows from the general commutative law of addition, and needs no further proof. The following example illustrates the theorem.

Example 7-7

$$\sum_{i=4}^{7} (2^i + i^2) = (2^4 + 4^2) + (2^5 + 5^2) + (2^6 + 6^2) + (2^7 + 7^2)$$

$$= (2^4 + 2^5 + 2^6 + 2^7) + (4^2 + 5^2 + 6^2 + 7^2)$$

$$= \sum_{i=4}^{7} 2^i + \sum_{i=4}^{7} i^2.$$

Theorem 7-5. If $u = (a_0, a_1, a_2, \ldots)$ and $v = (b_0, b_1, b_2, \ldots)$ are polynomials in $D[x]$ for an integral domain D, then in the product $uv = (c_0, c_1, c_2, \ldots)$, $c_n = \sum_{i=0}^{n} a_i b_{n-i}$ for each nonnegative integer n.

The only proof needed is to apply the definition of the summation notation to the expression $\sum_{i=0}^{n} a_i b_{n-i}$ and to verify that this is exactly the same formula as given in Section 7-1. Thus

$$\sum_{i=0}^{n} a_i b_{n-i} = a_0 b_n + a_1 b_{n-1} + a_2 b_{n-2} + \cdots + a_n b_0,$$

and this is the formula given for the product of polynomials.

It often happens that the function $f(i)$, which appears in the summation notation, is itself a summation. Suppose, for example, that $f(i) = \sum_{k=1}^{3} a_k b_i$. Then $f(i) = a_1 b_i + a_2 b_i + a_3 b_i$. Now consider the summation

$$\sum_{i=3}^{4} \left(\sum_{k=1}^{3} a_k b_i \right).$$

Replacing $\Sigma_{k=1}^3 a_k b_i$ by the formula above, we have

$$\sum_{i=3}^4 \left(\sum_{k=1}^3 a_k b_i \right) = \sum_{i=3}^4 (a_1 b_i + a_2 b_i + a_3 b_i)$$

$$= (a_1 b_3 + a_2 b_3 + a_3 b_3) + (a_1 b_4 + a_2 b_4 + a_3 b_4).$$

Now, if each a_k and each b_i is in an integral domain where we have associative and commutative laws, we may rewrite the sum above as follows:

$$\sum_{i=3}^4 \left(\sum_{k=1}^3 a_k b_i \right) = (a_1 b_3 + a_1 b_4) + (a_2 b_3 + a_2 b_4) + (a_3 b_3 + a_3 b_4)$$

$$= \sum_{k=1}^3 (a_k b_3 + a_k b_4) = \sum_{k=1}^3 \left(\sum_{i=3}^4 a_k b_i \right).$$

That is, in the special case we have been able to reverse the order of summation symbols without changing the sum.   Note, however, that the limits of summation are all specific numbers.   The next theorem gives a general statement of this type.   First, however, a definition is given to explain the standard custom of omitting parentheses in such expressions.   We refer to such sums as *double sums*.

Definition 2. $\sum_{i=m}^n \Sigma_{j=s}^t f(i,j) = \Sigma_{i=m}^n \left(\Sigma_{j=s}^t f(i,j) \right).$

In this definition, $f(i,j)$ refers to an expression involving both i and j.   A formal definition could be made of the symbol as follows.   A *function of two variables* u and v, where u is an element in a set U and v is an element in a set V, is a function (in the usual sense) whose range is some set B and whose domain is a subset of $U \times V$.   Thus for each pair (u, v) in the domain of $f(u, v)$, a unique element in B is determined.

Theorem 7–6.   If all functional values $f(i,j)$ are elements of an integral domain D, then $\Sigma_{i=m}^n \Sigma_{j=s}^t f(i,j) = \Sigma_{j=s}^t \Sigma_{i=m}^n f(i,j).$

To prove this theorem, we need only to consider the sums indicated in each case.   Each represents the sum of all $f(i,j)$ which can be written with $m \le i \le n$ and $s \le j \le t$.   The order of the terms is not important because of the associative and commutative laws of addition in the integral domain.   Thus the expressions are equal.

Theorem 7–6 is somewhat involved, but the manipulation of summation needed for the proofs in the next section is even more so.   A special notation is useful for such theorems.   The difficulty that arises can be seen by considering the sum which results in connection with the product of three polynomials.   Let $u = (a_0, a_1, a_2, \ldots)$, $v = (b_0, b_1, b_2, \ldots)$, and $w = (c_0, c_1, c_2, \ldots)$ be three polynomials in $D[x]$, where D is an integral.   Further, let product $vw = (d_0, d_1, d_2, \ldots)$

and the product $u(vw) = (e_0, e_1, e_2, \dots)$. The mth coefficient in vw is given by $d_m = \sum_{i=0}^{m} b_i c_{m-i}$, and the nth coefficient of $u(vw)$ is given by $e_n = \sum_{j=0}^{n} a_j d_{n-j}$. To evaluate e_n in terms of a's, b's, and c's, we need to use the formula for d_{n-j}, which is $d_{n-j} = \sum_{i=0}^{n-j} b_i c_{n-j-i}$, obtained by replacing m in the formula for d_m by $n - j$. Thus e_n is given by $e_n = \sum_{j=0}^{n} a_j \sum_{i=0}^{n-j} b_i c_{n-j-i}$. It is necessary to interchange the order of summation in proving the associative law of multiplication. This process is similar to Theorem 7–6, but now the inner sum has as its upper limit $n - j$, which depends on the value of j, rather than on a constant, as in Theorem 7–6. We can avoid this difficulty by noting, first, that in the formula for d_m, the subscript i in b_i and the subscript $m - i$ in c_{m-i} have m as their sum. In fact, the subscripts that occur in the sum can be identified as all combinations of nonnegative integers which have m as their sum. This leads to the definition of a new type of summation symbol.

Definition 3. The notation $\sum_{i+j=m} f(i, j)$ means the sum of all terms $f(i, j)$ which be formed with i and j nonnegative integers whose sum is m.

This definition specifies the terms of the summation but does not specify the order in which they are to be added. This is of no consequence in an integral domain, since addition is commutative. The following example illustrates the meaning of this definition.

Example 7–8. The terms of the summation $\sum_{i+j=4} a_i b_j$ can be written out as follows:

$$\sum_{i+j=4} a_i b_j = a_0 b_4 + a_1 b_3 + a_2 b_2 + a_3 b_1 + a_4 b_0.$$

This follows from the definition, since the pairs of nonnegative integers whose sum is 4 are $(0, 4)$, $(1, 3)$, $(2, 2)$, $(3, 1)$, and $(4, 0)$. We could, of course, write this equally well as $a_1 b_3 + a_2 b_2 + a_0 b_4 + a_4 b_0 + a_3 b_1$, since addition is commutative. It can be seen, then, that the formula for d_m in the preceding paragraph may be written as $d_m = \sum_{i+j=m} a_i b_j$. And in a similar way, we may write the formula for e_n as $e_n = \sum_{i+j+k=n} a_i b_j c_k$. This notation does not mention the order in which terms are summed and hence avoids the necessity for interchanging the order in which summation symbols are written.

Example 7–9. We will write out the terms of the sum $\sum_{i+j+k=3} a_i b_j c_k$. The triples (i, j, k), which sum to 3, are $(0, 0, 3)$, $(0, 1, 2)$, $(0, 2, 1)$, $(0, 3, 0)$, $(1, 0, 2)$, $(1, 1, 1)$, $(1, 2, 0)$, $(2, 0, 1)$, $(2, 1, 0)$ and $(3, 0, 0)$. Hence

$$\sum_{i+j+k=3} a_i b_j c_k = a_0 b_0 c_3 + a_0 b_1 c_2 + a_0 b_2 c_1 + a_0 b_3 c_0 + a_1 b_0 c_2 + a_1 b_1 c_1$$

$$+ a_1 b_2 c_0 + a_2 b_0 c_1 + a_2 b_1 c_0 + a_3 b_0 c_0.$$

Any other order of terms would do equally well.

EXERCISES

1. Write out, term by term, each of the following sums of integers.

a) $\sum_{i=1}^{5} i^2$
b) $\sum_{j=2}^{7} 2^j$
c) $\sum_{k=3}^{5} 4$
d) $\sum_{n=1}^{5} \dfrac{n-1}{n(n+1)}$

e) $\sum_{m=4}^{7} (m-2)(m-1)m$
f) $\sum_{p=1}^{5} p^{2p}$
g) $\sum_{i=0}^{3} m$

2. Assume that each a_i, b_j, and c_k in the following is an element in an integral domain. Write out, term by term, each of the indicated sums.

a) $\sum_{i=3}^{7} a_i$
b) $\sum_{i=3}^{7} a_i b_j$
c) $\sum_{i=3}^{5} \sum_{j=1}^{3} a_i b_j$
d) $\sum_{i=0}^{3} \sum_{j=0}^{i} a_i b_j$

e) $\sum_{j=0}^{3} a_i b_{3-j}$
f) $\sum_{j=0}^{3} \sum_{i=0}^{3-j} a_j b_i c_{3-j-i}$
g) $\sum_{i+j+k=2} a_i b_j c_k$

3. Let $a_0 = 2$, $a_1 = -3$, $a_2 = 1$, $a_3 = 0$, $b_0 = 1$, $b_1 = -1$, $b_2 = 3$, and $b_3 = -2$. Compute the numerical value of each of the following sums of integers.

a) $\sum_{i=0}^{3} a_i$
b) $\sum_{i=0}^{3} a_i^2$
c) $\left(\sum_{i=0}^{3} a_i \right)^2$
d) $\sum_{i+j=3} a_i b_j$

e) $\sum_{i=0}^{3} a_i b_{3-i}$
f) $\sum_{i=0}^{3} \sum_{j=0}^{i} a_i b_j$
g) $\sum_{i=0}^{3} \sum_{j=0}^{3} a_i b_j$
h) $\sum_{i=-1}^{2} 3$

i) $\sum_{i=3}^{5} 10$
j) $\sum_{i=0}^{3} (a_i + b_i)$
k) $\sum_{i=0}^{3} a_i + \sum_{i=0}^{3} b_i$

4. Write each of the following in summation notation.

a) $1^2 + 2^2 + 3^2 + \cdots + 10^2$
b) $2^5 + 2^6 + 2^7 + 2^8 + 2^9 + 2^{10}$
c) $a_{-1} + a_0 + a_1 + a_2 + a_3$
d) $b_0^2 + b_1^2 + b_2^2 + b_3^2$
e) $a_0 b_2 + a_1 b_2 + a_2 b_2 + a_3 b_2$
f) $a_0 b_5 + a_1 b_4 + a_2 b_3 + a_3 b_2 + a_4 b_1 + a_5 b_0$

5. Prove by mathematical induction that

$$\sum_{i=1}^{n} i = \frac{n}{2}(1 + n)$$

6. Prove by mathematical induction that

$$\sum_{i=1}^{n} 4i = 2n(n + 1)$$

7. Prove by mathematical induction that

$$\sum_{i=1}^{n} (4i - 3) = n(2n - 1)$$

8. Evaluate the following sums of integers.

a) $\displaystyle\sum_{i+j=3} (i-2)(j+1)$

b) $\displaystyle\sum_{i+j=5} i^2(j-2)$

c) $\displaystyle\sum_{i+j=4} \frac{i-1}{j+1}$

d) $\displaystyle\sum_{i+j=3} (ij)^{i-j}$

7-3 THE STRUCTURE OF **D[x]**

Operations of addition and multiplication have been defined in $D[x]$ where D is an integral domain. It is natural to ask what the structure of $D[x]$ is. Is it a ring? an integral domain? or maybe even a field? Does the answer depend on whether or not D is a field? The answers to these questions are given in Theorems 7–7 and 7–8, which follow. The proofs are long, but not difficult, and are included in their entirety.

Many of the steps in the proofs of Theorems 7–7 and 7–8 will require us to show that two elements are equal. Recall that to be equal, two polynomials must have identical coefficients. After reading the section on mathematical induction, the student should be wary of proving that a theorem holds in a few cases and then assuming it is always true. In order that our proofs concerning the equality of two polynomials may be complete, it is necessary to be sure that every coefficient of one equals the corresponding coefficient of the other. Hence it will not be sufficient to list only the first two or three coefficients. For this reason, we will modify our notation slightly and write each polynomial by giving the zeroth coefficient and the nth coefficient. Our proofs will show that equality holds for the nth coefficient for every natural number n. The notation for a polynomial will read $(a_0, \ldots, a_n, \ldots)$.

> **Theorem 7–7.** If D is an integral domain, then $D[x]$ is an integral domain with respect to the operations of addition and multiplication of polynomials given in Section 7–1.

First, we will show $D[x]$ to be an additive abelian group. Addition is commutative, since if $u = (a_0, \ldots, a_n, \ldots)$ and $v = (b_0, \ldots, b_n, \ldots)$ are any two elements of $D[x]$,

$$u + v = (a_0 + b_0, \ldots, a_n + b_n, \ldots)$$
$$= (b_0 + a_0, \ldots, b_n + a_n, \ldots) = v + u.$$

The reason for the middle step is the commutative law of addition in D.

The set $D[x]$ is closed with respect to addition by the fact that the sum of two polynomials has been defined to be another polynomial in every case. The sum of two sequences is certainly a sequence, and if only finitely many terms of each sequence are nonzero, then the sum can have only finitely many terms that are nonzero.

The associative law of addition holds in $D[x]$. We consider any three elements of $D[x]$, say, $u = (a_0, \ldots, a_n, \ldots)$, $v = (b_0, \ldots, b_n, \ldots)$, and $w = (c_0, \ldots, c_n, \ldots)$. Then,

$$u + (v + w) = (a_0, \ldots, a_n, \ldots) + (b_0 + c_0, \ldots, b_n + c_n, \ldots)$$
by definition of $+$ in $D[x]$,

$$= (a_0 + [b_0 + c_0], \ldots, a_n + [b_n + c_n], \ldots)$$
by definition of $+$ in $D[x]$,

$$= ([a_0 + b_0] + c_0, \ldots, [a_n + b_n] + c_n, \ldots)$$
associative law in D,

$$= (a_0 + b_0, \ldots, a_n + b_n, \ldots) + (c_0, \ldots, c_n, \ldots)$$
by definition of $+$ in $D[x]$,

$$= (u + v) + w \qquad \text{by definition of } + \text{ in } D[x].$$

The zero element of $D[x]$ is $\mathbf{0} = (0, \ldots, 0, \ldots)$, since for any

$$u = (a_0, \ldots, a_n, \ldots) \text{ in } D[x],$$

$$u + \mathbf{0} = (a_0 + 0, \ldots, a_n + 0, \ldots) = (a_0, \ldots, a_n, \ldots) = u.$$

By commutativity of addition, $\mathbf{0} + u = u$, as well.

The negative of any element $u = (a_0, \ldots, a_n, \ldots)$ in $D[x]$ is given by $-u = (-a_0, \ldots, -a_n, \ldots)$, since

$$(a_0, \ldots, a_n, \ldots) + (-a_0, \ldots, -a_n, \ldots) = (0, \ldots, 0, \ldots),$$

the zero of $D[x]$. Clearly $-u$ is an element of $D[x]$. This completes the proof that $D[x]$ is an additive abelian group.

The set $D[x]$ is closed with respect to multiplication. To see this, let $u = (a_0, \ldots, a_n, \ldots)$ and $v = (b_0, \ldots, b_n, \ldots)$ be two elements of $D[x]$. By the definition of product, the product of two polynomials is a sequence. To prove that this sequence is a polynomial, we need only to show that it has at most a finite number of nonzero terms. If either u or v is the zero polynomial, then from the definition of product, it is clear that uv is also zero and hence is an element of $D[x]$. Suppose that neither u nor v is zero, then each has a degree. (By definition, every nonzero polynomial has finite degree.) By Theorem 7–1 the product uv has degree equal to the sum of the degrees of u and v, a finite integer. But this statement is equivalent to saying that the sequence for uv has only a finite number of nonzero terms. Hence the sequence for uv represents a polynomial, and $uv \in D[x]$. This means that $D[x]$ is closed with respect to multiplication.

Next, in order to show that $D[x]$ is a ring, we will prove the associative law of multiplication and the distributive laws. Let $u = (a_0, \ldots, a_n, \ldots)$, $v = (b_0, \ldots, b_n, \ldots)$, and $w = (c_0, \ldots, c_n, \ldots)$ by any three elements of $D[x]$. In each of the following proofs, remember that the coefficients which are written are the zeroth and the nth terms. Thus the general formula for the nth term in each product or sum appears in the notation representing that product or sum.

$$u(vw) = (a_0, \ldots, a_n, \ldots)[(b_0, \ldots, b_n, \ldots)(c_0, \ldots, c_n, \ldots)]$$

$$= (a_0, \ldots, a_n, \ldots)(b_0c_0, \ldots, \sum_{j+k=n} b_jc_k, \ldots) \qquad \text{by definition of } \cdot \text{ in } D[x],$$

$$= \left(a_0b_0c_0, \ldots, \sum_{i+j+k=n} a_ib_jc_k, \ldots\right) \qquad \text{by definition of } \cdot \text{ in } D[x],$$

Similarly,

$$(uv)w = [(a_0, \ldots, a_n, \ldots)(b_0, \ldots, b_n, \ldots)](c_0, \ldots, c_n, \ldots)$$

$$= \left(a_0b_0, \ldots, \sum_{i+j=n} a_ib_j, \ldots\right)(c_0, \ldots, c_n, \ldots) \qquad \text{by definition of } \cdot \text{ in } D[x],$$

$$= \left(a_0b_0c_0, \ldots, \sum_{i+j+k=n} a_ib_jc_k, \ldots\right) \qquad \text{by definition of } \cdot \text{ in } D[x].$$

Now, since both $u(vw)$ and $(uv)w$ equal the same thing, they are equal. This follows from the symmetric and transitive properties of equality. Hence the associative law of multiplication holds in $D[x]$.

In order to prove the left-distributive law, we consider u, v, and w as in the preceding paragraph. Then,

$$u(v + w) = (a_0, \ldots, a_n, \ldots)[(b_0, \ldots, b_n, \ldots) + (c_0, \ldots, c_n, \ldots)]$$

$$= (a_0, \ldots, a_n, \ldots)(b_0 + c_0, \ldots, b_n + c_n, \ldots)$$
$$\qquad\qquad\qquad\qquad\qquad \text{by definition of } + \text{ in } D[x],$$

$$= \left(a_0[b_0 + c_0], \ldots, \sum_{i+j=n.} a_i(b_j + c_j), \ldots\right) \qquad \text{by definition of } \cdot \text{ in } D[x],$$

$$= \left(a_0b_0 + a_0c_0, \ldots, \sum_{i+j=n} (a_ib_j + a_ic_j), \ldots\right) \qquad \text{by distributive law in } D,$$

$$= \left(a_0b_0 + a_0c_0, \ldots, \sum_{i+j=n} a_ib_j + \sum_{i+j=n} a_ic_j, \ldots\right) \qquad \text{by Theorem 7-4,}$$

$$= \left(a_0b_0, \ldots, \sum_{i+j=n} a_ib_j, \ldots\right) + \left(a_0c_0, \ldots, \sum_{i+j=n} a_ic_j, \ldots\right)$$
$$\qquad\qquad\qquad\qquad\qquad \text{by definition of } + \text{ in } D[x],$$

$$= (a_0, \ldots, a_n, \ldots)(b_0, \ldots, b_n, \ldots)$$
$$+ (a_0, \ldots, a_n, \ldots)(c_0, \ldots, c_n, \ldots) \qquad \text{by definition of } \cdot \text{ in } D[x],$$

$$= uv + uw.$$

This establishes the left-distributive law of multiplication over addition in $D[x]$, and the right-distributive law follows from the fact that multiplication is commutative, as we will show next.

Let u and v be arbitrary elements of $D[x]$, as in the preceding paragraphs. Then,

$$uv = (a_0, \ldots, a_n, \ldots)(b_0, \ldots, b_n, \ldots)$$

$$= \left(a_0 b_0, \ldots, \sum_{i+j=n} a_i b_j, \ldots \right) \qquad \text{by definition of multiplication in } D[x],$$

$$= \left(b_0 a_0, \ldots, \sum_{i+j=n} b_j a_i, \ldots \right) \qquad \text{by the commutative law in } D,$$

$$= (b_0, \ldots, b_n, \ldots)(a_0, \ldots, a_n, \ldots) \qquad \text{by definition of multiplication in } D[x],$$

$$= vu.$$

This shows that multiplication is commutative in $D[x]$. With this, we have completed the proof that $D[x]$ is a commutative ring.

The unity in $D[x]$ is $\mathbf{1} = (1, 0, \ldots, 0, \ldots)$, since for any $t = (d_0, \ldots, d_n, \ldots)$ in $D[x]$, $\mathbf{1}t = (1, 0, \ldots, 0, \ldots)(d_0, \ldots, d_n, \ldots) = (d_0, \ldots, d_n, \ldots)$ by definition of multiplication in $D[x]$. Note that for any coefficient in the product of these polynomials, the formula for multiplication gives a sum of products $a_i b_j$, but in this case, each such product is zero except the first. That is, $\sum_{i+j=n} a_i b_j$ reduces to $1 \cdot b_n$ for the nth coefficient in $\mathbf{1}t$.

Finally, we need to show that $D[x]$ has no zero divisors. To show this, we will use the notion of the degree of a polynomial. In Theorem 7–1, we proved that the degree of the product of two polynomials is the sum of their respective degrees. Recall, also, that a polynomial is zero if and only if it has no degree. Consider any two nonzero polynomials in $D[x]$ having degrees s and t, respectively. The product of these polynomials has degree $s + t$, and hence cannot be zero. This means that $D[x]$ has no zero divisors. With this, the proof that $D[x]$ is an integral domain is complete.

The next theorem answers the question as to whether or not $D[x]$ may be a field. Note that the proof does not depend on whether or not D is also a field.

Theorem 7–8   The polynomial domain $D[x]$ is not a field for any integral domain D.

To prove that $D[x]$ is not a field, we need only to exhibit a single nonzero element of $D[x]$ which has no multiplicative inverse. We will prove an even stronger statement which will be useful later. No element of $D[x]$ which has degree greater than zero has an inverse. Clearly, there are elements in $D[x]$ such as $(0, 1, 0, \ldots, 0, \ldots)$. Let v be any element in $D[x]$ of degree greater than zero. If v has an inverse, it is not the zero polynomial, since the product of v with the zero polynomial gives zero and not the identity of $D[x]$. Suppose, then, that v' is any nonzero element of $D[x]$. The product vv' has degree greater than zero, since the degree of the product is the sum of the degrees of the factors. The unity element, $(1, 0, \ldots, 0, \ldots)$, of $D[x]$ has degree zero, and hence vv' is not the unity of $D[x]$. That is, v' is not the inverse of v. Now since v' was an arbitrary element of $D[x]$ other than zero, v has no inverse in $D[x]$. This proves that $D[x]$ is not a field, no matter what the integral domain D may be.

Corollary. No element of the polynomial domain $D[x]$, for an integral domain D, has an inverse if the degree of the element is greater than zero.

It is true, of course, that the integral domain $D[x]$ may be extended to a field of quotients, by the method described in Section 6–5. We have no particular need to make this extension. We will consider division of polynomials in a way which does not involve this field directly. This treatment will be delayed until later, when the division algorithm for polynomials is discussed.

EXERCISES

For the polynomials in the exercises of this set, as previously, all coefficients not specifically given are to be considered as zero.

1. Given the polynomial $u = (3, 1, 2, 4, 0, \ldots)$, find $-u$ and check the sum $u + (-u)$ to show that it is the zero polynomial in each of the following cases:
   a) assuming $u \in \mathbf{Z}[x]$, where $\mathbf{Z}$ is the set of integers;
   b) assuming $u \in Z_5[x]$, where Z_5 is the set of integers modulo 5;
   c) assuming $u \in Z_{11}[x]$, where Z_{11} is the set of integers modulo 11.

2. Given that $u = (3, 4, 0, 2, 0, \ldots)$ and $v = (0, 2, 3, 0, 1, 0, \ldots)$, show that $uv = vu$ by direct computation:
   a) assuming that u and v are polynomials in $\mathbf{Z}[x]$;
   b) assuming that u and v are polynomials in $Z_5[x]$.

3. Let $u = (3, 4, 0, 2, 0, \ldots)$ and $e = (1, 0, \ldots, 0, \ldots)$. Check by direct computation that $eu = ue = u$:
   a) assuming that u and e are polynomials in $\mathbf{Z}[x]$;
   b) assuming that u and e are polynomials in $Z_5[x]$.

4. Let $u = (2, 0, -4, 1, 0, \ldots)$, $v = (0, -3, 0, \ldots)$, and $w = (-1, 0, 0, 2, 0, \ldots)$ be considered as polynomials in $\mathbf{Z}[x]$. Check by direct computation that these polynomials satisfy each of the following identities.
   a) $u + (v + w) = (u + v) + w$ b) $u(vw) = (uv)w$
   c) $u(v + w) = uv + uw$ d) $(u + v)w = uw + vw$

5. Let $u = (3, 0, 0, 2, 0, \ldots)$, $v = (0, 1, 2, 0, \ldots)$, and $w = (0, 0, 4, 0, \ldots)$ be considered as polynomials in $Z_5[x]$. Check by direct computation that these polynomials satisfy each of the following identities.
   a) $u + (v + w) = (u + v) + w$ b) $u(vw) = (uv)w$
   c) $u(v + w) = uv + uw$ d) $(u + v)w = uw + vw$

6. Let $u = (i, 0, 2, 0, \ldots)$, $v = (0, 2 - 3i, 0, \ldots)$, and $w = (\frac{1}{2}, 1 + 5i, 0, \ldots)$ be considered as polynomials in $S[x]$, where S is the field given in Exercise 2 of Section 6–5. That is, the coefficients of u, v, and w are complex numbers, where $i^2 = -1$. Check by direct computation that these polynomials satisfy each of the following identities.
   a) $u + (v + w) = (u + v) + w$ b) $u(vw) = (uv)w$
   c) $u(v + w) = uv + uw$ d) $(u + v)w = uw + vw$

7. Find a nonzero element in $D[x]$ for an arbitrary integral domain D which has no inverse. Do not use the example in the text, namely, $(0, 1, 0, \ldots, 0, \ldots)$. Prove that your answer is correct.

8. Let D be a field and let S be the subset of $D[x]$ consisting of all polynomials which have degree zero or no degree. That is, $S = \{(a, 0, \ldots, 0, \ldots) \mid a \in D\}$. Prove that each non-zero polynomial in S has an inverse in S. Note that these are the only polynomials in $D[x]$ which have inverses, according to the corollary to Theorem 7–8.

7-4   *D* AS A SUBSET OF *D*[x]

In this section, we will justify the contention made earlier that $D[x]$ is an extension of the integral domain D. While D is not actually a subset of $D[x]$, there is a set D' isomorphic to D which is a subset of $D[x]$. It is in this sense that we use the word "extension." Recall a similar circumstance in the extension of the integers to the set of rational numbers.

Let D be an arbitrary integral domain, and denote by D' the set of all poly-nomials in $D[x]$ whose coefficients are all zero except for the constant term, which may be either zero or nonzero. That is,

$$D' = \{(a_0, 0, \ldots, 0, \ldots) \mid a_0 \in D\}.$$

We refer to D' as the set of *constant polynomials* in $D[x]$.

Theorem 7–9. If D is an integral domain and D' is the set of constant poly-nomials in $D[x]$, then D' is isomorphic to D.

To prove this theorem, we need to find a one-to-one mapping from D' onto D which preserves the operations of addition and multiplication. For this purpose, define the mapping τ from D' into D by $\tau(a_0, 0, \ldots, 0, \ldots) = a_0$, for each constant polynomial $(a_0, 0, \ldots, 0, \ldots)$ in D'. The mapping τ is one-to-one from D' onto D, since, for each element $x \in D$, there is one and only one constant polynomial having x as its zeroth coefficient, and for each constant polynomial $(y, 0, \ldots, 0, \ldots)$, y is a unique element of D.

Now, in order to prove that operations are preserved by τ, we consider any two elements in D', say $u = (a, 0, \ldots, 0, \ldots)$ and $v = (b, 0, \ldots, 0, \ldots)$. Then,

$$\begin{aligned}
\tau(u + v) &= \tau[(a, 0, \ldots, 0, \ldots) + (b, 0, \ldots, 0, \ldots)] \\
&= \tau(a + b, 0, \ldots, 0, \ldots) && \text{by definition of } + \text{ in } D[x], \\
&= a + b && \text{by definition of } \tau, \\
&= \tau(a, 0, \ldots, 0, \ldots) + \tau(b, 0, \ldots, 0, \ldots) && \text{by definition of } \tau, \\
&= \tau(u) + \tau(v).
\end{aligned}$$

Similarly, we consider the image of the product uv, noting that the product of two constant polynomials is also a constant polynomial whose zeroth term is the product of the zeroth terms of the two factors.

$$\tau(uv) = \tau[(a, 0, \ldots, 0, \ldots)(b, 0, \ldots, 0, \ldots)]$$
$$= \tau(ab, 0, \ldots, 0, \ldots) \qquad \text{by definition of product in}$$
$$\qquad\qquad\qquad\qquad\qquad\qquad D[x],$$
$$= ab \qquad\qquad\qquad\qquad\qquad \text{by definition of } \tau,$$
$$= \tau(a, 0, \ldots, 0, \ldots)\tau(b, 0, \ldots, 0, \ldots) \qquad \text{by definition of } \tau,$$
$$= \tau(u)\tau(v).$$

Thus we have shown that τ preserves the operations of addition and multiplication. This completes the proof that τ is an isomorphism and hence that D' is isomorphic to D.

As we have said before, when two mathematical systems are isomorphic, they differ only in notation. Hence it would make sense to denote each symbol $(x, 0, \ldots, 0, \ldots)$ for an element of D' by the symbol x. In the next section we will make this replacement and also reduce the symbol for a general element of $D[x]$ to a new symbol more easily recognizable as related to elementary algebra.

EXERCISES

1. List all polynomials of degree two or less in $Z_2[x]$.

2. Prove that if D is a field, then the subset D' of $D[x]$ given by

$$D' = \{(a, 0, \ldots, 0, \ldots) \mid a \in D\}$$

   is a field. (That is, D' is the set of constant polynomials in $D[x]$.)

3. Let D be an integral domain, and define the subset S of $D[x]$ by

$$S = \{(0, a, 0, \ldots, 0, \ldots) \mid a \in D\}.$$

   Let the mapping ρ of S onto D be defined by

$$\rho(0, a, 0, \ldots, 0, \ldots) = a \text{ for each } (0, a, 0, \ldots, 0, \ldots) \text{ in } S.$$

   Prove that ρ is *not* an isomorphism of S onto D. (This suggests the fact the set D' in Theorem 7–9 is the only subset of $D[x]$ isomorphic to D.)

4. Let D' be the subset of $D[x]$ defined in Theorem 7–9 for an integral domain D. Suppose that σ is an isomorphism of D onto D. (Note that although the domain and the range of σ are the same set, σ need not be the identity mapping.) If τ is the mapping of Theorem 7–9, prove $\sigma\tau$ is an isomorphism of D' onto D, where the mapping $\sigma\tau$ is defined by $\sigma\tau(x) = \sigma(\tau(x))$ for each $x \in D'$. (This problem correctly suggests that there may be more than one mapping of D' onto D which is an isomorphism.)

7-5   THE INDETERMINATE x

We have discussed the polynomial domain $D[x]$ for an integral domain D in a way which shows clearly what a polynomial is. The set $D[x]$ is an extension of D to a larger integral domain with elements that are quite different from those of D. Operations in $D[x]$ are defined in terms of operations in D, but they are new operations. The notation used up to now has helped in keeping the systems

D and $D[x]$ separate as we investigated properties of $D[x]$.   However, this notation is not used (and probably should never be used) in high school or college freshman courses dealing with polynomials.   If our work is to help in the reader's understanding of elementary algebra, it is necessary to show how our polynomials are related to those he has met in earlier courses.

As a first step in this direction, we have pointed out in Section 7–4 that the constant polynomials may be written more simply as elements of D, since D is isomorphic to the set.   We will agree, then, that for each $a \in D$, we will write $a = (a, 0, \ldots, 0, \ldots)$.

As the next step, we define the symbol x to be the polynomial

$$(0, 1, 0, \ldots, 0, \ldots).$$

That is, x is to be the name for the specific polynomial in $D[x]$ which has 1 as its first coefficient and 0 for all other coefficients, including the zeroth coefficient. We write

$$x = (0, 1, 0, \ldots, 0, \ldots).$$

Theorem 7–10. If $x = (0, 1, 0, \ldots, 0, \ldots)$ in the polynomial domain $D[x]$, then $x^2 = (0, 0, 1\ 0, \ldots)$ and, in general, for each positive integer n, $x^n = (c_0, \ldots, c_n, \ldots)$, where $c_n = 1$ and $c_i = 0$ for all integers $i \neq n$.

The proof of the theorem is by induction on n.   If $n = 1$, then $x^1 = x = (0, 1, 0, \ldots, 0, \ldots)$, by definition, and the theorem clearly holds in this case. Assume next that the theorem holds when $n = k$ (the induction hypothesis).   That is, $x^k = (c_0, \ldots, c_n, \ldots)$, where $c_k = 1$ and $c_i = 0$ for all $i \neq k$.   Then,

$$x^{k+1} = x^k x = (c_0, \ldots, c_n, \ldots)(0, 1, 0, \ldots, 0, \ldots) = (d_0, \ldots, d_n, \ldots),$$

where $d_0, d_1, \ldots$ are yet to be determined.   If we denote x by $(x_0, \ldots, x_n, \ldots)$, then we can say that $x_1 = 1$ and $x_i = 0$ for all $i \neq 1$.   The formula for multiplication gives $d_n = \Sigma_{i+j=n}\, c_i x_j$.   Since $c_k = 1$, while all $c_i = 0$ for $i \neq k$, and $x_1 = 1$, while all $x_j = 0$ for $j \neq 1$, the only product $c_i x_j$ which is nonzero is the product $c_k x_1$, and this product is 1.   But $c_k x_1$ appears only in the summation for d_{k+1}.   Thus, $d_{k+1} = 1$, while $d_n = 0$ for all $n \neq k + 1$.   That is, x^{k+1} is that polynomial whose $(k + 1)$-coefficient is 1 and all others are zero.   This establishes the theorem for the case $n = k + 1$, and by the principle of mathematical induction, the theorem is valid for all positive integers n.

We are now ready to formulate the theorem which allows us to write a polynomial in the form usually encountered in elementary courses in algebra.

Theorem 7–11. If $(a_0, \ldots, a_n, \ldots)$ is a polynomial of degree k in $D[x]$ for an integral domain D, then

$$(a_0, \ldots, a_n, \ldots) = a_0 + a_1 x + a_2 x^2 + \cdots + a_k x^k,$$

where $x = (0, 1, 0, \ldots, 0, \ldots)$ and $u = (u, 0, \ldots, 0, \ldots)$ for each $u \in D$.

To prove this theorem, we will show first that the product $a_m x^m$ for $0 \le m \le k$ is a polynomial whose mth coefficient is a_m, with all other coefficients zero. This follows directly from the definition of multiplication of polynomials, since the only nonzero coefficient in $a_m = (a_m, 0, \ldots, 0, \ldots)$ is the zeroth coefficient a_m, and the only nonzero coefficient in x^m is the mth coefficient, which is 1. Hence the only nonzero coefficient in the product will be the one involving $a_m \cdot 1$. This is the mth coefficient of the product. That is, $a_m x^m = (b_0, \ldots, b_n, \ldots)$, where $b_m = a_m$ and $b_i = 0$ for all $i \ne m$. Now, since $(a_0, \ldots, a_n, \ldots)$ is of degree k, all coefficients a_i for $i > k$ are zero. The sum $a_0 + a_1 x + \cdots + a_k x^k$ is now clearly equal to $(a_0, \ldots, a_n, \ldots)$, since to add two or more polynomials, we merely add corresponding coefficients. With this, the proof is complete.

Example 7–10. Consider the polynomial $(2, 3, 0, 4, 0, \ldots)$ in $\mathbf{Z}[x]$. By Theorem 7–10, $x^2 = (0, 0, 1, 0, \ldots, 0, \ldots)$ and $x^3 = (0, 0, 0, 1, 0, \ldots, 0, \ldots)$. Then

$$
\begin{aligned}
2 + 3x + 0x^2 + 4x^3 &= (2, 0, \ldots) + (3, 0, \ldots)(0, 1, 0, \ldots) \\
&\quad + (0, \ldots)(0, 0, 1, 0, \ldots) \\
&\quad + (4, 0, \ldots)(0, 0, 0, 1, 0, \ldots) \\
&= (2, 0, \ldots) + (0, 3, 0, \ldots) + (0, \ldots) \\
&\quad + (0, 0, 0, 4, 0, \ldots) \\
&= (2, 3, 0, 4, 0, \ldots).
\end{aligned}
$$

Each step above resulted from direct computation by definitions of operations in $\mathbf{Z}[x]$. In each polynomial all nonzero coefficients are written explicitly. This illustrates the content of Theorem 7–11 in a specific numerical case. The general proof given for the theorem depends only upon the same computational procedures.

Since we have introduced the familiar notation for polynomials, which we will use from now on, it is well to point out some of the common errors that are made in the use of the notation. First, since the expression $a_0 + a_1 x + \cdots + a_n x^n$ involves letters a_i, which represent elements of D, and the letter x, which looks much like a symbol for an element of D, it is easy to believe that the operations of addition and multiplication appearing in the expression are the operations of D. This is not the case. The reader should remember that addition and multiplication in this expression are operations in $D[x]$, not in D. Further, the symbol x does *not* represent an element of D, but is a special polynomial in $D[x]$. The symbols in $a_0 + a_1 x + \cdots + a_n x^n$ represent elements of a new and larger mathematical system which extends D. For proofs of theorems about polynomials, we must rely on known properties of $D[x]$ rather than those of D. If these facts are kept clearly in mind, many of the common errors in treating polynomials would be avoided.

A final comment is in order. If we should write the equation $2 + 3x = 0$, the only interpretation possible at the present stage is that this equation implies that $2 = 0$ and $3 = 0$. The term $2 + 3x$ is an abbreviation for the polynomial

$(2, 3, 0, \ldots)$, and 0 is an abbreviation for the zero polynomial $(0, 0, \ldots)$. Hence we have stated that $(2, 3, 0, \ldots) = (0, 0, \ldots)$. From the definition of equality of polynomials, this means that $2 = 0$ and $3 = 0$. If 2 and 3 are integers, as they appear to be, this is absurd.

On the other hand, we often write equations such as

$$x^2 - 1 = (x + 1)(x - 1),$$

where the meaning is exactly what our treatment gives. This equation can be rewritten as

$$(-1, 0, 1, 0, \ldots) = (1, 1, 0, \ldots)(-1, 1, 0, \ldots).$$

A careful check reveals that this equation is valid in $Z[x]$.

The examples of the preceding paragraphs illustrate two common uses for equations in elementary mathematics. The first is termed a *conditional equation* and the second is termed an *identical equation*, or simply an *identity*. Equality of polynomials, as we have defined it, is synonymous with the second usage. We need new definitions and new terminology to treat conditional equations. This will be the subject of some of the remaining sections of this chapter.

The symbol $D[x]$ has been justified, in part, by the introduction of the shortened notation for polynomials. The following definition explains terminology frequently used in connection with polynomials.

Definition 1. The symbol x, as used in a polynomial

$$a_0 + a_1 x + \cdots + a_n x^n \text{ in } D[x],$$

is called an *indeterminate*. The domain $D[x]$ is referred to as the domain of *polynomials in the indeterminate x* over the integral domain D. We also speak of $a_0 + 1_1 x + \cdots + a_n x^n$ as a *polynomial in the indeterminate x with coefficients in D.*

The word "indeterminate" refers to the use of x to represent a polynomial. Of course, any other letter might be used as well. We could consider $D[y]$ or $D[z]$ instead of $D[x]$. From our definitions, it should be clear that these sets are indistinguishable.

A comparison of the definitions of addition and multiplication of polynomials, written as sequences with the familiar rules for operations with polynomials written in terms of x, will reveal that these operations are identical. Now that the notation for a polynomial in terms of x has been introduced, operations may be performed in the same way that they were performed in high school algebra. We will frequently refer to a polynomial as $a(x)$, $f(x)$, or a similar symbol whether it is written as a sequence or otherwise. The following example illustrates the meaning of these remarks.

Example 7–11. Let $a(x) = (3, 0, 2, 0, \ldots)$ and $b(x) = (0, 1, 3, 4, 0, \ldots)$. We may also write $a(x) = 3 + 2x^2$ and $b(x) = x + 3x^2 + 4x^3$. The product $a(x)b(x)$ can be computed from either notation. For instance,

$$a(x)b(x) = (3, 0, 2, 0, \ldots)(0, 1, 3, 4, 0, \ldots) = (0, 3, 9, 14, 6, 8, 0, \ldots).$$

On the other hand,

$$a(x)b(x) = (3 + 2x^2)(x + 3x^2 + 4x^3) = 3x + 9x^2 + 14x^3 + 6x^4 + 8x^5.$$

Comparison shows that these answers are the same, although written in different notations.

A final definition extends the treatment of polynomials to polynomials in two indeterminates. We will make no use of this definition, but it is included as a matter of interest.

Definition 2. A *polynomial in two indeterminates* x and y is a polynomial in y with coefficients in $D[x]$. The set of all such polynomials is written as $(D[x])[y]$ or, more simply, as $D[x, y]$.

Example 7–12. $P = 2x^2 + 3xy + y^2$ is a polynomial in $Z[x, y]$. We could, of course, write it more precisely as $P = (2x^2, 3x, 1, 0, \ldots)$. The ultimate in precision would show P as an infinite sequence, each of whose terms was itself an infinite sequence of elements in Z. This is rarely done. One might also think of P as a polynomial in x, with coefficients in $Z[y]$. A sequence notation for P would then be $(y^2, 3y, 2, 0, \ldots)$.

As illustrated in the example, the order in which the two indeterminates are given makes no difference. It is relatively easy to prove that for any integral domain D, $D[x, y]$ is isomorphic to $D[y, x]$, and hence the only difference is in the notation used in the sequences. When a polynomial from one of these sets is written in terms of x and y, it is not possible to tell which set is intended, as with the polynomial in Example 7–12.

EXERCISES

1. Express each of the following polynomials in $Z[x]$ in the form $a_0 + a_1x + \cdots + a_nx^n$.

    a) $(0, 2, 0, -3, 0, 5, 0, \ldots)$ b) $(3, 0, 0, 4, 0, \ldots)$
    c) $(0, 0, 0, 0, 7, 0, \ldots)$ d) $(2, 5, -2, 4, 1, 0, 3, 0, \ldots)$

2. Express each of the following polynomials in $Z[x]$ in the form $(a_0, \ldots, a_n, \ldots)$.

    a) $x^2 - 3$ b) 5 c) $3x$
    d) $5x^2 - 3x + 4$ e) x^7 f) $x^5 + 3x^2 + 2$

3. Show by substitution similar to that in Example 7–10 that

$$3 + 2x^2 - 4x^4 = (3, 0, 2, 0, -4, 0, \ldots).$$

4. Show by substitution similar to that in Example 7–10 that

$$4x^2 - 3x - 2x^3 = (0, -3, 4, -2, 0, \ldots).$$

5. Write the polynomial $x^2 - 2xy + y^2 - 3x + 2y$ as:

    a) a polynomial $(a_0, \ldots, a_n, \ldots)$ in $D[x]$, where $D = Z[y]$; that is, where each a_i is a polynomial in y (see Example 7–12).
    b) a polynomial $(b_0, \ldots, b_n, \ldots)$ in $D[y]$ where $D = Z[x]$.

6. Determine which of the following equations are valid, considering the polynomials as elements of $Z_5[x]$.

 a) $x^2 + 1 = (x + 2)(x + 3)$ b) $x^2 + 2x + 2 = (2x + 3)(3x + 4)$
 c) $3x^2 + x + 4 = (3x + 2)(x + 2)$ d) $(x + 2)^5 = x^5 + 2$

7. a) Let $u = (2, 0, 1, -2, 0, \ldots)$ and $v = (0, -2, 3, 0, \ldots)$ be polynomials in $\mathbf{Z}[x]$. Compute each of following from the definitions given for polynomials as sequences.

 i) $u + v$ ii) $u - v$ iii) uv iv) u^2 v) v^2

 b) Write u and v in the notation $a + bx - cx^2 + \cdots$. Now compute quantities (i) through (v) in part (a), using the familiar rules for operations with polynomials given in previous courses. Check the answers against those found in part (a).

8. Let $u = (3, 0, 2, 4, 0, \ldots)$ and $v = (0, 2, 4, 0, \ldots)$ be polynomials in $Z_5[x]$. Repeat Exercise 7 for these polynomials.

7-6   DIVISIBILITY OF POLYNOMIALS

The terminology relating to divisibility for polynomials is essentially the same as for integers, as presented in Section 2–8. If $a(x)$ and $f(x)$ are elements of $D[x]$, then $a(x)$ is a *divisor* (or *factor*) of $f(x)$ if and only if there is a polynomial $b(x)$ in $D[x]$ such that $f(x) = a(x)b(x)$. We write $a(x) \mid f(x)$, and read the notation as $a(x)$ divides $f(x)$. If $f(x) \mid g(x)$ and $g(x) \mid f(x)$, then we call $f(x)$ and $g(x)$ *associates*.

A *unit* is an element of an integral domain which has an inverse. If two polynomials $f(x)$ and $g(x)$ in a domain $D[x]$ are associates, then $f(x) = a(x)g(x)$ and $g(x) = b(x)f(x)$ for some polynomials $a(x)$ and $b(x)$. Substituting for $g(x)$ in the first equation, we have $f(x) = a(x)b(x)f(x)$. By the cancellation law for multiplication in $D[x]$, $1 = a(x)b(x)$. That is, $a(x)$ and $b(x)$ are inverses of each other. We have already shown that the only elements in $D[x]$ which have inverses are the constant polynomials, that is, elements of D. These may or may not have inverses depending on D. If D is a field, all nonzero elements have inverses. Otherwise, some elements in D may have inverses while others do not. In any case, $a(x)$ and $b(x)$ above must be elements of D. The foregoing remarks prove the following theorem.

Theorem 7–12. If $f(x)$ and $g(x)$ are polynomials in $D[x]$ which are associates, then $f(x) = d[g(x)]$ for some element $d \in D$.

Because of this theorem, we wish to differentiate between two types of divisors. Since any polynomial is divisible by its associates and by all units, these divisors are of little interest and are referred to as *improper divisors*. All other divisors are *proper divisors*.

Example 7–13. Consider $3x + 2$ as an element of $Z_5[x]$. Then $3x + 2$ and $x + 4$ are associates, since $2(3x + 2) = x + 4$ and $3(x + 4) = 3x + 2$. Hence $3x + 2$ is an improper divisor of $x + 4$, and $x + 4$ is an improper divisor of $3x + 2$.

Example 7–14. Every number $a \neq 0$ in the field **R** of real numbers is a divisor of each polynomial $f(x)$ in **R**$[x]$. Thus $2 \mid x^2 + 1$, since $x^2 + 1 = 2(\frac{1}{2}x^2 + \frac{1}{2})$ and $\sqrt{2} \mid 3x - 5$, since

$$3x - 5 = \sqrt{2}\left(\frac{3}{\sqrt{2}}x - \frac{5}{\sqrt{2}}\right).$$

Definition of irreducible polynomial. A polynomial $f(x)$ in $D[x]$, for an integral domain D, is *irreducible over D* (or *prime*) if and only if it has no proper divisors in $D[x]$; $f(x)$ is *reducible over D* if it has a proper divisor in $D[x]$.

Note that this definition of an irreducible polynomial refers to the polynomial domain to which the polynomial and its divisors belong. This is essential. It is entirely possible that a polynomial may be irreducible when considered as an element of one domain and yet reducible in another.

Example 7–15. $x^2 - 2$ is irreducible over the field of rational numbers but is reducible over the field of real numbers, since $x^2 - 2 = (x + \sqrt{2})(x - \sqrt{2})$.

Example 7–16. $3x^2 + 6$ is reducible over the integers but irreducible over the rational numbers: $3x^2 + 6 = 3(x^2 + 2)$. Since 3 is not a unit in the set of integers, 3 is a proper divisor and $3x^2 + 6$ is reducible over the integers. On the other hand, 3 is a unit in the field **Q** of rational numbers and is therefore an improper divisor in **Q**$[x]$. Hence $3x^2 + 6$ is irreducible over **Q**$[x]$.

These examples point out that instructions to "factor $f(x)$" are not sufficient. Before the problem will make sense, it must be understood which coefficients are to be allowed in the factorization. We should not say that $x^2 - 2$ cannot be factored, but that it cannot be factored into factors with rational coefficients.

Most factoring problems in high school algebra are restricted to factorization over the integers. This is unfortunate because in solving quadratic equations and other problems, it would help greatly to be able to consider factoring over other sets as well, particularly over the rational numbers, the real numbers, and the complex numbers. Of course, it must be kept clear in each problem which set or sets are being considered.

EXERCISES

1. Prove that $f(x) = x^2 + 6$ is reducible over Z_7 and Z_{11}, and over the complex numbers. To prove this, merely show a correct factorization of $f(x)$.
2. Find three different associates of $3x^2 + 4x + 2$ considered as an element in **Q**$[x]$.
3. Find three different associates of $3x^2 + 4x + 2$ considered as an element in $Z_5[x]$.
4. Find all units in each of the following domains. Describe them explicitly.
   (a) **Z**. (b) **Q**. (c) Z_5. (d) $S = \{a + b\sqrt{2} \mid a \text{ and } b \text{ are integers}\}$. (e) **Z**$[x]$. (f) $Z_5[x]$.
5. Decide whether $f(x) = 2x^2 + 2x - 2$ is reducible or irreducible over each of the following integral domains. Do not show proof, but give the factors in each case where $f(x)$ is reducible.
   (a) **Z**. (b) **Q**. (c) **R**. (d) **C**.

6. Decide whether $g(x) = x^2 + 3x + 5$ is reducible or irreducible over each of the following fields.   Do not show proof, but give the factors in each case where $g(x)$ is reducible.

   (a) **Q**.   (b) **R**.   (c) **C**.

7. Factor $x^4 - 4$ into irreducible factors over each of the following integral domains.

   (a) **Z**.   (b) **Q**.   (c) **R**.   (d) **C**.

8. Factor each of the following polynomials into irreducible factors over the given field.

   a) $6x^2 + 2x + 6$ over Z_7 b) $2x^2 + 8x + 1$ over Z_{11}
   c) $3x^2 + 3x + 2$ over Z_7 d) $10x^2 + 9x + 8$ over Z_{11}
   e) $x^2 + 3$ over Z_7 f) $3x^2 + 2$ over Z_7

7-7   VALUE OF A POLYNOMIAL AT $x = a$

Consider a polynomial $f(x) = a_0 + a_1x + \cdots + a_nx^n$ in $D[x]$ for an arbitrary integral domain D. It has been emphasized that the indicated operations of addition and multiplication are operations in $D[x]$, not in D.   Many applications of polynomials make use of an element of D obtained by replacing x in the symbol $a_0 + a_1x + \cdots + a_nx^n$ by an element, say c, of D and performing operations in D indicated by the resulting expression.   This element of D is called the *value of* $f(x)$ *at* $x = c$ and is denoted by $f(c)$.   A formal definition of $f(c)$ follows.   The summation notation is used to make the definition explicit.

Definition 1. Let $f(x) = \Sigma_{i=0}^n a_ix^i$ be a polynomial over D, and let c be an element of D.   Then $f(c) = \Sigma_{i=0}^n a_ic^i$, where the indicated addition and multiplication are interpreted as operations in D.

We might say that each polynomial $f(x)$ in $D[x]$ serves to define a mapping of D into D, given by $\{(c, f(c)) \mid c \in D\}$. Note that $f(c)$ is a single element of D, and that $f(x)$ is never equal to $f(c)$.   Hence $f(x)$ is an element of $D[x]$ and $f(c)$ is an element of D.

Example 7–17. If $f(x) = 2 - 3x + 4x^2$ is considered an element in $Z[x]$, then

$$f(2) = 2 - 3(2) + 4(2)^2 = 12$$

and

$$f(-3) = 2 - 3(-3) + 4(-3)^2 = 47.$$

Now that we have defined the value of a polynomial $f(x)$ at $x = c$ for c an element of the domain of coefficients, let us consider the meaning of the symbols which appear in the following standard problem in elementary algebra.

1)   Solve the equation $x^2 - 5x + 6 = 0$.

The expression $x^2 - 5x + 6$ is not a polynomial in this usage.   If it were, the equation would represent the statement that the polynomial $x^2 - 5x + 6$ is the zero polynomial. This is absurd, since our definition of equality of poly-nomials would then require that $1 = 0$, $-5 = 0$, and $6 = 0$.

Whenever we write Problem (1) above we really intend the student to find all numbers c such that $c^2 - 5c + 6 = 0$. In the notation just introduced, if we let $f(x) = x^2 - 5x + 6$, we are asking for numbers c such that $f(c) = 0$. This statement makes sense. Problem (1) does not refer to a polynomial as such but to the value of a polynomial at $x = c$ for an unknown element c in the domain of coefficients. In the usage of Problem (1), the symbol x is referred to as an *un-known*.

Of course, whether one uses the letter x or the letter c in stating a problem such as (1) makes no real difference. The difficulty is that when the same symbol is used to represent an indeterminate and an unknown, confusion is apt to result.

This difficulty might be avoided by using two sets of symbols for each of the operations of addition and multiplication and two sets for equality. When an equation is written which states that two polynomials are equal, such as in the equation, $x^2 - 4 = (x + 2)(x - 2)$, the operations and equality are those of $D[x]$ for the appropriate polynomial domain. When one asks the student to solve the equation $x^2 - 4 = 0$, the operations and equality are those of D for the appropriate integral domain of numbers. To distinguish these usages, we might agree to write $\oplus$, $\ominus$, $\odot$, and $\equiv$ for addition, subtraction, multiplication, and equality in $D[x]$. We could continue the usual notation for D. Then the first equation would be written

$$(x \odot x) \ominus 4 \equiv (x \oplus 2) \odot (x \ominus 2).$$

This would solve the problem of ambiguity but is not a pleasant notation to use.

Some authors use $\equiv$ as the symbol for equality in a polynomial domain $D[x]$ and $=$ as the symbol for equality in D. Then in any equation involving $\equiv$, the indicated operations are automatically assumed to be those of $D[x]$. Should $=$ appear, one would assume that the operations are those of D. When this is done, we read the symbol $\equiv$ as "is identical to" rather than as "is equal to." This is probably the best solution to the problem.

Whatever symbolism is used, a teacher should feel obligated to distinguish carefully between the uses of the symbol x as an indeterminate and as an unknown.

Definition 2. If $f(x)$ is a polynomial in $D[x]$ for an integral domain D, and $f(c) = 0$ for an element c in D, then c is called a *zero* of $f(x)$.

The problem of finding the zeros of a polynomial is central to elementary algebra. In this problem, as with factorization, it is necessary to specify clearly the integral domain from which the coefficients are taken.

Example 7–18. The polynomial $f(x) = x^2 - 2$ has no zeros when considered as an element of $Z[x]$. However, if $f(x)$ is considered as an element in $R[x]$, both $\sqrt{2}$ and $-\sqrt{2}$ are zeros of $f(x)$. If $f(x)$ is considered as a polynomial in $Z_7[x]$, then 3 and 4 are zeros of $f(x)$.

EXERCISES

1. Given $f(x) = 2 + 3x + 4x^2$ in $Z_5[x]$. Find: (a) $f(0)$, (b) $f(1)$, (c) $f(2)$, (d) $f(3)$, and (e) $f(4)$.

2. Polynomials may be defined over rings which are not integral domains; however, not all the theorems that we have proved still hold. Prove by counterexample that the degree of a product of two polynomials is not always the sum of the degrees of the factors if the ring of coefficients is not an integral domain.

3. Let

$$f(x) = \begin{pmatrix} 2 & 1 \\ 0 & 3 \end{pmatrix} - \begin{pmatrix} 0 & 2 \\ 4 & 3 \end{pmatrix} x + \begin{pmatrix} 1 & -1 \\ 1 & 1 \end{pmatrix} x^2$$

be considered as a polynomial with coefficients in the ring of 2×2 matrices. Find:

a) $f\left[\begin{pmatrix} 0 & 1 \\ 1 & 0 \end{pmatrix}\right]$

b) $f\left[\begin{pmatrix} 1 & 2 \\ 0 & 2 \end{pmatrix}\right]$

c) $f\left[\begin{pmatrix} 2 & 0 \\ 1 & 3 \end{pmatrix}\right]$

d) $f\left[\begin{pmatrix} 1 & 1 \\ 1 & 0 \end{pmatrix}\right]$

4. Find two polynomials of at least second degree in $Z_7[x]$ such that $x = 5$ is a zero of the polynomial.

5. Show that the polynomial $2x^2 + 3x + 2$ has no zeros if considered as a polynomial in $Z_5[x]$ but has a zero if considered as a polynomial in $Z_7[x]$. Find this zero.

6. Determine, without proof, whether or not the polynomial $2x^2 + x - 6$ has zeros when considered an element of each of the following polynomial domains. List any zeros that exist in each case. (A proof that the polynomial does not have zeros is impossible at present, since we have not yet proved the necessary factorization theorems.)

   (a) $Z_{11}[x]$ (b) $Z_7[x]$ (c) $Z[x]$ (d) $Q[x]$ (e) $R[x]$ (f) $C[x]$

7. Repeat Exercise 6 for the polynomial $x^2 + x + 1$.

8. Prove that

$$\begin{pmatrix} 1 & 2 \\ -1 & 3 \end{pmatrix}$$

is a zero of the polynomial $f(x)$ given by

$$f(x) = \begin{pmatrix} -3 & 9 \\ -12 & 11 \end{pmatrix} + \begin{pmatrix} 2 & 1 \\ 3 & 4 \end{pmatrix} x + \begin{pmatrix} -2 & 0 \\ -1 & -3 \end{pmatrix} x^2,$$

where the coefficients are from the ring of 2×2 matrices.

9. Determine whether the symbol x in each of the following equations is used as an indeterminate or as an unknown. Consider all polynomials as elements of $Z[x]$. Recall that an indeterminate appears in an equation (identity) in $Z[x]$, while an unknown will appear in an equation (conditional equation) in Z.

   a) $3x + 6 = 3(x + 2)$

   b) $x^2 - 5 = 0$

   c) $(x + 2)^2 = x^2 + 4x + 4$

   d) $(x + 3)(x - 2) = x^2 + x - 6$

   e) $x^2 + 7x = 5$

   f) $x^3 = 1$

7-8   THE DIVISION ALGORITHM

In considering questions of factoring and divisibility for polynomials, it is customary to restrict the domain of coefficients to a field. Otherwise, the statements of theorems become quite involved and the results depend so heavily upon the nature of the coefficient domain that the properties of polynomials are obscured. From this point on, then, we will consider polynomials over a field F and change the notation for the polynomial domain to $F[x]$ to remind the reader that further restrictions have been placed on the sets of coefficients.

> **Definition.** Let $f(x) = a_0 + a_1x + \cdots + a_nx^n$, with $a_n \neq 0$, be a polynomial in $F[x]$ for a field F. a_n is called the *leading coefficient* of $f(x)$, and $f(x)$ is said to be *monic* if $a_n = 1$, the unity in F.

Example 7–19. $2x - 3x^2$ has -3 as its leading coefficient, and $x^3 - 2x + 4$ has leading coefficient 1, and is therefore monic.

> **Theorem 7–13 (the division algorithm for polynomials).** If $f(x)$ and $g(x)$ are polynomials in $F[x]$ for a field F, and $g(x) \neq 0$, there exist unique polynomials $q(x)$ and $r(x)$ in $F[x]$ such that
>
> 1) $f(x) = q(x)g(x) + r(x)$, and
>
> 2) either $r(x) = 0$ or the degree of $r(x)$ is less than the degree of $g(x)$.

If the degree of $f(x)$ is less than the degree of $g(x)$, or if $f(x) = 0$, the theorem is clearly valid, since $f(x) = 0 \cdot g(x) + f(x)$. That is, we may take $q(x) = 0$ and $r(x) = f(x)$. Then, either $r(x) = 0$ or the degree of $r(x)$ is less than the degree of $g(x)$, as required. We could also prove that $q(x)$ and $r(x)$ are unique in this case, but we will leave the proof of uniqueness until last.

Now let $f(x) = a_0 + a_1x + \cdots + a_nx^n$, with $a_n \neq 0$, so that the degree of $f(x)$ is n. Let $g(x) = b_0 + b_1x + \cdots + b_mx^m$, with $b_m \neq 0$, so that the degree of $g(x)$ is m. Since we have already taken care of the cases where $n < m$ and $f(x) = 0$, we will prove the theorem assuming that $n \geq m$ and $f(x) \neq 0$. The proof is by induction on n, the degree of $f(x)$.

First, if $n = 0$, then $f(x) = a_0$, where $a_0 \neq 0$. But $m \leq n$, so that $g(x) = b_0$. Further, $b_0 \neq 0$, since $g(x) \neq 0$. Therefore, b_0^{-1} exists. Hence, $f(x) = (a_0b_0^{-1})b_0 + 0$. That is, $q(x) = a_0b_0^{-1}$ and $r(x) = 0$ will satisfy the requirements of the theorem.

Next assume that the theorem holds for all polynomials $f(x)$ with degree less than k. (This is the induction hypothesis.) We need to prove that the theorem holds for a polynomial $f(x)$ of degree k. Consider $f(x) = a_0 + a_1x + \cdots + a_kx^k$, where $a_k \neq 0$, and $g(x) = b_0 + b_1x + \cdots + b_mx^m$, where $b_m \neq 0$ and $m \leq k$. We construct, first, an auxiliary polynomial $h(x)$. Since $b_m \neq 0$, b_m^{-1} exists.

(1) $\qquad\qquad$ Let $h(x) = f(x) - a_kb_m^{-1}x^{k-m}g(x)$.

If we replace $f(x)$ and $g(x)$ by their respective polynomial forms, we obtain

$$h(x) = (a_0 + a_1x + \cdots + a_kx^k) - a_kb_m^{-1}x^{k-m}(b_0 + b_1x + \cdots + b_mx^m)$$
$$= (a_0 + a_1x + \cdots + a_kx^k) - (a_kb_m^{-1}b_0x^{k-m} + \cdots + a_kx^k).$$

Note that $h(x)$ is the difference of two polynomials of degree k, each with leading coefficient a_k. Upon subtraction, the term involving x^k vanishes, leaving the degree of $h(x)$ less than k. By the induction hypothesis,

$$h(x) = q^*(x)g(x) + r(x),$$

where $q^*(x)$ and $r(x)$ are polynomials and $r(x)$ is zero or has degree less than the degree of $g(x)$. Substituting into equation (1), we have

$$q^*(x)g(x) + r(x) = f(x) - a_k b_m^{-1} x^{k-m} g(x).$$

Solving for $f(x)$, we obtain

$$f(x) = q^*(x)g(x) + a_k b_m^{-1} x^{k-m} g(x) + r(x)$$
$$= [q^*(x) + a_k b_m^{-1} x^{k-m}]g(x) + r(x).$$

Now if we let $q(x) = q^*(x) + a_k b_m^{-1} x^{k-m}$, we can say that $f(x) = q(x)g(x) + r(x)$, as required. The restrictions on $r(x)$ have been established above, so the theorem holds (except possibly for uniqueness) when $n = k$. By the second principle of mathematical induction, the theorem holds for all n.

To show that $q(x)$ and $r(x)$ are unique, assume that

$$f(x) = q_1(x)g(x) + r_1(x) = q_2(x)g(x) + r_2(x).$$

Then $[q_1(x) - q_2(x)]g(x) = r_2(x) - r_1(x)$. But unless $q_1(x) - q_2(x) = 0$, the degree of the product in the left member of this equation is at least m, the degree of $g(x)$. On the other hand, the degree of $r_2(x) - r_1(x)$ must be less than m, since the degrees of $r_1(x)$ and $r_2(x)$ are both less than m. This contradiction implies that $q_1(x) - q_2(x) = 0$, or that $q_1(x) = q_2(x)$. Then $r_2(x) - r_1(x) = 0$, and $r_1(x) = r_2(x)$. This proves that the polynomials $q(x)$ and $r(x)$ are unique and completes the proof of the theorem.

In order to compute the polynomials $q(x)$ and $r(x)$ referred to in Theorem 7–13, we use the usual process of long division for polynomials taught in high school. The theorem serves only to prove that this can always be done. The polynomials $q(x)$ and $r(x)$ are referred to as the *quotient* and the *remainder*, respectively, in the division of $f(x)$ by $g(x)$. This terminology is the same as that used for the integers.

Example 7–20. Let $f(x) = 2x^3 - 4x^2 + 5$ and $g(x) = 2x^2 - 3x + 2$ be considered polynomials in $\mathbf{Q}[x]$, where $\mathbf{Q}$ is the field of rational numbers. We will find the quotient and remainder of the division of $f(x)$ by $g(x)$ and express $f(x)$ in the form $f(x) = q(x)g(x) + r(x)$, where $r(x)$ satisfies the conditions of Theorem 6–13.

$$
\begin{array}{r}
x - \frac{1}{2} \\
2x^2 - 3x + 2 \overline{)\,2x^3 - 4x^2 \qquad\;\; + 5} \\
\underline{2x^3 - 3x^2 + 2x} \\
-x^2 - 2x + 5 \\
\underline{-x^2 + \frac{3}{2}x - 1} \\
-\frac{7}{2}x + 6
\end{array}
$$

Then

$$2x^3 - 4x^2 + 5 = (x - \tfrac{1}{2})(2x^3 - 3x + 2) + (-\tfrac{7}{2}x + 6).$$

Here, $q(x)$ is $x - \tfrac{1}{2}$, the quotient, and $r(x)$ is $-\tfrac{7}{2}x + 6$, the remainder.

The next two theorems are highly useful for work with polynomials and follow easily from the division algorithm.

Theorem 7–14 (remainder theorem).   If $f(x) \in F[x]$ and $a \in F$, for any field F, the remainder in the division of $f(x)$ by $x - a$ is $f(a)$.

To prove the theorem, we note that by the division algorithm, polynomials $q(x)$ and $r(x)$ exist such that $f(x) = q(x)(x - a) + r(x)$.   Further, either $r(x) = 0$, or the degree of $r(x)$ is less than that of $x - a$.   Since the degree of $x - a$ is one, $r(x)$ has degree 0 or no degree.   Hence $r(x)$ is a constant polynomial, which may be interpreted as an element r in F.   Thus $f(x) = q(x)(x - a) + r$ where $r \in F$.   Substituting $x = a$ into this equation, we see that $f(a) = r$, which completes the proof.

The preceding theorem can be used in connection with the process often referred to as synthetic division to determine the value of a polynomial at $x = a$ for various elements a in the field of coefficients.   It also has value in proving theorems about polynomials, such as the following.

Theorem 7–15 (factor theorem).   If $f(x) \in F[x]$ and $a \in F$, for a field F, then $x - a$ divides $f(x)$ if and only if $f(a) = 0$.

By the remainder theorem, $f(a)$ is the remainder on division of $f(x)$ by $x - a$. Hence if $f(a) = 0$, then $x - a$ divides $f(x)$.   Conversely, suppose that $x - a$ divides $f(x)$.   Then the remainder on division of $f(x)$ by $x - a$ is zero.   But this remainder is $f(a)$, by the remainder theorem, and the proof is complete.

Example 7–21.   Determine whether $x - 3$ and $x + 2$ are divisors of $f(x) = x^5 + 32$, considered as polynomials in $\mathbf{Q}[x]$.   Since $f(3) = 275 \neq 0$, $x - 3$ does not divide $x^5 + 32$.   However, $f(-2) = 0$, so that $x + 2$ divides $x^5 + 32$.   The reader is urged to perform the necessary long division to check these results.

EXERCISES

1. Find the quotient and remainder referred to in Theorem 7–13 when the polynomial $f(x)$ is divided by $g(x)$ in each of the following cases.   Express $f(x)$ in the form $f(x) = q(x)g(x) + r(x)$.   Assume that all polynomials are elements of $\mathbf{Q}[x]$.

   a) $f(x) = 4x^4 - 3x^2 + 2$ and $g(x) = x^3 - 2x + 1$
   b) $f(x) = 3x^3 - 2x^2 + x - 1$ and $g(x) = 3x^2 + 2x - 3$
   c) $f(x) = 6x^3 + 17x^2 + 7x - 20$ and $g(x) = 3x + 4$
   d) $f(x) = x + 5$ and $g(x) = x^2 - 2x + 6$
   e) $f(x) = 3x^2 + 2x$ and $g(x) = 2x^2 - 5$
   f) $f(x) = 2x^2 + 6x - 3$ and $g(x) = 7$

2. Find the quotient and remainder referred to in Theorem 7–13 when the polynomial $f(x)$ is divided by $g(x)$ in each of the following cases.   Express $f(x)$ in the form $f(x) = q(x)g(x) + r(x)$.   Assume that all polynomials are elements of $\mathbf{C}[x]$.

   a) $f(x) = \sqrt{2}x^2 + 3x - \sqrt{3}$ and $g(x) = x - \sqrt{2}$
   b) $f(x) = 2.3x^3 - 3.6x^2 + 0.04$ and $g(x) = x^2 - 1.32$
   c) $f(x) = x^3 - (2 + i)x + 3i$ and $g(x) = 2x - 1 + 2i$
   d) $f(x) = x^3 - 1$ and $g(x) = x + \frac{1}{2} - \frac{1}{2}\sqrt{3}\,i$

3. Find the quotient and remainder referred to in Theorem 7–13, when the polynomial $f(x)$ is divided by $g(x)$ in each of the following cases.   Express $f(x)$ in the form $f(x) = q(x)g(x) + r(x)$.   Assume that all polynomials are elements of $Z_5[x]$.

   a) $f(x) = 3x^3 + 2x^2 + x + 1$ and $g(x) = x^2 + 3x + 2$
   b) $f(x) = 3x^3 + 3x^2 + 3x + 1$ and $g(x) = 3x + 2$
   c) $f(x) = 3x^4 + x^2 + 3$ and $g(x) = 2x^2 + 2$
   d) $f(x) = x^5 + 1$ and $g(x) = x + 2$

4. Use the factor theorem to determine whether or not the polynomial $g(x)$ is a factor of the polynomial $f(x)$ in each of the following cases.

   a) $f(x) = x^4 - 2x^3 - 3$ and $g(x) = x + 1$ for $f(x)$ and $g(x)$ in $\mathbf{Q}[x]$
   b) $f(x) = 2x^3 + 3x^2 + 2x + 1$ and $g(x) = x + 2$, for $f(x)$ and $g(x)$ in $Z_5[x]$
   c) $f(x) = x^7 + 2x + 1$ and $g(x) = x + 3$, for $f(x)$ and $g(x)$ in $Z_7[x]$
   d) $f(x) = x^4 - 2ix^3 + x^2 + (2 + 5i)x - (3 + 6i$ and $g(x) = x - 3i$, for $f(x)$ and $g(x)$ in $\mathbf{C}[x]$
   e) $f(x) = x^3 + 2x^2 - 3$ and $g(x) = x - \sqrt{2}$, for $f(x)$ and $g(x)$ in $\mathbf{R}[x]$

7–9   THE GREATEST COMMON DIVISOR

The material in this section parallels that in Section 2–8 for integers.   There are minor differences that should be noted, but most of the former results apply directly to the case of polynomials.

> **Definition.**   A *greatest common divisor* (GCD) of two polynomials $f(x)$ and $g(x)$ is a polynomial $d(x)$ such that
>
> a) $d(x)$ is monic.
> b) $d(x)\,|\,f(x)$ and $d(x)\,|\,g(x)$.
> c) If $c(x)$ is a polynomial such that $c(x)\,|\,f(x)$ and $c(x)\,|\,g(x)$, then $c(x)\,|\,d(x)$.

The definition refers to *a* greatest common divisor.   We will prove that there is only one GCD for any two given polynomials.   The requirement that the GCD be monic is necessary in order to guarantee uniqueness.   For instance, if $f(x) = x^2 - 4$ and $g(x) = x^2 + 4x + 4$, then conditions (b) and (c) of the definition are satisfied by $c(x + 2)$ for any element c in the field of coefficients.   The restriction that the GCD be monic specifies $x + 2$ as the unique GCD of $f(x)$ and $g(x)$.

Example 7–22.   The GCD of $3x^3 - 24$ and $3x^2 - 12x + 12$, considered as elements of $\mathbf{Q}[x]$, is $x - 2$.   It is true, of course, that $3x - 6$ is a divisor of both polynomials, but $3x - 6$ is not monic.

Example 7–23. The GCD of $x^2 - 4$ and $x^2 + 6x + 9$, considered as elements of $Q[x]$, is 1, since the two polynomials have no common divisors other than constant polynomials. The only monic constant polynomial is 1.

The restriction that the GCD of two polynomials be monic may seem unnatural to the reader. In Example 7–22, it could be argued that $3x - 6$ is a more suitable GCD than $x - 2$. This is because 3 is greater than 1, and hence $3(x - 2)$ would appear to deserve the title of *greatest* common divisor. However, for polynomials over arbitrary fields, it would be impossible to describe a unique GCD in any other reasonable way. Not all fields are ordered, and there is therefore no way to select a *largest* constant multiplier. The restriction to monic polynomials is the only reasonable way to guarantee uniqueness for an arbitrary field of coefficients.

Theorem 7–16. Let F be a field and $f(x)$ and $g(x)$ be any two polynomials in $F[x]$, not both of which are zero. Then $f(x)$ and $g(x)$ have a unique greatest common divisor $d(x)$ which can be expressed in the form

$$d(x) = m(x)f(x) + n(x)g(x)$$

for polynomials $m(x)$ and $n(x)$ in $F[x]$.

Let $f(x)$ and $g(x)$ be two polynomials in $F[x]$, with $g(x) \neq 0$. This is no restriction, since at least one of the polynomials is nonzero and we denote it merely by $g(x)$. By the division algorithm, there exist polynomials $q_1(x)$ and $r_1(x)$ such that

$$f(x) = q_1(x)g(x) + r_1(x),$$

where $r_1(x)$ is zero or has lower degree than $g(x)$. Now if $r(x) \neq 0$, we apply the division algorithm to $g(x)$ and $r_1(x)$. [We omit until later the case where $r_1(x) = 0$.] By the algorithm, we may express $g(x)$ as

$$g(x) = q_2(x)r_1(x) + r_2(x),$$

where $r_2(x)$ is zero or has lower degree than $r_1(x)$. Next apply the algorithm to $r_1(x)$ and $r_2(x)$ if $r_2(x) \neq 0$. Continuing in this way, we determine the following sequence of equations.

$$f(x) = q_1(x)g(x) + r_1(x),$$
$$g(x) = q_2(x)r_1(x) + r_2(x),$$
1) $$r_1(x) = q_3(x)r_2(x) + r_3(x),$$
$$\vdots$$
$$r_{i-2}(x) = q_i(x)r_{i-1}(x) + r_i(x),$$
$$r_{i-1}(x) = q_{i+1}(x)r_i(x) + 0.$$

Here, each $r_j(x)$ is either 0 or has lower degree than $r_{j-1}(x)$. This process terminates with a remainder which is zero, since the degree of $r_1(x)$ is finite and each succeeding remainder has lower degree or is zero. If any remainder is a nonzero constant, say c, then the next step produces a zero remainder, since, as was shown in Section 7–7, each such element is a unit and a divisor of every polynomial.

Now $r_i(x)$ divides $r_{i-1}(x)$ by the final equation of (1). Working backward through the set of equations, we see that $r_i(x)$ divides $r_{i-2}(x)$, since it is a divisor of the right member of the next-to-last equation of (1), and hence must be a divisor of the left member. Continuing in this way, $r_i(x)$ divides each $r_j(x)$ for $j < i$ and also divides both $f(x)$ and $g(x)$.

Next, if $c(x)$ divides $f(x)$ and $g(x)$, then $c(x)$ must divide $r_1(x)$, from the first of equations (1), and $c(x)$ must also divide $r_2(x)$, by the second equation, since it divides $g(x)$ and $r_1(x)$. From the third equation, we see that $c(x)$ divides $r_3(x)$, etc. Continuing, we have that $c(x)$ divides $r_i(x)$.

From these facts, $r_i(x)$ satisfies conditions (b) and (c) in the definition of greatest common divisor. If the leading coefficient of $r_i(x)$ is b, then $d(x) = b^{-1}r_i(x)$ is monic. Further, $d(x)$ also satisfies (b) and (c) of the definition, since it differs from $r_i(x)$ by a factor which is a unit in F. Hence in case $r_1(x) \neq 0$, we have proved that $d(x) = b^{-1}r_i(x)$ is the greatest common divisor of $f(x)$ and $g(x)$.

Suppose, now, that $r_1(x)$ is zero. Then $g(x)$ divides $f(x)$. If $f(x)$ has leading coefficient c, then $c^{-1}g(x)$ is the greatest common divisor of $f(x)$ and $g(x)$. If we call this polynomial $d(x)$, we can clearly write $d(x)$ in the form $d(x) = c^{-1}[g(x)] + 0[f(x)]$. That is, $m(x) = c^{-1}$ and $n(x) = 0$ are the polynomials required by the final statement of the theorem.

When $r_1(x) \neq 0$, so that the greatest common divisor $d(x)$ is of the form $d(x) = b^{-1}r_i(x)$, we proceed as with integers to find the polynomials $m(x)$ and $n(x)$ required. First, we solve the next-to-last equation of (1) for $r_i(x)$. Then we employ each of the preceding equations of (1) to eliminate successively all $r_j(x)$ for $j < i$. This leaves $r_i(x)$ expressed in the form

$$r_i(x) = m'(x)f(x) + n'(x)g(x).$$

Now, multiplying through by b^{-1}, we obtain $d(x) = m(x)f(x) + n(x)g(x)$, where $m(x) = b^{-1}m'(x)$ and $n(x) = b^{-1}n'(x)$. This completes the proof of the theorem except for uniqueness of the GCD.

To prove uniqueness, assume that $d(x)$ and $d'(x)$ are both greatest common divisors of $f(x)$ and $g(x)$. By the definition of GCD, $d(x)\,|\,d'(x)$ and $d'(x)\,|\,d(x)$, which means that $d(x)$ and $d'(x)$ are associates. By Theorem 7–12, $d'(x) = kd(x)$ for $k \in F$. Let the leading coefficients of $d'(x)$ and $d(x)$ be t' and t, respectively. The above equation requires that $kt = t'$. But since $d'(x)$ and $d(x)$ are monic, $t' = t = 1$, so that $k = 1$. Hence $d'(x) = d(x)$, and the proof is complete.

The process of successive division represented by equations (1) is referred to as *Euclid's algorithm for polynomials*. We illustrate the procedure in the following example

Example 7–24. Find the GCD, $d(x)$, of $f(x) = x^3 - 2x^2 + 3x - 7$ and $g(x) = x^2 + 2$, and express it in the form

$$d(x) = m(x)f(x) + n(x)g(x),$$

as described in the theorem.   The equations similar to (1) in Euclid's algorithm
are
$$x^3 - 2x^2 + 3x - 7 = (x - 2)(x^2 + 2) + x - 3,$$
$$x^2 + 2 = (x + 3)(x - 3) + 11,$$
$$x - 3 = \left(\frac{x}{11} - \frac{3}{11}\right)(11) + 0.$$

Hence 11 is the polynomial $r_i(x)$ mentioned in the theorem, so that 1 is the GCD
of $f(x)$ and $g(x)$.   From the second equation we have that $11 = (x^2 + 2) - (x + 3)(x - 3)$.   Solving for $x - 3$ in the first equation and substituting, we get
$$11 = (x^2 + 2) - (x + 3)[x^3 - 2x^2 + 3x - 7 - (x - 2)(x^2 + 2)]$$
$$= (x^2 + 2) - (x + 3)(x^3 - 2x^2 + 3x - 7) + (x^2 + x - 6)(x^2 + 2)$$
$$= (x^2 + x - 5)(x^2 + 2) + (-x - 3)(x^3 - 2x^2 + 3x - 7).$$
Dividing by 11, we obtain the GCD, 1, expressed as
$$1 = \left(\frac{1}{11}x^2 + \frac{1}{11}x - \frac{5}{11}\right)(x^2 + 2) + \left(\frac{-1}{11}x - \frac{3}{11}\right)(x^3 - 2x^2 + 3x - 7).$$

Example 7–25.   Find the GCD of $f(x) = x^3 - 3x^2 + 2x - 6$ and $g(x) = x^3 - 4x^2 + 4x - 3$, and express it in the form $m(x)f(x) + n(x)g(x)$.   Applying the
procedure of Euclid's algorithm, we find
$$x^3 - 3x^2 + 2x - 6 = 1(x^3 - 4x^2 + 4x - 3) + x^2 - 2x - 3,$$
$$x^3 - 4x^2 + 4x - 3 = (x - 2)(x^2 - 2x - 3) + 3x - 9,$$
$$x^2 - 2x - 3 = (\tfrac{1}{3}x + \tfrac{1}{3})(3x - 9) + 0.$$
Hence the GCD of $f(x)$ and $g(x)$ is $\tfrac{1}{3}(3x - 9)$, or $x - 3$.   Then,
$$3x - 9 = (x^3 - 4x^2 + 4x - 3) - (x - 2)(x^2 - 2x - 3)$$
$$= (x^3 - 4x^2 + 4x - 3)$$
$$\quad - (x - 2)[x^3 - 3x^2 + 2x - 6 - (x^3 - 4x^2 + 4x - 3)]$$
$$= (x - 1)(x^3 - 4x^2 + 4x - 3) + (-x + 2)(x^3 - 3x^2 + 2x - 6).$$
Hence $x - 3$, the GCD of $f(x)$ and $g(x)$, can be expressed as
$$x - 3 = (\tfrac{1}{3}x - \tfrac{1}{3})(x^3 - 4x^2 + 4x - 3)$$
$$\quad + (-\tfrac{1}{3}x + \tfrac{2}{3})(x^3 - 3x^2 + 2x - 6).$$

EXERCISES

1. Reduce the following fractions to lowest terms.   [*Hint:* Reduce the fractions by dividing
numerator and denominator by their GCD.]

a) $\dfrac{x^3 + 2x^2 - 3x - 6}{2x^3 + x^2 - 6x - 3}$

b) $\dfrac{x^5 + 1}{x^3 + 1}$

c) $\dfrac{x^5 + x^3 + 2x^2 + 2}{x^3 + 2}$

d) $\dfrac{x^5 + 3x^3 + 2x^2 + 6}{x^5 + 5x^3 + x^2 + 3x + 3}$

2. Find the GCD of $f(x)$ and $g(x)$ in each of the following cases, and express it in the form $m(x)f(x) + n(x)g(x)$. Interpret all polynomials as elements of $\mathbf{Q}[x]$.

a) $f(x) = 6x^3 + 5x^2 - 2x + 35$ and $g(x) = 2x^2 - 3x + 5$
b) $f(x) = x^3 + 1$ and $g(x) = x^2 + 3x - 5$
c) $f(x) = x^4 - 4x^3 + 5x^2 - 4x + 2$ and $g(x) = x^3 - 3x + 2$
d) $f(x) = 2x^4 - 2x^3 + 5x^2 - 3x + 3$ and $g(x) = 2x^4 + 2x^3 + x^2 + 3x - 3$

3. Find the GCD of $f(x)$ and $g(x)$ in each of the following cases, and express it in the form $m(x)f(x) + n(x)g(x)$. Interpret all polynomials as elements of $Z_5[x]$.

a) $f(x) = x^3 + 3x^2 + 3x + 3$ and $g(x) = 4x^3 + 2x^2 + 2x + 2$
b) $f(x) = x^6 + 3x^5 + 3x^4 + x^3 + x + 3$ and $g(x) = 2x^3 + 3x + 1$
c) $f(x) = 2x^2 + x + 2$ and $g(x) = x^2 + x + 4$
d) $f(x) = 3x^3 + 2x^2 + 4$ and $g(x) = x^4 + 3x^2 + 1$

7-10   THE UNIQUE FACTORIZATION THEOREM

One of the most important theorems on polynomials is the unique factorization theorem, which we will prove in this section.   We will show that every polynomial can be factored uniquely into irreducible factors.   This theorem is primarily of theoretical interest.   It has little value for computation, since it provides no general procedure for determining the factors.   The theorem states only that such a set of factors exists and that they are unique.   The principal value to teachers of elementary algebra is the assurance it gives that there can be only one correct answer to any given factoring problem.

Before stating the factorization theorem, we will give two preliminary theorems that are needed for its proof.

Theorem 7-17.   Let $f(x)$, $g(x)$, and $h(x)$ be polynomials in $F[x]$ for a field F. If $f(x) \mid g(x)h(x)$ and the GCD of $f(x)$ and $g(x)$ is 1, then $f(x) \mid h(x)$.

By Theorem 7-16, if the GCD of $f(x)$ and $g(x)$ is 1, then there exists polynomials $m(x)$ and $n(x)$ in $F[x]$ such that $1 = m(x)f(x) + n(x)g(x)$.   Multiplying both members of this equation by $h(x)$, we obtain $h(x) = m(x)f(x)h(x) + n(x)g(x)h(x)$.   But $f(x) \mid g(x)h(x)$, so that $g(x)h(x) = f(x)q(x)$ for some polynomial $q(x)$ in $F[x]$.   Thus

$$h(x) = m(x)f(x)h(x) + n(x)f(x)q(x) = f(x)[m(x)h(x) + n(x)q(x)],$$

which shows that $f(x)$ divides $h(x)$.

The next theorem is really a corollary of Theorem 7-17, although its proof depends also upon a use of the principle of mathematical induction.   Except for the notation indicating polynomials rather than integers, this proof is identical, to the proof of the corollary to Theorem 2-16.   We will leave this proof for the reader to supply.

Theorem 7-18.   If $f(x)$ is an irreducible polynomial in $F[x]$ for a field F, and if $f(x)$ divides the product $g_1(x)g_2(x) \ldots g_k(x)$ of polynomials in $F[x]$, then $f(x)$ divides $g_i(x)$ for some i, $1 \le i \le k$.

Theorem 7–19 (the unique factorization theorem for polynomials). If $f(x)$ is a nonzero polynomial in $F[x]$, where F is a field, then $f(x) = cp_1(x)p_2(x) \ldots p_m(x)$, where each $p_i(x)$, for $i = 1, 2, \ldots, m$, is an irreducible polynomial in $F[x]$ and $c \in F$. Further, the factors $p_1(x), p_2(x), \ldots, p_m(x)$ are unique, except for the order in which they appear.

The constant c appearing in the formula of this theorem is the leading coefficient of $f(x)$. The restriction that each $p_i(x)$ be monic is made to ensure uniqueness. For instance, the polynomial $x^2 - 4$ in $\mathbf{Q}[x]$ can be factored as $(x + 2)(x - 2)$ and also as $(3x + 6)(\frac{1}{3}x - \frac{2}{3})$, and in many other ways, into factors which are not monic.

The proof of the theorem is in two parts. We first prove that $f(x)$ can be factored as required, and then prove that the factors are unique. The proof of the first part uses the second principle of mathematical induction on the degree of $f(x)$ and parallels closely the proof of the analogous theorem for integers.

Suppose that $f(x)$ is of degree one. Then $f(x) = ax + b$ for $a, b \in F$. We may write $f(x)$ as $f(x) = a(x + ba^{-1})$. Thus the theorem holds in the case where $f(x)$ has degree one, since $x + ba^{-1}$ is irreducible and monic.

Now assume, as the induction hypothesis, that every polynomial of degree less than n can be factored as stated in the theorem. Consider an arbitrary polynomial $f(x)$ of degree n. If a is the leading coefficient of $f(x)$, then $f(x) = af'(x)$, where $f'(x) = a^{-1}f(x)$ and $f'(x)$ is monic. If $f'(x)$ is irreducible, the theorem holds. If $f'(x)$ is reducible, then it can be factored as $f'(x) = g(x)h(x)$, where neither $g(x)$ nor $h(x)$ is a unit. Since every nonzero element of F is a unit, $g(x)$ and $h(x)$ must be of degree one or larger. Since the degree of $f'(x)$ is the sum of the degrees of $g(x)$ and $h(x)$, both $g(x)$ and $h(x)$ have degree less than n. By the induction hypothesis, $g(x) = b(b_1(x)b_2(x)\ldots b_s(x))$, and $h(x) = d(d_1(x)d_2(x) \ldots d_t(x))$, where each $b_i(x)$ and each $d_j(x)$ is monic and irreducible, and where b and d are elements of F. Then

$$f(x) = (abd)b_1(x)b_2(x) \cdots b_s(x)d_1(x)d_2(x) \cdots d_t(x).$$

This factorization of $f(x)$ satisfies the requirements of the theorem, where $c = abd$. Hence the theorem holds for all polynomials of degree n, and by the second principle of mathematical induction, for all polynomials of arbitrary degree.

In order to prove that the factors are unique, suppose that a polynomial $f(x)$ can be factored in one way as $f(x) = cp_1(x)p_2(x) \cdots p_s(x)$, and also as $f(x) = dq_1(x)q_2(x) \cdots q_t(x)$. We assume that both factorizations satisfy all conditions stated in the theorem. We need to show that these factors are identical in the two cases, except for the order in which they are written. We prove this by induction on s, the number of factors in one factorization. If $s = 1$, then $f(x) = cp_1(x) = dq_1(x)q_2(x) \cdots q_t(x)$. Since $p_1(x)$ is irreducible, $p_1(x) \mid q_i(x)$ for some i, by Theorem 7–18. Further, this implies that the degree of $q_i(x)$ is not less than that of $p_1(x)$, and hence $t = 1$ and $q_i(x) = q_1(x)$. Now, since $f(x) = cp_1(x) = dq_1(x)$,

$p_1(x)$ and $q_1(x)$ are associates. Since each is monic, $p_1(x) = q_1(x)$, and the theorem holds in the case $s = 1$.

Assume as an induction hypothesis that if $s = k$, the factors are unique. Consider a polynomial $f(x)$ that factors as $f(x) = cp_1(x) \cdots p_{k+1}(x)$ and also as $f(x) = dq_1(x) \cdots q_t(x)$. Then

$$p_{k+1}(x) \mid q_1(x)q_2(x) \cdots q_t(x),$$

and by Theorem 7–18, $p_{k+1}(x) \mid q_i(x)$ for some i. As before, since both $p_{k+1}(x)$ and $q_i(x)$ are monic and irreducible, $p_{k+1}(x) = q_i(x)$. Then by the cancellation law,

$$cp_1(x)p_2(x) \cdots p_k(x) = dq_1(x) \cdots q_{i-1}(x)q_{i+1}(x) \cdots q_t(x).$$

But now one factorization contains only k factors, and by the induction hypothesis, these factors are unique. Hence the theorem holds in the case $s = k + 1$ and, by the principle of mathematical induction, holds for all s. This completes the proof of the theorem.

EXERCISES

1. Prove Theorem 7–18. [*Hint:* Refer to the proof of the corollary to Theorem 2–16, and give a similar proof here.]

7-11 ZEROS AND ROOTS

In this final section, we will establish a few results dealing with the zeros of a polynomial which are of value in solving equations. First, we will give a definition that relates the zeros of a polynomial to the solution of equations.

Definition 1. If $f(x)$ is a polynomial in $F[x]$ for a field F, and a is a zero of $f(x)$, we say that a is a *root* of the equation $f(x) = 0$. A root of an equation is also often called a *solution* of the equation.

From this definition it should be clear that any theorem on zeros of a polynomial is also a theorem on roots of equations. Theorem 7–20, which follows, is such a theorem, obtained as a consequence of the remainder theorem (see Section 7–8).

Theorem 7–20. Let $f(x)$ be a polynomial in $F[x]$ for a field F with leading coefficient c and degree n. Then if $a_1, a_2, \ldots, a_n$ are n distinct zeros of $f(x)$,

$$f(x) = c(x - a_1)(x - a_2) \cdots (x - a_n).$$

Conversely, if $(x - a_1)$, $(x - a_2), \ldots, (x - a_n)$ are divisors of $f(x)$, then each a_i for $i = 1, 2, \ldots, n$ is a zero of $f(x)$.

The second statement in the theorem follows immediately from the factor theorem. That is, if $x - a_i$ is a divisor of $f(x)$, then $f(a_i) = 0$.

The first statement of the theorem will be proved by induction on n. If $f(x)$ has degree one, $f(x) = cx + d$ for c, $d \in F$. If a_1 is a zero of $f(x)$, $f(a_1) = 0$, and hence $ca_1 + d = 0$, or $d = -ca_1$. Then we have

$$f(x) = cx + d = cx - ca_1 = c(x - a_1),$$

as required.

Now suppose that the theorem holds for all polynomials of degree k, and let $f(x)$ be of degree $k + 1$, with leading coefficient c, and distinct zeros $a_1, \ldots, a_{k+1}$. Then, since a_{k+1} is a zero of $f(x)$, $f(x) = (x - a_{k+1})g(x)$ for some $g(x) \in F[x]$, by the factor theorem. We note that the degree of $g(x)$ must be k and that $g(x)$ has leading coefficient c. Further, for any zero a_i of $f(x)$, with $i \leq k$, $f(a_i) = (a_i - a_{k+1})g(a_i)$. Since the zeros of $f(x)$ are distinct,

$$a_i - a_{k+1} \neq 0,$$

and therefore $g(a_i) = 0$, so that a_i is also a zero of $g(x)$. Thus $g(x)$ has k distinct zeros $a_1, \ldots, a_k$. By the induction hypothesis,

$$g(x) = c(x - a_1)(x - a_2) \cdots (x - a_k).$$

Substituting this in the expression for $f(x)$, we have established that

$$f(x) = c(x - a_1)(x - a_2) \cdots (x - a_k)(x - a_{k+1}),$$

and the proof is complete.

Before we illustrate this theorem with an example, we need a definition to extend some of the terminology of polynomials to equations of the type $f(x) = 0$, where $f(x)$ is a polynomial.

Definition 2. Let $f(x)$ be a polynomial of degree n over a field F. We say that the equation $f(x) = 0$ is an *equation over the field F*, and n is the *degree* of the equation.

Example 7–26. Write an equation over $\mathbf{Q}$ having $\frac{1}{2}$, -2, and 3 as roots. By Theorem 7–19,

$$f(x) = (x - \tfrac{1}{2})(x + 2)(x - 3) = x^3 - \tfrac{3}{2}x^2 - \tfrac{11}{2}x + 3$$

has $\frac{1}{2}$, -2, and 3 as zeros. Hence the equation $x^3 - \tfrac{3}{2}x^2 - \tfrac{11}{2}x + 3 = 0$ has roots $\frac{1}{2}$, -2, and 3. We could also write this equation as $2x^3 - 3x^3 - 11x + 6 = 0$.

In an earlier section, we made quite a point of the fact that factorization depends upon the domain of coefficients of a polynomial. From the preceding theorem and the definition of a zero of a polynomial, it is clear that similar comments can be made concerning roots of equations. For instance, the equation $x^2 + 4 = 0$ has no roots in the field of real numbers, but has two roots in the field of complex numbers, namely $2i$ and $-2i$. Thus the number of roots of this equation depends upon whether the equation is considered as an equation over the real or over the complex numbers.   In one case it has no roots, and in the other it has two roots.   This example leads one to inquire as to the number of roots a given equation may have in the general case.

The reader is aware that the number of roots of an equation depends upon the degree of the equation as well as upon the field of coefficients being considered. However, the degree alone does not give the number of roots.   The equation $(x - 2)^3 = 0$ over the rational numbers is of degree three and has two as its only root.   On the other hand, the equation $(x - 2)(x - 3)(x - 4) = 0$ over the rational numbers is also of degree three and has two, three, and four as roots.

From these remarks, one would expect that although something can be said about the number of roots of an equation of a given degree, we will not be able to specify the exact number of roots for all cases.   The best that can be done is the following result, which holds for polynomial equations over an arbitrary field.

Theorem 7–21.   If $f(x)$ is a polynomial of degree n over a field F, the equation $f(x) = 0$ has at most n distinct roots in F.

To prove the theorem, suppose that an equation $f(x) = 0$ over F has n distinct roots in F.   Call these roots $r_1, r_2, \ldots, r_n$.   We will show that $f(x)$ can have no other root in F, and hence the greatest possible number of distinct roots is n.

Suppose that r is any root of $f(x) = 0$.   Since roots of the equation $f(x) = 0$ are zeros of $f(x)$, we may factor $f(x)$ as

$$f(x) = c(x - r_1)(x - r_2) \ldots (x - r_n),$$

where c is the leading coefficient of $f(x)$ (Theorem 7–20).   Now, r is a root of $f(x) = 0$, so that $f(r) = 0$.   Substituting r for x in the factored form of $f(x)$ gives

$$0 = f(r) = c(r - r_1)(r - r_2) \ldots (r - r_n).$$

Since F has no zero divisors, one of the factors $r - r_i = 0$, where $1 \leq i \leq n$.   Hence $r = r_i$.   That is, any root r of $f(x) = 0$ must equal one of the n roots $r_1, r_2, \ldots, r_n$. This completes the proof of the theorem.

The reader has probably seen the statement, "An equation of degree n has exactly n solutions."   This statement is false unless qualified.   The equation $x^2 + 4 = 0$ has no roots if considered as an equation over the rational numbers, or over the real numbers.   The statement is usually intended to refer to the field of complex numbers.   Even in this case it is necessary to count roots in a special way for the statement to hold.   The equation $(x - 2)^3 = 0$ has only one root in the complex field $\mathbf{C}$.   However, when the claim is made that the equation has three roots, we are supposed to interpret it as meaning that the equation has three equal roots, all of which are 2.   Such a root is referred to as a *multiple root*.   We will not use this point of view, but the remarks are included to aid the reader in comparing Theorem 7–21 with theorems appearing in other texts.

No discussion of polynomial equations would be complete without mention of the theorem usually referred to as the fundamental theorem of algebra.   The proof is not given because we believe it to be beyond the scope of a first course in algebra.   Relatively easy proofs can be given which depend upon topology or upon the theory of complex variables, but a strictly algebraic proof is very difficult and tedious.

Theorem 7–22 (the fundamental theorem of algebra).   If $f(x)$ is a polynomial of degree one or greater, with coefficients in the field $\mathbf{C}$ of complex numbers, then the equation $f(x) = 0$ has at least one root in $\mathbf{C}$.

As a final theorem, we include a result for equations having rational zeros which can be of considerable value in solving equations or in factoring polynomials.

Theorem 7–23.   Let $f(x) = a_0 + a_1 x + \ldots + a_n x^n$ be a polynomial with coefficients which are integers.   Let p/q be a rational number in lowest terms. (That is, the integers p and q are relatively prime.)   If p/q is a root of the equation $f(x) = 0$, then $p \mid a_0$ and $q \mid a_n$.

If p/q is a root of $f(x) = 0$, then

$$a_0 + a_1 \left(\frac{p}{q}\right) + a_2 \left(\frac{p}{q}\right)^2 + \ldots + a_{n-1}\left(\frac{p}{q}\right)^{n-1} + a_n\left(\frac{p}{q}\right)^n = 0.$$

Multiplying both members of this equation by q^n, we obtain

1) $$a_0 q^n + a_1 p q^{n-1} + \ldots + a_{n-1}p^{n-1}q + a_n p^n = 0.$$

Solving equation (1) for $a_0 q^n$, we have

$$a_0 q^n = -a_1 p q^{n-1} - \cdots - a_{n-1}p^{n-1}q - a_n p^n$$
$$= p(-a_1 q^{n-1} - \cdots - a_{n-1}p^{n-2}q - a_n p^{n-1}).$$

In the last step, we have merely factored p from the sum of terms appearing in the right member of the equation.   Thus $p \mid a_0 q^n$, and since p and q are relatively prime, $p \mid a_0$, as was to be proved.   (See the corollary to Theorem 2–16.)
Now we solve equation (1) for $a_n p^n$ to obtain

$$a_n p^n = -a_0 q^n - a_1 p q^{n-1} - \cdots - a_{n-1}p^{n-1}q$$
$$= q(-a_0 q^{n-1} - a_1 p q^{n-2} - \cdots - a_{n-1}p^{n-1}).$$

In the last step we have merely factored q from the sum of terms in the right member of the preceding equation.   Thus $q \mid a_n p^n$, and p is relatively prime to q.   Hence $q \mid a_n$, and this completes the proof of the theorem.
Theorem 7–23 gives a practical method of solving an equation (or factoring a polynomial) where rational roots are involved.   The possible rational roots may be determined by inspection and checked by direct substitution.

Example 7-27.   Find all roots of the equation $2x^4 + x^3 - 10x^2 - 2x + 12 = 0$. By Theorem 7–23, the possible rational roots are $\pm 1, \pm 2, \pm 3, \pm 4, \pm 6, \pm 12,$

$\pm\frac{1}{2}$, and $\pm\frac{3}{2}$. Substituting these values into the equation, we find that -2 and $3/2$ are roots. By the factor theorem, if $f(x)$ denotes the left member of the given equation, $f(x)$ contains $x + 2$ and $x - 3/2$ as factors. By long division we determine that $f(x) = 2(x - \frac{3}{2})(x + 2)(x^2 - 2)$. Now the third factor, $x^2 - 2$, can be set equal to zero and yields two further roots, $\sqrt{2}$ and $-\sqrt{2}$. Thus the complete set of roots is $\{-2, 3/2, \sqrt{2}, -\sqrt{2}\}$. Note that in the process of solving the equation, we have also succeeded in factoring $f(x)$.

Of course, not all equations with integers as coefficients have rational roots. Unfortunately, there are no general methods for solving equations (or equivalently for factoring polynomials) of arbitrary degree. For equations of degrees one, two, three, or four, solutions can always be found by algebraic methods. It is not possible to solve all equations of degree five or more. Some special types, such as those having rational roots, can be solved, but it is possible to prove that equations of degree five exist which are not solvable by methods similar to those used for equations of lower degree. In such cases methods which approximate the roots are usually employed. Modern high-speed computers can be programmed to find such approximate solutions to any desired degree of accuracy.

EXERCISES

1. Find four equations over **Q** all of degree three and such that (a) the first has no roots in **Q**. (b) the second has one root in **Q**, (c) the third has two roots in **Q** and (d) the fourth has three roots in **Q**.

2. Find three equations over **C**, all of degree three and such that (a) the first has one root in **C**, (b) the second has two roots in **C**, and (c) the third has three roots in **C**.

3. Find an equation over Z_5 which has roots 2 and 3.

4. Find an equation over the complex numbers that has roots $\frac{2}{3}, -\frac{1}{2}, 2 + i$, and $2 - i$.

5. (For students who have had calculus.) Prove that if $f(x)$ is a polynomial of degree n over the real numbers **R**, the equation $f(x) = 0$ always has a root in **R** if n is any odd integer. Give a counterexample to show that is not always the case if n is an even integer. [*Hint:* The function $y = f(x)$ is continuous and there must exist real numbers x_1 and x_2 such that $f(x_1)$ and $f(x_2)$ have opposite signs.]

6. For the following equations over the complex numbers find all rational roots and find the remaining roots in those cases where all but two of the roots are rational.

a) $x^4 + 2x^3 - 12x^2 - 10x + 3 = 0$ b) $x^3 - 3x^2 - 12x + 54 = 0$
c) $x^4 + 6x^3 - 7x^2 - 35x + 42 = 0$ d) $3x^3 - 8x^2 - 8x + 8 = 0$
e) $27x^3 - 36x + 8 = 0$ f) $2x^3 + 22x^2 - 23x + 12 = 0$

7. Determine all factors of the form $x - r$, where r is rational, for each of the following polynomials over the complex numbers. Factor each polynomial into irreducible factors whenever the only factor not of this form is of second or lower degree.

a) $x^4 + 2x^3 + x + 2$ b) $x^5 - 34x^3 + 29x^2 + 212x - 300$
c) $x^4 - 15x^3 + 66x^2 - 116x + 72$ d) $3x^4 + 14x^3 + 3x^2 - 27x - 12$
e) $6x^4 - 7x^3 + 8x^2 - 7x + 2$ f) $8x^3 - 6x + 1$

REFERENCES: GROUP I

Elementary mathematics texts illustrating the new uses of material contained in this text in the teaching of elementary and secondary school courses.

1. Banks, J. J., M. A. Sobel, and W. C. Walsh, *Algebra: Its Elements and Structure*, McGraw-Hill, New York, 1971

2. Beberman, M., H. Vaughan, H. Gabai, and S. Szabo, *High School Mathematics, Course 4*, D. C. Heath, Lexington, Mass., 1970

3. Beberman, M., M. S. Wolfe, and R. E. Zwoyer, *Algebra I — A Modern Course*, D. C. Heath, Lexington, Mass., 1970

4. Brumfiel, C. F., R. E. Eicholz, and M. E. Shanks, *Introduction to Mathematics*, Addison-Wesley, Reading, Mass., 1961

5. ———, *Algebra I*, Addison-Wesley, Reading, Mass., 1961

6. ———, *Algebra II*, Addison-Wesley, Reading, Mass., 1962

7. ———, *Geometry*, Addison-Wesley, Reading, Mass., 1960

8. Case, D. H. V., *Modern Mathematical Topics*, Philosophical Library, New York, 1968

9. Cavanagh, T. D., *Modern Trigonometry*, Wadsworth, Belmont, Calif., 1971

10. Douglis, Avron, *Ideas in Mathematics*, W. B. Saunders, Philadelphia, 1970

11. Dupree, D. E., and F. L. Harmon, *Introduction to Analysis*, Dickenson, Belmont, Calif., 1970

12. Fitzgerald, W. M., J. P. Zetterberg, and L. C. Dalton, *Algebra I, Theory and Application*, Laidlaw Brothers, River Forest, Ill., 1967

13. Johnson, R. E., L. L. Lendsey, and W. E. Slesnick, *Modern Algebra, First Course*, Addison-Wesley, Reading, Mass., 1961

14. Johnson, R. E., L. L. Lendsey, W. E. Slesnick, and G. E. Bates, *Modern Algebra, Second Course*, Addison-Wesley, Reading, Mass., 1962

15. Keedy, M. L., and M. L. Bittinger, *Introductory Algebra: A Modern Approach*, Addison-Wesley, Reading, Mass., 1971

16. Lang, S., *Basic Mathematics*, Addison-Wesley, Reading, Mass., 1971

17. Ore, O., *Invitation to Number Theory*, Random House, New York, 1969

18. Papy, G., and F. Papy, *Modern Mathematics*, Vol. I, Macmillan, New York, 1968

19. Stevens, L. H., *Elementary Algebra*, Wadsworth, Belmont, Calif., 1970

20. Wilcox, M. S., and J. E. Yarnelle, *Mathematics, A Modern Approach*, Addison-Wesley, Reading, Mass., 1963

21. Wisner, R. J., *A Panorama of Numbers*, Scott, Foresman, Glenvier, Ill., 1970

22. Wooton, W., and I. Drooyan, *Elementary Functions*, Wadsworth, Belmont, Calif., 1971

REFERENCES: GROUP II

General texts for background material and supplementary reading.

23. Andree, R. V., *Selections from Modern Abstract Algebra*, Henry Holt, New York, 1958

24. Beaumont, R. A., and R. S. Pierce, *The Algebraic Foundations of Mathematics*, Addison-Wesley, Reading, Mass., 1963

25. Birkhoff, G., and S. Maclane, *A Survey of Modern Algebra*, Macmillan, New York, 1948

26. Bittinger, M. L., *Logic and Proof*, Addison-Wesley, Reading, Mass., 1970

27. Courant, R., and H. Robbins, *What Is Mathematics?*, Oxford University Press, New York, 1941

28. Crouch, R., and E. Walker, *Introduction to Modern Algebra and Analysis*, Holt, Rinehart, and Winston, New York, 1962

29. Euclid, *The Elements of Euclid*, St. John's College Press, 1947

30. Felgzamen, A. N., *Numbers and Such: A Lively Guide to the New Math for Parents and Other Perplexed Adults*, Prentice-Hall, Englewood Cliffs, N.J., 1968

31. Freund, J. E., *A Modern Introduction to Mathematics*, Prentice-Hall, Englewood Cliffs, N.J., 1956

32. Gardner, K. L., *Discovering Modern Algebra*, Oxford, New York, 1966

33. Halmos, P. R., *Naive Set Theory*, Van Nostrand, Princeton, N.J., 1960

34. Hardy, G. H., *A Mathematician's Apology*, Cambridge University Press, Cambridge, 1967

35. Henkin, L., W. N. Smith, V. J. Varineau, and M. Walsh, *Retracing Elementary Mathematics*, Macmillan, New York, 1962

36. Keedy, M. L., *A Modern Introduction to Basic Mathematics*, Addison-Wesley, Reading, Mass., 1963

37. Kline, Morris, *Mathematics: A Cultural Approach*, Addison-Wesley, Reading, Mass., 1962

38. Lightstone, A. H., *Symbolic Logic and the Real Number System*, Harper and Row, New York, 1965

39. McCoy, N. H., *Introduction to Modern Algebra*, Allyn and Bacon, Boston, 1960

40. Meserve, B. E., and M. A. Sobel, *Mathematics for Secondary Schoool Teachers*, Prentice-Hall, Englewood Cliffs, N. J., 1962

41. Moise, E., *Elementary Geometry from an Advanced Standpoint*, Addison-Wesley, Reading, Mass., 1963

42. O'Nan, M., *Linear Algebra*, Harcourt Brace Jovanovich, New York, 1971

43. Paley, A., and P. M. Weichsel, *Elements of Abstract and Linear Algebra*, Holt, Rinehart, and Winston, New York, 1972

44. Peterson, J. M., *Foundations of Algebra and Number Theory*, Markham, Chicago, 1971

45. Polya, G., *How to Solve It*, Princeton University Press, Princeton, N. J., 1957

46. Reiner, I., *Introduction to Matrix Theory and Linear Algebra*, Holt, Rinehart and Winston, New York, 1971

47. Sanders, P., *Elementary Mathematics: A Logical Approach*, International Textbook Co., Scranton, Pa., 1963

48. Sawyer, W. W., *A Concrete Approach to Abstract Algebra*, Freeman, San Francisco, Calif., 1959

49. Selby, S., and L. Sweet, *Sets, Relations, Functions*, McGraw-Hill, New York, 1963

50. Sloyer, C. W., *Algebra and Its Applications: A Problem-Solving Approach*, Addison-Wesley, Reading, Mass., 1970

51. Stark, H. M., *An Introduction to Number Theory*, Markham, Chicago, 1970

52. Stoll, R. R., *Set Theory and Logic*, Freeman, San Francisco, Calif., 1961

53. Thomas, G. B., *Calculus and Analytic Geometry*, third edition, Addison-Wesley, Reading, Mass., 1960

54. Wexler, C., *Analytic Geometry: A Vector Approach*, Addison-Wesley, Reading, Mass., 1961

55. Whitesitt, J. E., *Boolean Algebra and Its Applications*, Addison-Wesley, Reading, Mass., 1961

56. Wilder, R. L., *The Foundations of Mathematics*, Wiley, New York, 1952

THE GENERALIZED ASSOCIATIVE, COMMUTATIVE AND DISTRIBUTIVE LAWS

The generalized laws treated in this appendix have been introduced for rings in the text, but without proof. Although the laws are intuitively clear, the proofs are lengthy and are usually omitted from a first course. They are included here for the sake of completeness.

It is convenient to have available a specific sequence of operations called the general product. Let $a_1, a_2, \ldots, a_n$ be any n elements of a system in which an operation referred to as product is associative. The *general product* of these elements, written $GP(a_1, a_2, \ldots, a_n)$, is defined inductively to be $a_1 \cdot a_2$ if $n = 2$, and to be

$$[GP(a_1, a_2, \ldots, a_{n-1})] \cdot a_n$$

if n is greater than 2. Thus

$$GP(a_1, a_2, a_3) = (a_1 a_2) a_3,$$
$$GP(a_1, a_2, a_3, a_4) = [(a_1 a_2) a_3] a_4,$$

etc. This sequence of operations is often referred to by saying that association is to the left, since it indicates multiplying the two left-most elements first, then multiplying by the next factor to the right, and so on. We will use the general product by proving that any arrangement of grouping symbols leaves the product equal to the general product and hence each such product equals any other.

THE GENERALIZED ASSOCIATIVE LAW

Let S be a set which is closed with respect to an associative binary operation, which for convenience we write as a product. Then the product formed by the elements $a_1, a_2, \ldots, a_n$ of S (for $n \geq 2$), taken in that order and with parentheses in any position whatever, is equal to $GP(a_1, a_2, \ldots, a_n)$.

The proof will use the second principle of mathematical induction. In the case $n = 2$, the only product possible is $a_1 a_2$ and this is exactly $GP(a_1, a_2)$, so the theorem holds. Now assume that the theorem holds for every product involving less than n factors, and consider any product p of n factors. Every product, such as p, must involve a "last" multiplication, indicated by the grouping symbols. This final multiplication is between two expressions, each having less than n factors. By our induction hypothesis, any product of less than n factors equals the general product, so that p may be written as

$$p = GP(a_1, a_2, \ldots, a_k) \cdot GP(a_{k+1}, a_{k+2}, \ldots, a_n)$$

for some natural number k. By definition of GP,

$$GP(a_{k+1}, \ldots, a_n) = [GP(a_{k+1}, \ldots, a_{n-1})] \cdot a_n.$$

Thus

$$p = GP(a_1, \ldots, a_k)[GP(a_{k+1}, \ldots, a_{n-1})a_n]$$
$$= [GP(a_1, \ldots, a_k)GP(a_{k+1}, \ldots, a_{n-1})]a_n.$$

The factor in brackets in the last expression has $n - 1 < n$ factors so by our induction hypothesis is the general product of these $n - 1$ factors.   That is,

$$p = [GP(a_1, a_2, \ldots, a_{n-1})]a_n.$$

Now by definition of the general product, $p = GP(a_1, a_2, \ldots, a_n)$, and this establishes the validity of the theorem for n factors.   By the second principle of mathematical induction, the theorem holds for every natural number n.

Now that the generalized associative law has been proven, we omit parentheses from a sum (or product) of more than two terms (or factors) unless a particular grouping is to be emphasized.

Generalizations of the left- and right-distributive laws are proved by the first principle of induction, and are valid in all systems having the usual distributive laws and the associative law of addition.   We will phrase the theorem in terms of multiplication and addition, but the theorem is valid for any pair of operations satisfying analogous conditions.

THE GENERALIZED DISTRIBUTIVE LAW

Let S be a set which is closed with respect to two binary operations, written as addition and multiplication.   If addition is associative, and multiplication is left-distributive over addition, then

$$a(b_1 + b_2 \cdots + b_n) = ab_1 + ab_2 + \cdots + ab_n$$

for every natural number $n \geq 2$, where a and $b_1, b_2, \ldots, b_n$ are arbitrary elements of S.

If $n = 2$, the theorem reduces to the left-distributive law in S and is valid. Assume that the theorem is true in the case of n term $b_1, b_2, \ldots, b_n$, and consider the case of $n + 1$ terms.

$a(b_1 + b_2 + \ldots + b_{n+1})$

$\qquad\qquad = a[(b_1 + b_2 + \ldots + b_n) + b_{n+1}]$ by the previous theorem,

$\qquad\qquad = a(b_1 + b_2 + \ldots + b_n) + ab_{n+1}$ by distributive law,

$\qquad\qquad = ab_1 + ab_2 + \ldots + ab_n + ab_{n+1}$ by induction hypothesis.

Thus the theorem holds for $n + 1$ terms and by the first principle of mathematical induction it holds for every natural number n.   The theorem is also true if the word "left" is replaced by the word "right."

THE GENERALIZED COMMUTATIVE LAW

Let S be a set that is closed with respect to an associative and commutative operation, which we will write as a product.   Then the product of n factors from S is independent of the order in which the factors are written.

First, let us change the form of the theorem to allow an easier application of the induction principle.   Any ordering of n factors may be thought of as having been obtained from any other ordering by a sequence of steps, each of which involves the interchange of two adjacent factors.   Thus the ordering 3214 may be obtained from 1234 by the sequence $1234 \rightarrow 2134 \rightarrow 2314 \rightarrow 3214$.   Hence the theorem is equivalent to the statement that the product of n factors is not changed by a succession of m interchanges of adjacent factors for any natural number m.   The proof by the first principle of induction, applied with respect to m, is now straightforward.   For the inductive step in the proof, the generalized associative law is used to group the adjacent factors to be interchanged and the commutative law justifies the interchange.

Other laws or formulas we have discussed can also be generalized.   For example, the fact that $(-a)(-b) = ab$ in a ring can be extended to read that $(-a_1)(-a_2) \cdots (-a_n)$ equals $a_1 a_2 \cdots a_n$ if n is even, and equals $-a_1 a_2 \cdots a_n$ if n is odd.   This and other such generalizations are not sufficiently important to justify inclusion of their proofs, but it is hoped that the discussion will make the student at least recognize instances of the use of such generalizations, and recognize the fact that proofs are necessary.

APPENDIX B

CONGRUENCE OF INTEGERS

Congruence of integers has been introduced in the text to describe the rings Z_n in precise fashion. However, the subject is of interest in its own right. This appendix is included to give a brief introduction to linear congruences with the hope of stimulating further investigation on the part of the reader.

Recall that if a and b are integers, *a is congruent to b modulo m*, written $a \equiv b$ (mod m), if and only if $a - b$ is divisible by m. Congruence modulo m is an equivalence relation on the set of integers, as we saw in Section 4–7.

Congruences have properties similar, in many ways, to properties of equations. Because of the similarity, the student should be careful not to assume that all rules for manipulating equations are valid for congruences. The following theorems illustrate permissible operations on congruences. Any other operations must be assumed invalid until they have been formally proved. In all theorems in this section, the letters a, b, c, m, x refer to arbitrary integers unless we specifically state the contrary.

Theorem 1. If $a \equiv b$ (mod m), then $a \pm c \equiv b \pm c$ (mod m) and $ac \equiv bc$ (mod m) for any integer c.

The proof follows directly from the definition. We will prove only that $ac \equiv bc$ (mod m), as an indication of the method. If $a \equiv b$ (mod m), then from the definition, $a - b = km$ for some integer k. Multiplying by c, we have $ac - bc = kcm$. That is, $ac - bc$ is divisible by m, and hence $ac \equiv bc$ (mod m), as was to be proved.

Theorem 2. If $a \equiv b$ (mod m) and $c \equiv d$ (mod m), then $a \pm c \equiv b \pm d$ (mod m) and $ac \equiv bd$ (mod m).

Again the proof follows from the definition. We will illustrate this by proving only that $a + c \equiv b + d$ (mod m). Since it is assumed that $a \equiv b$ (mod m) and $c \equiv d$ (mod m), $a - b = k_1 m$ and $c - d = k_2 m$ for integers k_1 and k_2. (Note that k_1 is not necessarily equal to k_2.) Then

$$(a + c) - (b + d) = (a - b) + (c - d) = k_1 m + k_2 m = (k_1 + k_2)m.$$

We see that $k_1 + k_2$ is an integer, since it is the sum of two integers, and $(a + c) -$

$(b + d)$ is divisible by m.   This means that $a + c \equiv b + d \pmod{m}$, which completes the proof.

Theorem 3. If $ca \equiv cb \pmod{m}$ and d is the GCD of c and m, where $m = dm'$, then $a \equiv b \pmod{m'}$.

Since d is the GCD of c and m, we may write $c = dc'$ and $m = dm'$; $ca \equiv cb$ (mod m) means that $ca - cb = km$ for an integer k.   Substituting for c and m, we obtain $dc'a - dc'b = kdm'$.   Since $d \neq 0$, the cancellation law for integers may be applied to give $c'(a - b) = km'$.   Thus m' divides $c'(a - b)$.   But by the definition of GCD, c' and m' contain no common factors.   By Theorem 2–16, m' divides $a - b$ and hence $a \equiv b \pmod{m'}$.   This completes the proof of Theorem 3.

Corollary. If $ca \equiv cb \pmod{m}$ and c and m are relatively prime, then $a \equiv b$ (mod m).

This corollary is the special case of Theorem 3, where $d = 1$.   It is included for convenience of reference.

In summarizing the preceding theorems, we note that it has been proved that an integer may be added to or subtracted from both sides of a congruence and that both sides of a congruence may be multiplied by the same integer.   However, it is not possible to divide both sides of a congruence by the same integer unless this integer is relatively prime to the modulus involved.   In addition, two congruences may be combined by addition or multiplication, just as we combine equations.   Many properties of equations, then, carry over to congruences, but there are significant differences.

Example 1. From the congruence $7 \equiv 4 \pmod{3}$, we may deduce that $9 \equiv 6 \pmod{3}$, $4 \equiv 1 \pmod{3}$, and $21 \equiv 12 \pmod{3}$.   In the first case, 2 was added to both members of the given congruence.   In the second, 3 was subtracted from each member of the given congruence.   In the third, both members of the given congruence were multiplied by 3.

Example 2. From the congruence $7 \equiv 28 \pmod{3}$, we may deduce that $1 \equiv 4$ (mod 3) by division by 7, since $D(3, 7) = 1$.   However, from $6 \equiv 36 \pmod{10}$ we may *not* deduce $1 \equiv 6 \pmod{10}$ but only that $1 \equiv 6 \pmod{5}$.   Here the GCD of 6 and 10 is 2 and $10 = 5 \cdot 2$.   Therefore the congruence resulting from division by 6 is a congruence modulo 5, as indicated in Theorem 3.

We now turn our attention to the solution of congruences of the type $ax \equiv b$ (mod m), called *linear congruences*.   A *solution* of such a congruence is an integer such that the congruence becomes valid upon replacing x by this integer.   Another way of describing a solution is as a replacement for x which converts the open sentence $ax \equiv b \pmod{m}$ into a true statement.   Not all linear congruences can be solved, and when solution is possible, there may be one or many solutions.   The situation is described in the following theorem.

Theorem 4. The linear congruence $ax \equiv b \pmod{m}$ has a solution if and only if $d \mid b$, where $d = D(a, m)$. In this case, there are exactly d incongruent solutions modulo m which can be expressed in the form $x_0 + im'$ for $i = 0, 1, 2, \ldots, d - 1$, where x_0 is an arbitrary solution and $m = dm'$.

Assume first that $d = D(a, m)$ and that d divides b. There exist integers u and v such that $ua + vm = d$. Since d divides $b, b = b'd$. Multiplying the equation $ua + vm = d$ by b', we have that $uab' + vmb' = db' = b$. Transposing terms, $a(ub') - b = b'vm$, or in other words, $a(ub') \equiv b \pmod{m}$ and ub' is a solution of the congruence. We have shown that a solution exists if $d \mid b$.

Next, suppose that x_0 is a solution of the congruence $ax \equiv b \pmod{m}$. That is, $ax_0 - b = km$ for some integer k. Since $d \mid a$ and $d \mid m$, $a = a'd$ and $m = m'd$. Hence

$$b = ax_0 - km = a'dx_0 - km'd = d(a'x_0 - km'),$$

showing that $d \mid b$. This shows that if a solution exists, then d divides b. Together with the first part of the proof, this establishes the necessary and sufficient condition for the existence of a solution.

Now suppose that $d \mid b$, so that a solution exists. Let $a = a'd$, $b = b'd$, and $m = m'd$ for integers a', b', and m'. If x_0 is a solution of $ax \equiv b \pmod{m}$, then by Theorem 3, x_0 is a solution of the congruence $a'x \equiv b' \pmod{m'}$. (This application uses d as a special case of the letter c in the theorem.) Suppose that x_1 is also a solution of $ax \equiv b \pmod{m}$ and hence of $a'x \equiv b' \pmod{m'}$. Then $a'x_0 \equiv b' \pmod{m'}$ and $a'x_1 \equiv b' \pmod{m'}$. Applying Theorem 2,

$$a'x_1 - a'x_0 \equiv b' - b' \pmod{m'}, \qquad \text{or} \qquad a'x_1 - a'x_0 = km'$$

for some integer k. But $D(a', m') = 1$ and hence m' divides $x_1 - x_0$, by Theorem 2–16. That is, $x_1 - x_0 = im'$ for some integer i or, equivalently, $x_1 = x_0 + im'$. Hence every solution x_1 of the congruence $ax \equiv b \pmod{m}$ can be expressed in the form $x_0 + im'$ for some integer i.

Suppose next that $d \leq i$. Then by the division algorithm, $i = qd + r$, for integers q and r, where $0 \leq r \leq d$. We will show that $x_0 + im' \equiv x_0 + rm' \pmod{m}$ and hence using $i = 0, 1, \ldots, d - 1$ gives all solutions not congruent modulo m:

$$(x_0 + im') - (x_0 + rm') = im' - rm'$$
$$= (qd + r)m' - rm' = qdm' = qm,$$

and hence

$$x_0 + im' \equiv x_0 + rm' \pmod{m}, \qquad \text{where } 0 \leq r < d.$$

Finally, suppose that $0 \leq j \leq i \leq d$. Assume that

$$x_0 + im' \equiv x_0 + jm' \pmod{m}.$$

Then $im' \equiv jm' \pmod{m}$ by Theorem 1 and $i \equiv j \pmod{d}$ by Theorem 3. This implies that $i - j = kd$ for an integer k, which is a contradiction of the statement that $i - j < d$. Hence no two solutions among the set

$$\{x_0 + im' \,|\, 0 \leq i < d\}$$

are congruent modulo m. This completes the proof of Theorem 4.

The method for solving linear congruences is indicated in the proof of Theorem 4. The procedure is to first determine whether or not solutions exist, and if they exist, to determine d and m'. Next, a particular solution is found by trial and error combined with applications of Theorems 1, 2, or 3. Once a solution x_0 is found, all other solutions which are incongruent modulo m can be determined by substituting $1, 2, \ldots, d - 1$ for i in the expression $x_0 + im'$.

Example 3. Consider the problem of solving the congruence

$$52x \equiv 28 \,(\text{mod } 20).$$

Since $D(52, 20) = 4$ and $4 \,|\, 28$, there are four solutions incongruent modulo 20. In the notation of the theorem, $d = 4$ and $m' = 5$. Any solution will be a solution of $13x \equiv 7 \,(\text{mod } 5)$. A solution x_0 for this congruence may be found by trial and error, but considerable work is saved if we make use of the theorems in this section before resorting to guesswork. Since $0 \equiv 5 \,(\text{mod } 5)$, we may subtract this congruence from the above to obtain the simpler congruence $13x \equiv 2 \,(\text{mod } 5)$. Again $10x \equiv 0 \,(\text{mod } 5)$, and upon subtraction we obtain $3x \equiv 2 \,(\text{mod } 5)$. In this form a solution can be easily determined by guessing. We could also proceed as follows: Multiplying by 2 gives $6x \equiv 4 \,(\text{mod } 5)$, and subtracting the congruence $5x \equiv 0 \,(\text{mod } 5)$ leaves $x \equiv 4 \,(\text{mod } 5)$, indicating that $x_0 = 4$ is a solution. The four required solutions of $52x \equiv 28 \,(\text{mod } 20$ are $4 + 0(5) = 4$, $4 + 1(5) = 9$, $4 + 2(5) = 14$ and $4 + 3(5) = 19$. The student should check each of these solutions to verify that no errors were made.

As an application of the notion of congruence, we prove the following familiar theorem.

Theorem 5. An integer n is divisible by 9 if and only if the sum of its digits is divisible by 9.

First we note that $10 \equiv 1 \,(\text{mod } 9)$. Assuming that $10^k \equiv 1 \,(\text{mod } 9)$ and multiplying by the first congruence, we obtain $10^{k+1} \equiv 1 \,(\text{mod } 9)$. By the first principle of mathematical induction, $10^m \equiv 1 \,(\text{mod } 9)$ for every positive integer m. Any integer n may be written as

$$n = a_0 + 10a_1 + 10^2 a_2 + \cdots + 10^k a_k,$$

where $a_0, a_1, \ldots, a_k$ are the digits in n. Since $a_i \equiv a_i \,(\text{mod } 9)$, and we have shown that $10^i \equiv 1 \,(\text{mod } 9)$, multiplication gives $10^i a_i \equiv a_i \,(\text{mod } 9)$ for $i = 0, 1, 2, \ldots, k$. Adding these $k + 1$ congruences, we obtain

$$n \equiv (a_0 + a_1 + \cdots + a_k) \,(\text{mod } 9).$$

That is,

$$n - (a_0 + a_1 + \cdots + a_k) = 9s$$

for an integer s.   Now, clearly, n is divisible by 9 if and only if the sum of its digits, $a_0 + a_1 + \cdots + a_k$, is divisible by 9.

Casting out nines is a method of checking arithmetic familiar to most students. Theorem 5 gives the principal justification for the method.   The method also involves arithmetic modulo 9, although these words seldom appear in arithmetic texts where casting out nines is discussed.   To illustrate the procedure, we will give an example of an addition problem and a check of the work by casting out nines.

Example 4. Consider the addition problem below.

$$
\begin{array}{r}
814 \\
683 \\
756 \\
\hline
2253
\end{array}
$$

To cast out nines means to reduce the numbers modulo 9.   However, in accord with Theorem 5, we may work with the sum of the digits in each number rather than with the number itself.   Thus $8 + 1 + 4 = 13$.   If 13 is reduced modulo 9, we obtain 4.   (This can be obtained by adding the digits 1 and 3 in the number 13.) This is the same result that would be obtained if the number 814 were divided by 9 and the remainder of 4 were retained.

The phrase "casting out nines" is suggested by the fact that the multiples of 9 are disregarded, or cast out, and only the remainder is kept.   The number 683 is then reduced modulo 9 by adding the digits 6, 8, and 3 to obtain 17.   Then 17 is reduced modulo 9 either by division by 9 to obtain a remainder of 8 or by again adding the digits 1 and 7 to obtain 8.   Similarly, 756 is reduced by adding digits to obtain 18, then adding again to obtain 9.   But 9 reduces to 0 modulo 9, so that 756 is reduced to 0 modulo 9.   Now the numbers 4, 8, and 0 are added modulo 9 (or added in the usual fashion and then reduced by casting out nines).   The result is checked against the first answer after it is also reduced modulo 9.   Here 3 is the result in each case, indicating a successful check.   The problem is repeated below to show the check.

$$
\begin{array}{rll}
814 & \text{casting out nines leaves} & 4 \\
683 & \text{casting out nines leaves} & 8 \\
756 & \text{casting out nines leaves} & \underline{0} \\
\hline
2253 & & 12
\end{array}
$$

Casting out nines from 2253 leaves 3 and casting out nines from 12 also leaves 3.

It should be mentioned that the check is only a partial one.   If the answer is correct, then the check will always come out correctly.   However, a correct check does not always indicate a correct problem.   It will catch most, but not all, errors. Consider, for example, the problem below.

Example 5. Suppose we have performed the following incorrect addition, and checked by casting out nines.

$$275 \quad \text{casting out nines leaves} \quad 5$$
$$388 \quad \text{casting out nines leaves} \quad 1$$
$$\overline{672} \qquad\qquad\qquad\qquad\qquad\quad \overline{6}$$

Now casting out nines in 672 leaves 6.   In this case the check failed to show that the answer was incorrect.   Can you give other examples?

Example 5 shows that this check is not infallible, although it is helpful.   One could prove the following theorem, but not its converse.

Theorem 6.   If an arithmetic problem is correct, then the results can be successfully checked by casting out nines.

It would be more satisfying if the converse were also true, but the practical value of the check comes from the fact that *most* errors are caught.   The advantage of the above check over the check using arithmetic modulo 7 comes from Theorem 5, which allows us to use the sum of the digits in a number rather than the number itself, and thus reduce the amount of work involved.   An added advantage is that one would expect that a larger percentage of errors would be detected by casting out nines than by reducing modulo 7.   Can you explain why?

ANSWERS AND HINTS TO SELECTED EXERCISES

Section 1–2

1. a) Either three is even or six is odd.
   c) There is a triangle which is isosceles in which no median to any side is perpendicular to that side.

2. a) Converse: If $2a$ is less than $2b$ then a is less than b. Contrapositive: If $2a$ is not less than $2b$ then a is not less than b.

3. a) a is less than b only if $2a$ is less than $2b$.

4. a) In order that $2a$ is less than $2b$ it is sufficient that a is less than b.

5. a) In order that a is less than b, it is necessary that $2a$ is less than $2b$.

Section 1–3

1. $\emptyset$, $\{a\}$, $\{b\}$, $\{c\}$, $\{d\}$, $\{a,b\}$, $\{a,c\}$, $\{a,d\}$, $\{b,c\}$, $\{b,d\}$, $\{c,d\}$, $\{a,b,c\}$, $\{a,b,d\}$, $\{a,c,d\}$, $\{b,c,d\}$, $\{a,b,c,d\}$

2. a) The set of prime integers

3. a) $\{11, 12, 13\}$ c) $\{y \mid y = \sin x$ and x is a real number$\}$ e) $\{(x, y) \mid x + y > 1$ and x and y are real numbers$\}$

4. *One* partition is the set of sets $\{X_1, X_2, X_3, X_4\}$ where $X_1 = \{x \mid x$ is an integer and $x < 0\}$, $X_2 = \{x \mid x$ is an integer and $0 \leq x \leq 10\}$, $X_3 = \{11, 12, 13, 14\}$, and $X_4 = \{x \mid x$ is an integer and $x \geq 15\}$.

5. a) $\{1, 2, 3, 4, 5, 6\}$ d) $\emptyset$ f) $\{4, 6\}$

6. a) Since $\emptyset$ has no elements the condition of the definition that $\emptyset \subseteq X$ is vacuously satisfied.
   c) By definition of union, each element of X is an element in $X \cup Y$ so that $X \subseteq X \cup Y$.
   d) Prove that $X \cup X \subseteq X$ and that $X \subseteq X \cup X$.
   e) Prove that $X \cap X \subseteq X$ and that $X \subseteq X \cap X$.
   f) Since $\emptyset$ contains no elements, argue that $a \in X \cup \emptyset$ if and only if $a \in X$.
   g) By definition of intersection each element of $X \cap \emptyset$ must be an element of $\emptyset$. Hence $X \cap \emptyset$ contains no elements and is just the set $\emptyset$.

7. Prove that $X \cap Y \subseteq X$ and that $X \subseteq X \cap Y$, using the fact that $X \subseteq Y$.

8. T, F, T, T, F, F, T, T, T, T

Section 1-4

2. $M \times N = \{(1, 2), (1, 4), (1, 6), (3, 2), (3, 4), (3, 6), (4, 2), (4, 4), (4, 6)\}$ $N \times M = \{(2, 1), (4, 1), (6, 1), (2, 3), (4, 3), (6, 3), (2, 4), (4, 4), (6, 4)\}$.

3. The set of points in quadrant I, including points on both axes, whose coordinates are integers.

5. Let $S = \{p, n, d, q\}$ and $T = \{h, t\}$, where the letters used represent penny, nickel, dime, quarter, heads, and tails. Then $S \times T$ is a possible answer.

6. b) $A \cap B = \{3, 5\}$. Hence $C \times (A \cap B) = \{(0, 3), (0, 5), (1, 3), (1, 5)\}$.
   d) $\varnothing$.

7. $\{(1, 1, 1), (1, 1, 2), (1, 2, 1), (2, 1, 1), (1, 2, 2), (2, 1, 2), (2, 2, 1), (2, 2, 2)\}$

Section 1-5

1. a) The domain and the range are each the set of real numbers.
   b) The domain is the set of integers, the range is the set of even integers.

2. a) The domain is the set of real numbers, the range is the set of nonnegative real numbers.

8. The domain is $\{2, 3, 4, 5\}$, the range is $\{1, 2, 3\}$.

7. Let ABC denote a triangle with vertices A, B, C. Two triangles are similar if corresponding angles are equal. Let S denote this relation. Then $S = \{(ABC, PQR) \mid < A \cong < P, < B \cong < Q$, and $< C \cong < R\}$.

Section 1-6

1. a) $\{1, 2, 3\}$ b) $\{1, 2, 4\}$ c) No d) Yes

3. a) Yes b) Yes c) Yes d) Yes

5. $F(0) = 4, F(1) = 10/3$

6. The set of integers which are multiples of 3.

7. $F = \{(x, y) \mid y = 3x$ and $0 < x < 1\}$

9. Assume that (a, b) and $(a, c) \in F$. Prove that then $b = c$. Then prove that if $n \in Z$ there is an integer m such that $(m, n) \in F$.

10. Do this by counterexample. That is, find two pairs (a, b) and (a, c) in G for which $b \neq c$. Also find a number t such that no pair in G has a second element t.

Section 1-7

1. a) Yes; b) $3 - 8 = -5$, for example.

2. a) For example, $5 - 3 = 2$ and $3 - 5 = -2$.

3. Yes

4. Use a counterexample to prove division is not left-distributive over addition. The right-distributive property is the well-known procedure for adding fractions with a common denominator. Show this.

5. Use a specific numerical counterexample to prove it does not hold.

6. a) 9 c) 40

7. It is commutative and associative. Use a counterexample for the distributive property.

8. a) Yes   b) No   c) $ is associative   d) Use a counterexample   e) Give a proof   f) Use a counterexample

9. No

10. a) $\frac{5}{4}$ b) No

11. a) 3   b) 2

Section 1–8

1. No, yes, no

2. $2 \neq 3$ and $3 \neq 2$ but $2 = 2$

3. b) $\{a, b\} \subseteq \{a, b, c\}$ but $\{a, b, c\} \nsubseteq \{a, b\}$

5. See Example 1-20.

6. $\{(1, 1), (2, 2), (3, 3), (4, 4), (5, 5), (1, 3), (3, 1), (1, 5), (5, 1), (3, 5), (5, 3), (2, 4), (4, 2)\}$

7. a) $[a] = \{a, b, c\}$ b) No

8. No.   Prove by counterexample that it is not reflexive, or that it is not transitive.

9. The relation $<$ on the set Z is an example.

11. a) $\{(1, 2), (2, 1)\}$ is an example.   c) The empty set of pairs is an example   e) $\{(1, 1), (2, 2), (3, 3), (4, 4), (1, 2), (2, 3)\}$ is an example.

Section 2–1

1. The even integers greater than zero form a nonempty subset of Z^+ but has no largest integer.

2. By the well-ordering principle there is a smallest natural number (the integer 1).   Prove that if $n < m$ then $1/n \geq 1/m$ and hence the largest element of S is the number $1/1 = 1$.

8. In the general step $(a^m)^{k+1} = (a^m)^k a^m$ by definition of exponent.   Now the induction hypothesis can be applied to give $a^{mk} a^m$ which equals a^{mk+m}, using another theorem on exponents.   This can also be written as $a^{m(k+1)}$ which is the desired form.

10. In the general step, consider a polygon with $k + 1$ sides and vertices $P_1, P_2, \ldots, P_{k+1}$. Join vertex P_1 to P_3 forming a new polygon with k sides, to which the induction may be applied, and a triangle.   From this figure compute the sum of interior angles of the original polygon of $k + 1$ sides.

11. It does hold.   Each nonempty subset of the positive even integers is also a subset of Z^+, hence has a least element.

Section 2–2

1. In the even integers all properties hold except (i).   In the set Z^+ all properties except (c) and (d) hold.

2. There is none.   Although $a - 0 = a, 0 - a = -a \neq a$, and zero is not an identity.   Further, 0 is the only possibility since if $a - x = a$, then $x = 0$.

3. a) $\emptyset$ b) The set T itself   d) No

5. All that you need to prove is that $(a + b) + [(-a) + (-b)] = 0$.

6. See Example 2–3.

9. a) No   b) No   c) No   d) Yes, if $x \neq 0$.

10. Use the definition of $<$ and the closure property of Z^+ under addition.

Section 2–3

1. a) 4   c) 1   e) 6

2. a) 2   c) 5   e) 1 and 6   g) 3, 5, 6   i) 3

8. a) 5   c) 3   e) 0

4. a) 0, 2, 3, 5

5. $3 \cdot 0 = 0$, $3 \cdot 1 = 3$, $3 \cdot 2 = 0$, $3 \cdot 3 = 3$, $3 \cdot 4 = 0$, $3 \cdot 5 = 3$, so 3 has no inverse in Z_6.

7. b) Suppose $ab = 0$ for $a, b \in Z_7$ and that $b \neq 0$. Then $ab = 0 \cdot b$ and hence $a = 0$ by the cancellation law.

9. a) 4   c) 3

10. a) 0   c) 3   e) 3   g) No solution, since $0^2 = 0$, $1^2 = 1$, $2^2 = 4$, $3^2 = 4$, and $4^2 = 1$ in Z_5.

Section 2–4

1. a), b), d), f)

5. w is the zero.   All nonzero elements are zero divisors.

6. The zero is the function $f(x) = 0$ for all x.   If

$$f(x) = \begin{cases} 0 \text{ for } 0 \leq x \leq 1/2 \\ x - 1/2 \text{ for } 1/2 < x \leq 1 \end{cases} \qquad \text{and } g(x) \begin{cases} 1/2 - x \text{ for } 0 \leq x \leq 1/2 \\ 0 \text{ for } 1/2 < x \leq 1 \end{cases}$$

then $fg(x) = 0$ but $f \neq 0$ and $g \neq 0$, so f and g are zero divisors.

7. Prove T is a ring.

10. a) $\{0, \pm 15, \pm 30, \ldots\}$ b) Yes   c) $\{x \mid x = 3t$ for t an integer or $x = 5s$ for s an integer$\}$ d) The set is not closed under addition.

Section 2–5

1. a) $\begin{pmatrix} 5 & -5 \\ 1 & 9 \end{pmatrix}$ b) $\begin{pmatrix} 6 & -16 \\ 3 & 18 \end{pmatrix}$ c) $\begin{pmatrix} 4 & -19 \\ 4 & 20 \end{pmatrix}$

2. Note that the answers to (a) and (b) are equal, the answers to (c) and (d) are equal and that the answers to (e) and (f) are equal.   Perform all operations to check these facts.

6. For example, $\begin{pmatrix} 1 & 2 \\ 2 & 4 \end{pmatrix} \begin{pmatrix} 3 & 4 \\ 1 & 0 \end{pmatrix} = \begin{pmatrix} 1 & 2 \\ 2 & 4 \end{pmatrix} \begin{pmatrix} -1 & -6 \\ 3 & 5 \end{pmatrix}$.

8. If $A = \begin{pmatrix} a & b \\ c & d \end{pmatrix}$ is any two-by-two matrix, compute IA and AI to show that both equal A.

9. Each element of A is multiplied by k.

10. a) The rows of A are interchanged.   b) The first row of A is multiplied by 2, the second by 3.

Section 2–6

1. c) The solution in Z_6 is 4, in Z_7 is 5, and in $\mathbf{Z}$ is -2.

2. a) $\begin{pmatrix} 1 & 6 \\ 4 & 1 \end{pmatrix}$

3. a) $a - b + cd + ce$

4. Model the proofs after the proofs given for parts (a) and (b) in Theorem 2–6.

5. See the proof given for the other part of Theorem 2–8.

6. See the proofs given in Theorem 2–9.

7. Use the definition of subtraction to write $a - b$ as $a + (-b)$ and the use the distributive property and Theorem 2–9.

9. Prove that if $0 = 1$ then every element x in the ring is equal to zero, using Theorem 2–8 and the definition of unity. Hence the ring cannot have two elements.

Section 2–7

1. a) If $a = 3$ then $3a = 3 + 3 + 3 = 3$.   c) If $a = 3$, then $a^3 = 3 \cdot 3 \cdot 3 = 3$.   e) $(-5)a$ $= 5(-a)$ and if $a = 3$ then $-a = 3$ so that $5(-a) = 3 + 3 + 3 + 3 + 3 = 3$.

2. g) If $a = 5$ then $a^{-1} = 3$, so that $a^{-2} = (a^{-1})^2 = 3^2 = 3 \cdot 3 = 2$.

6. Use a proof by induction on m.

7. Use a proof by induction on n.

10. Prove this by induction on n.

12. a) 13   b) 1   c) -3 d) -11

Section 2–8

1. a) $\{\pm 1, \pm 2, \pm 3, \pm 4, \pm 6, \pm 8, \pm 12, \pm 24\}$ b) $\{5k \mid k \text{ is an integer}\}$
   c) $\{11, 13, 17, 19, 23, 29\}$

3. e) $q = -11, r = 5, 126 = (-11)(-11) + 5$
   g) $q = -6, r = 13, -125 = (-6)(23) + 13$

5. $4307 = (59)(73)$

6. If $d \mid y$ and $d \mid z$ then $y = md$ and $z = nd$ for integers m and n. Then $x = (m + n)d$ and hence $d \mid x$.

9. 36

10. The restriction is that a and b are relatively prime.

Section 2–9

1. a) 8/9   d) Already in lowest terms.

2. a) $D(17,629) = 17 = (1)(17) + (0)(629)$
   c) $D(-120, 168) = 24 = (-3)(-120) + (-2)(168)$

3. Use the definition to show that if d and d' are both greatest common divisors then $d \mid d'$ and $d' \mid d$. Since both are positive, $d = d'$.

4. Use the definition of greatest common divisor.

5. Modify the definition in the text to include three integers a, b, c.

6. 71

Section 2–10

1. a) $2^4 \cdot 3^2$ c) Prime

2. For example, $10 = 7(10/7)$ and $10 = 5 \cdot 2$.

3. a) $3 = 2(3/2)$

6. a) 15 and 225

7. If m and n had a common factor $d > 1$, then d would be a divisor of 1, a contradiction.

8. Use induction.

Section 3–1

1. a) $[6,10]$ c) $[19,10]$ e) $[12,21]$

2. a) $[30,9]$ c) $[27,64]$ e) $[-60,8]$

9. b) $x = ab' + cd'$

10. This would prove the converse of the implication contained in the definition, rather than the implication itself.

Section 3–2

1. a) $[6,5]$ c) $[4,3]$ e) $[25,4]$ g) $[0,1]$ i) $[1,1]$

2. a) $[-26,11]$ c) $[-29,10]$ e) $[20,21]$ g) None

5. Use the fact that $-a \in Q$.   Prove that the solution is $(-a) + b$.

6. Use the fact that $c^{-1} \in Q$.   Prove that the solution is $c^{-1}d$.

7. Use the definition of addition and reduce by Theorem 3–4.

8. Use the fact that $-x$ is a rational number.

9. Use the fact that if $x \neq 0$ x has an inverse.

10. Use the existence of inverses or the cancellation law of Exercise 9.

Section 3–4

3. The proof that $\sqrt{3}$ is not rational is similar to that for $\sqrt{2}$.

5. Use Theorem 3–9 and write a proof by induction on n.

Section 3–5

1. a) $0.375000\ldots$ c) $10.428571428571\ldots$

2. a) $22/9$ c) $5219/99$

5. $\pi + e = 5.85987$

6. $(3.1, 3.2)$, $(3.14, 3.15)$, $(3.141, 3.142)$, $(3.1415, 3.1416)$, $(3.14159, 3.14160)$

Section 3-6

1. Prove that $\mathbf{Q}_p$ has properties (a), (b) of the definition.

3. If x and y are each the lub for a set S, then $x \le y$ and $y \le x$, by definition of lub.

4. $\{x \mid x^2 < 2\}$, for example.

5. a) -1 c) 1 e) 2

Section 3-7

1. a) $-2 - 3i, \frac{2}{13} - \frac{2}{13}i, 2 - 3i$ c) $-1, 1, 1$ i) $-i, -i, -i$

2. a) $5 - 6i$ c) $28 + 3i$ e) $18 + 92i$ g) $\frac{3}{10} + \frac{11}{10}i$

Section 4-1

3. a) $\begin{bmatrix} 1\ 2\ 3\ 4\ 5\ 6 \\ 2\ 6\ 4\ 3\ 1\ 5 \end{bmatrix}$ b) $\begin{bmatrix} 1\ 2\ 3\ 4\ 5\ 6 \\ 4\ 5\ 2\ 1\ 6\ 3 \end{bmatrix}$ c) $\begin{bmatrix} 1\ 2\ 3\ 4\ 5\ 6 \\ 3\ 2\ 1\ 4\ 6\ 5 \end{bmatrix}$

   e) $\begin{bmatrix} 1\ 2\ 3\ 4\ 5\ 6 \\ 5\ 1\ 4\ 3\ 6\ 2 \end{bmatrix}$

5. $\begin{bmatrix} 1\ 2\ 3 \\ 3\ 1\ 2 \end{bmatrix}^{-1} = \begin{bmatrix} 1\ 2\ 3 \\ 2\ 3\ 1 \end{bmatrix}$, for example.

9. Factorial n, that is, $n(n - 1)(n - 2)\ldots 3 \cdot 2 \cdot 1$

10. There are exactly three involutions in S_3.

Section 4-2

1. a) Yes   b) Yes   c) No   d) Yes   e) Yes   f) Yes   g) Yes   h) No   i) Yes   j) Yes
   k) Yes   l) Yes

2. Use counterexamples.

5. Merely quote the defining properties of a ring which imply that the set is a group.

7. The most significant fact is that each element of the group must appear once and only once in each row and in each column of the group table.

8. The group has six elements, three of which are rotations and three of which are reflections in an axis of symmetry.

10. This group is infinite and includes rotations through any angle and reflections in any diameter of the circle.

Section 4-3

1. a) 4   c) 8   e) 2

2. a) R_0, X, R_0 c) X e) X

3. a) $28, 28/27, 0$

5. Select an element, say a, as identity and then construct the table using Exercise 4.

6. No.   Use counterexamples for proof that none of the properties, except that of closure, hold.

9. The identity is 5.

Section 4-4

1. a) $\begin{bmatrix} 1 & 2 & 3 & 4 & 5 \\ 1 & 2 & 3 & 4 & 5 \end{bmatrix}$ c) $\begin{bmatrix} 1 & 2 & 3 & 4 & 5 \\ 4 & 3 & 1 & 5 & 2 \end{bmatrix}$

2. a) $(1\ 5\ 4\ 3\ 2)$ b) $(1\ 2\ 3\ 4\ 5)$ e) $(1\ 5\ 4\ 2)$

3. Merely compute $(rs)(rs)$.

4. a) $\begin{bmatrix} 1 & 2 & 3 & 4 & 5 \\ 3 & 2 & 1 & 5 & 4 \end{bmatrix}$ c) $(1\ 5\ 3)(2\ 6\ 4)$

5. a) $(1\ 2)(3\ 4)(5\ 6)$ c) $(1\ 4\ 3)(2\ 5\ 6)$

6. a) $(1\ 5)(1\ 3) = (1\ 5)(4\ 2)(1\ 3)(4\ 2)$

7. a) Even   c) Odd

10. b) Let α be a transposition. Prove that the mapping $f(\varphi) = \varphi\alpha$ for each φ in A_n is a one-to-one mapping from A_n onto the set of all odd permutations.

11. c) 0

Section 4-5

2. There are six, counting the subgroup consisting of the identity alone, and the entire group S_3. Of these three have 2 elements and one has 3 elements.

4. There are six.

5. For example, the order of a^3 is 4 and of a^5 is 12.

6. Each nonzero element has order 7; the zero element has order 1.

8. Prove that if a is an integer, then $na \neq 0$ for any positive integral coefficient n.

9. Every nonzero element generates Z_7.

Section 4-6

1. The left cosets are $\{R_0, R_1, R_2, R_3\}$ and $\{X, Y, D_1, D_2\}$.

2. For example $HD_1 = \{D_1, R_1\}$ and $D_1H = \{D_1, R_3\}$.

4. Let $a \in G$. Prove that if $b \in Ha$ then $Ha = Hb$. Do this by showing that $Ha \subseteq Hb$ and that $Hb \subseteq Ha$.

6. There are 7 cosets.

7. F, F, T, T, T, T

9. a) 1   c) 24   e) 3

10. There are eight.

Section 4-7

1. These sets are the cosets asked for in Exercise 6, Section 4-6.

3. a) [3]   c) [5]   e) [4]   g) [2]   i) [4]

9. a) [5]   c) [6]   e) [4]

10. a) [3]   c) [0]   Each part has a single solution.

Section 5–1

2. a) $= 180°$, $e = -1$, $c = 5$, $d = 2$

3. a) $(3, -2)$ and $(6, 9)$

4. a) $3x' + 2y' = 24$

5. a) $\delta(R) = (9/2 + \sqrt{3}, 3\,3/2 - 6)$, $\delta(S) = (3 - \sqrt{3}, -4)$.   The distance is 5 in both cases.

Section 5–2

1. Compute the distance from (a, b) to (p, q) and from $(a + c, b + d)$ to $(p + c, q + d)$.

3. a) α is the rotation through 180°, β is the reflection in the x-axis, and γ is the translation $x' = x + 3$, $y' = y - 2$.

   c) α is the rotation through 30°, β is the reflection in the x-axis, and γ is the translation $x' = x + 5$, $y' = y + 2$.

5. a) Ellipse   c) Parabola   e) Ellipse   g) Parabola

6. a) 45°   c) 30°

Section 6–1

1. a) $\{1, 3\}$ b) $\{2, 5\}$ c) $\{2, 3, 4\}$

3. a) p c) m e) m g) n

4. a) n

6. For example $\{a, b, c\}\{b, d\} = \{b, c\}\{a, b\}$.

7. For example $\{a, b\}$ is a zero divisor since $\{a, b\}\{c, d\} = \varnothing$.

9. Take a specific set U, and show that a particular subset would have no inverse with respect to union.

10. a) 7   c) zero

Section 6–2

1. Prove that the sum and the product of two matrices of this form have this form.   Note that the zero matrix is of this form with a and b equal to zero.   Prove that the negative of such a matrix is of the same form.   All other properties are inherited.

2. To prove that S is not a right ideal, exhibit specific matrices $A \in S$ and $B \notin S$ such that $AB \notin S$.

4. $\{m, n\}$ is one.

Section 6–3

1. A subset of $\mathbf{Z}$ is an ideal, and hence a principal ideal, if and only if it is the set of all multiples of a fixed integer.

2. One such ideal contains the three elements $\varnothing$, $\{1\}$, and $\{1, 2\}$.   The element $\{1, 2\}$ is the generator of the ideal.

4. Since every ideal forms a subgroup of the additive group of the ring, the theorem of Lagrange gives an immediate proof.

6. Multiplication on the right by a ring element may not give an element of the set.

Section 6–4

1. a) 4   c) 7   e) 5

2. a) $-1 - 9\sqrt{2}$ c) $-\frac{1}{17} - \frac{3}{17}\sqrt{2}$ e) $\frac{10}{3} - \frac{17}{6}\sqrt{2}$

3. a) 5   c) 8

5. $1^{-1} = 1, 2^{-1} = 8, 4^{-1} = 4, 7^{-1} = 13$, etc.

7. Prove by counterexample that the set is not closed under multiplication.

Section 6–5

1. The easiest examples are of the form $\mathbf{R}(a)$ for irrational real numbers a.

4. No.   The operations are not the same.

6. Closure properties are all you need to use.

8. This proof is analogous to the proof that the rational numbers from a field, given in Section 3–2.

Section 7–1

1. a) $(-1, 2, -1, 0, \ldots)$ b) $(0, -2, 3, 4, -6, 0, \ldots)$

2. a) $(4, 1, 0, \ldots)$ b) $(3, 0, 3, 0, \ldots)$ e) $(4, 0, 3, 0, 4, 0, \ldots)$

3. a) $(-1/3, 0, 9/10, 0, \ldots)$ c) $(0, 0, 0, 0, 1/4, 0, \ldots)$

   e) $(0, 0, 0, 0, 0, 0, 0, 0, 1/16, 0, \ldots)$

4. a) $(0, 1/2, 0, \sqrt{3}, 0, \ldots)$ b) $(-4, -1, 0, 2\sqrt{3}, \sqrt{3}/2, 0, \ldots)$

5. a) $(1 + 2i, 5/2 - i, \sqrt{2i}, 0, \ldots)$
   b) $(0, 4 + 3i, (1 - 2\sqrt{2}) + (\sqrt{2} - 1/2)i, \sqrt{2}/2\, i, 0, \ldots)$

10. In each case apply the definition to perform the multiplication in the right member and show that the result is the left member.

Section 7–2

1. a) $1^2 + 2^2 + 3^2 + 4^2 + 5^2$ c) $4 + 4 + 4$ e) $2 \cdot 3 \cdot 4 + 3 \cdot 4 \cdot 5 + 4 \cdot 5 \cdot 6 + 5 \cdot 6 \cdot 7$

2. a) $a_3 + a_4 + a_5 + a_6 + a_7$ c) $a_3 b_1 + a_3 b_2 + a_3 b_3 + a_4 b_1 + a_4 b_2 + a_4 b_3 + a_5 b_1 +$

   $a_5 b_2 + a_5 b_3$ f) As a first step, express the sum as $\sum\limits_{i=0}^{3} a_0 b_i c_{3-i} + \sum\limits_{i=0}^{2} a_1 b_i c_{2-i} +$

   $\sum\limits_{i=0}^{1} a_2 b_i c_{1-i} + \sum\limits_{i=0}^{0} a_3 b_i c_{-i}.$

3. a) 0   c) 0   e) -14 g) 0

4. a) $\sum\limits_{i=1}^{10} i^2$ c) $\sum\limits_{i=-1}^{3} a_i$ e) $\sum\limits_{i=0}^{3} a_i b_2$

8. a) -10 c) $62/15$

Section 7–3

1. b) $-u = (2, 4, 3, 1, 0, \ldots)$
2. a) $uv = vu = (0, 6, 17, 12, 7, 10, 0, 2, 0, \ldots)$
4. b) $(0, 6, 0, -12, -9, 0, 24, -6, 0, \ldots)$ c) $(-2, -6, 4, 15, -3, -8, 2, 0, \ldots)$
5. b) $(0, 0, 0, 2, 4, 0, 0, 3, 1, 0, \ldots)$
7. $(0, 0, 1, 0, \ldots)$ and similar elements. Only 0 and 1 may be used as coefficients, since an integral domain exists which has 0 and 1 as its only elements.

Section 7–4

1. There are seven such polynomials. Recall that the zero polynomial has no degree and hence is not one of the required set.
3. Let $s = (0, 1, 0, \ldots)$. Prove that $\rho(x^2)$ is not defined, since x^2 is not in S and hence $\rho(x^2) \neq \rho(x)\rho(x)$ as required for an isomorphism.

Section 7–5

1. a) $2x - 3x^3 + 5x^5$
2. a) $(-3, 0, 1, 0, \ldots)$ c) $(0, 3, 0, \ldots)$
5. a) $(y^2 + 2y, -2y - 3, 1, 0, \ldots)$
6. a) Valid   b) Valid   c) Invalid   d) Valid

Section 7–6

1. $f(x) = (x + 1)(x + 6)$ over Z_7
3. $x^2 + 3x + 4$ is one.
4. a) 1 and -1 only   c) $1, 2, 3, 4$ e) The two constant polynomials 1 and -1
5. a) $2(x^2 + x - 1)$ c) $\frac{1}{2}(2x + 1 - \sqrt{5})(2x + 1 + \sqrt{5})$
6. a) Irreducible   c) $\frac{1}{4}(2x + 3 + \sqrt{11}\,i)(2x + 3 - \sqrt{11}\,i)$
7. a) $(x^2 + 2)(x^2 - 2)$ c) $(x^2 + 2)(x + \sqrt{2})(x - \sqrt{2})$
8. a) $(6x + 1)(x + 6)$ c) Irreducible

Section 7–7

1. a) 2   c) 4

8. a) $\begin{pmatrix} 1 & 0 \\ -2 & 0 \end{pmatrix}$ c) $\begin{pmatrix} -1 & -14 \\ -2 & 3 \end{pmatrix}$

5. Use trial and error.

6. a) 7 and 9   c) -2

8. Evaluate $f\begin{pmatrix} 1 & 2 \\ -1 & 3 \end{pmatrix}$ to show it is zero.

9. a) Indeterminate   c) Indeterminate   e) Unknown

Section 7–8

1. a) $4x^4 - 3x^2 + 2 = (4x)(x^3 - 2x + 1) + 5x^2 - 4x + 2$

   c) $6x^3 + 17x^2 + 7x - 20 = (2x^2 + 3x - \frac{5}{3})(3x + 4) - \frac{40}{3}$

2. a) $\sqrt{2}x^2 + 3x - \sqrt{3} = (\sqrt{2}x + 5)(x - \sqrt{2}) + (5\sqrt{2} - \sqrt{3})$

3. a) $3x^3 + 2x^2 + x + 1 = (3x + 3)(x^2 + 3x + 2) + x$

4. a) $f(-1) = 0$ so $g(x) \mid f(x)$ c) $f(-3) = f(4) = 6$ so $g(x) \nmid f(x)$

Section 7–9

1. a) $\dfrac{x + 2}{2x + 1}$ c) $x^2 + 1$

2. The GCD is 1 and $1 = \frac{1}{20}(6x^2 + 5x - 17)g(x) - \frac{1}{20}(2x - 3)f(x)$.

3. a) The GCD is $x^3 + 3x^2 + 3x + 3$, which equals $f(x) + 0 \cdot g(x)$ or $3f(x) + 2g(x)$.

   c) The GCD is 1 and $1 = 4xf(x) + (2x + 4)g(x)$.

Section 9–11

3. $x^2 + 1 = 0$

4. $6x^4 - 25x^3 + 32x^2 + 3x - 10 = 0$

6. a) $-1, 3, -2 + \sqrt{5}, -2 - \sqrt{5}$ c) -6 e) None.

7. a) $\frac{1}{4}(x + 1)(x + 2)(2x - 1 - \sqrt{3}\,i)(2x - 1 + \sqrt{3}\,i)$,

   c) $(x - 2)^3(x - 9)$

INDEX

ABCDEFGH79876543